# THE SOVIET FAR EAST

# The Soviet Far East

## A SURVEY OF ITS
## PHYSICAL AND ECONOMIC
## GEOGRAPHY

by

### ERICH THIEL

*Professor of Economic Geography
in the University of Munich*

translated by
ANNELIE AND RALPH M. ROOKWOOD

FREDERICK A. PRAEGER
NEW YORK

*This book was originally published by the Isar Verlag, Munich, under the title* Sowjet-Fernost: Eine landes-und wirtschaftskundliche Ueber- sicht, *in 1953. It is Volume I of the Publications of the Osteuropa-Institut of Munich. It has been revised and brought up to date by the author and translated by Annelie and Ralph M. Rookwood.*

BOOKS THAT MATTER

*Published in the United States of America in 1957 by Frederick A. Praeger, Inc., Publishers, 150 East 52nd Street, New York 22, N.Y.*

*Library of Congress Catalog Card No 57–7732*

PRINTED IN GREAT BRITAIN BY
RICHARD CLAY AND COMPANY LTD
BUNGAY, SUFFOLK

# Preface

*

Having been occupied for several years with writing a comprehensive work on the geography of the Soviet Union, I have decided to finish one part of it now and to publish it in advance of the complete work. There were specific reasons for choosing the Far East for this purpose. It is well known that first Russia and now the Soviet Union have shifted the 'centre of gravity' of their political activities according to the circumstances of the period; sometimes it is to be found in Europe, where it is farthest to the west in relation to Russia as a whole, while at other times it will be found at the opposite end of this vast empire, which both the Russians and ourselves call the Far East. At present the latter is the case, and it is the Soviet-Russian Far Eastern territories which form the basis and starting point of political action. The main task of this book is to discuss these territories in relation to their geographical setting and their economic foundations.

The following work is based partly on personal knowledge acquired on my own journeys through the area, and partly on the intensive study of all available literature. I have not hesitated to discuss the whole of the Soviet-Russian Far East, although my personal knowledge is limited to only a part of this area. The decision to do this rested on the knowledge that even the best-known Russian geographers who have provided us with complete descriptions of Russia have known only part of the country from their own experience, and have had to rely at least partly on the descriptions and conclusions of other scholars, an observation which applies equally to this book. It must be mentioned that Soviet-Russian research has done much valuable work, and it is only to be regretted that the numerous important results of this research have not been made available to foreign science; this applies to some essential parts of geographic research and has particular force regarding the country's economy.

In its sub-title this work has been called a geographic and economic survey, and its intentions go no farther than this.

Limitations of space did not allow me to describe the historical development or the individual regions in as much detail as might have been desirable, since many volumes would have been required to make this possible. The subject-matter has therefore been dealt with only in broad outline in order to provide, in addition to the general survey, a clear picture of the individual areas. This has meant the omission of some detailed research in the interests of the whole. For the same reason the style of the book has been kept as simple as was compatible with its scientific character. I have constantly been guided by the conviction that this book should fill a gap not only in the German but also in the general literature.

The natural conditions of the country have been dealt with extensively, since they are of such decisive importance as the basis of the economy and its general lines of growth. An attempt has also been made to indicate the probable trends of future economic development which follow from the clearly marked pattern of present-day resource utilization. Because of the complete lack of official information, all other available sources (including news reports) have been used, subject to most careful consideration and critical evaluation, and have contributed to the assessment of the economy and its problems.

I am indebted to many friends for advice and stimulating ideas while working on this book, as well as for material which they have made available to me. I am specially grateful to Prof. Dr H. Lautensach of Stuttgart, Prof. Dr G. Ipsen of Dortmund, Forstmeister Dr R. Buchholz of Rheinbeck near Hamburg, and Dr Klocke of Wiesbaden. Finally, I should particularly like to mention my teacher, Prof. Dr Arved Schultz of Dusseldorf, who distinguished himself in the sphere of geographical research on the East, and who celebrates his seventieth birthday this year. I shall never forget him.

I thank the 'Osteuropa-Institut', Munich, and its director Prof. Dr H. Koch for reporting this work in the publications of the Institute.

*Munich*                                                                    May 1953

# Translators' Note

\*

Several corrections to the original German text have been received from the author, as well as several revisions providing additional information, either elaborating the original or bringing it more up-to-date. These have usually been incorporated in the general body of the work, except for one note on the most recent revision of administrative boundaries, where a footnote has seemed preferable to extensive re-writing of the original.

Transliteration of proper names has been done in accordance with the *Transcription of the Russian Alphabet* found at the end of the German edition and also included in this edition immediately preceding the index.

All metric measures have been converted into the equivalent English units, except for metric tons which are approximately equal to long tons and can be read as such. In calculating the English equivalents we have attempted to retain the same degree of accuracy used in the metric measures: the general rule is that decimal fractions, whole numbers, and hundreds, &c., of metric units have been converted into the nearest common fractions, whole numbers, or hundreds, &c., of the corresponding English units, except where the equivalent units differ greatly in size. (For example, 3·8 m. becomes 12½ ft., 52 km. becomes 32 miles, and 600 km. becomes 400 miles, but 6·5 cu. m. becomes 230 cu. ft.) When the use of this general rule appeared to be inadequate or misleading, the original metric measure has been retained, with the English equivalent given next to it in brackets. This occurs most commonly when data are presented within certain arbitrary limits, such as 'between 1,000 and 2,000 metres' or 'number per 1,000 hectares'.

Our thanks are due to Prof. Thiel, who has corresponded at some length regarding words and phrases for which exact English equivalents do not exist, and to Katherine B. Pailing for the time kindly and generously spent on a critical reading of the final

7

typescript.  Above all, we are particularly indebted to Hilde
Sluzewski for her invaluable help in the initial translation from
the German text.

                                                      A. R.
*February 29th, 1956*                                 R. M. R.

# Contents

*

# Maps and Diagrams

*

# Part I

# GENERAL

# CHAPTER I

# The Physical Background

*

## Significance, Situation, Size

The Soviet Far East: included under this name are all those Soviet Russian Eastern territories the rivers of which drain into the Pacific Ocean (which strongly influences the climate), and which are separated morphologically from the other parts of the Soviet Union by high mountain ridges. The area includes the whole of the Pacific coastal region from Vladivostok in the south to the Arctic latitudes of the Chukchen peninsula in the north. In its concept of 'Dalny Vostok' Soviet Russian science includes the same territories as described above, and thus follows the general division of Asia as worked out by Carl Ritter and Ferdinand Freiherr von Richthofen, who called the whole eastern peripheral slopes of the continent 'East Asia'.

To the extent that the hinterland of the coastal plain drains into the Pacific Ocean, it belongs to the Far Eastern territories and its natural boundary is obvious. But in this book the lake of Baikal will be set as the western boundary, and this calls for some words of explanation. Transbaikalia, situated between Lake Baikal in the west and the right-hand source of the Amur, the Argun, does not completely correspond to the definition of the concept given above. It forms an area of transition, belonging only partly to the drainage system of the Amur, and partly to those of the Yenesei and the Lena. It is not included in the Russian concept of the 'Dalny Vostok', and will not be included here in the restricted concept of the 'Far Eastern Territories'. Nevertheless Transbaikalia's communications and economy are much less closely linked with the West than with the East, meaning the Far East in the widest sense of the word. One is tempted to call Transbaikalia the base for the Soviet Russian position in Eastern Asia. Here is the source of the Amur, which showed the Russians the way to the east and which they followed first on foot and then by rail. In addition, Transbaikalia is not only the starting point of the important

Russian-built trade route that leads across Manchuria to the Pacific, but also of the historic routes, which today are equally essential, via Mongolia to China. For all these reasons the inclusion of Transbaikalia in the general concept of the 'Soviet Far East' seems to be not only justified but also necessary for a better understanding of the whole context.

The Soviet Union achieves through the Far Eastern territories a mainland coastline of more than 6,000 miles, making her an important neighbour to the Pacific. As a result of the Second World War, South Sakhalin and the Kuriles were also brought into the possession of the USSR, and the chain of Japanese territory blocking free access to the Pacific was broken. The Sea of Okhotsk (some 600,000 square miles in extent) became practically a Soviet inland sea and is now officially considered as coming under Russian sovereignty. This penetration of the Soviet sphere of influence into the Pacific Ocean opens up possibilities for the maritime development of the Soviet Union much more far-reaching than in the past, when this development was limited to the continental coast. In this context the island of Sakhalin, which points towards the island empire of Japan, and is separated from Hokkaido only by the Straits of La Pérouse, which are hardly 30 miles wide, needs special mention. By the construction of a dam which was completed in 1952, Sakhalin has been connected with the continent and has become virtually a part of it. The possession of the southwestern Sakhalin coast, together with the adjacent mainland coastal areas, has also made the Soviet Union an important neighbour to the Sea of Japan. Thus by her acquisition of a large share of the mainland coast and the possession of the islands in front of it, Russia has achieved conditions which, if not everywhere very favourable, are still sufficiently good to permit her development into a sea power on the Pacific. There is ample proof that the sea is by no means alien to the Russians, even though, as a continental people, they may have preferred to take the overland routes in the past. The fact that the Soviet Union does not as yet occupy an adequate position as a sea power does not mean that this situation will remain unchanged, and she has announced her claims in no uncertain terms by the intense development of the different harbours for trade and naval purposes.

It is the exit to the open sea provided by the Far Eastern territories which gives them their tremendous importance for the Soviet Union. The gateways to the ocean inside her own territory are reduced in importance by unfavourable natural conditions, but they are nevertheless there, and their individual inadequacy made it all the more necessary to expand and develop each one of them, as well as to enlarge the general access to the sea by making better and easier new routes, whether across her own territory or not. No other country in the world shows so clearly in its history an instinctive determination to reach the sea such as led the Russians east to the Pacific coast. The latter was reached for the first time in 1639 at the Sea of Okhotsk, which was the starting point for expeditions along the coast and on the sea. However, the difficulties of the long route from the hinterland and of the harsh climate made the Russians look farther towards the south. The discovery of the mighty River Amur, at whose mouth they expected to find a suitable exit to the sea, raised new hopes, but they soon realized that they had not yet reached their goal, and their search was pushed still farther south along the coast towards climatically more favourable areas. They then discovered a satisfactory natural harbour which, full of exaggerated hopes, they called the eastern 'Golden Horn'. Here Vladivostok was built, but here, too, the entrance is blocked by ice for three months of the year, and can be kept open only by the use of powerful ice-breakers. Tentatively searching for a better port, the Russians finally reached the Liaotung peninsula, where they found another natural harbour at Dalny, 'The Distant', and secured it by establishing a naval station nearby at Port Arthur. It mattered very little to the Russians that these two ports were on foreign territory; agreement with China was soon obtained, and after a short time railway tracks led from Transbaikalia right through Manchuria to Vladivostok and to Dalny (later called Dairen by the Japanese).

Even at this point the quest of the Russians for further connexions with the outside world has not ended. A railway has already been built from Ulan-Ude to Ulan-Bator in Outer Mongolia, and a stretch of only about 500 miles (already used by lorries throughout the year) has still to be completed in order to make a connexion at Kalgan with the railway which leads by way of Peking to the port of Tientsin.[1] In this way a further exit to the sea will be reached. For this development, of course, it is essential that the neighbouring states, in this case Outer Mongolia and China, should not object and should find themselves in political

---

[1] Author's footnote: According to a report in *Pravda* (13.11.54) the line from Ulan-Bator to Kalgan has been completed. The line was probably opened in 1955.

and economic harmony with the great continental power to the north.

The pivot of the north–south arc from the mouth of the Amur to Tientsin is in Transbaikalia, from which radiate all the lines of communication. The continual movement south has cut this radial distance (as the crow flies) from 1,400 miles to about 1,000 miles. Apart from representing the starting point for Soviet penetration to the east, it is its great size relative to the Far Eastern territories as a whole which forms the real basis of Soviet power in the Far East, because through it the Soviet Union becomes an important East Asian continental power, a position of which she is extremely conscious.

The encirclement of Manchuria in the north-west, north, and east, and the construction of the railways across it to Vladivostok and Dalny, had already brought these Chinese territories under Russian economic influence in the time of the Tsars. By regaining, as a result of the Second World War, these positions in Manchuria which had been lost during the period from 1904 to 1945, the Soviet Union obtained once more the possession, or rather the use, of the principal Manchurian railways and the South Manchurian ports. This means for the Soviet Union a renewed extension of her economic sphere of influence, which is now at least equal to that of the Tsarist empire at the height of its power and, taking into account the political events of recent years in East Asia, may even surpass it.

Nevertheless the stability of the Soviet Russian position in East Asia depends essentially on the development of her own Far Eastern territories. The present state of settlement and the general economy both in Transbaikalia and in the Far Eastern territories proper, shows that they are only at the beginning of their development. Only a small percentage of the land suitable for agriculture has so far been cultivated, and the utilization of the natural resources has been started in only a few parts of these territories. However, the progress that has been made, particularly under the Soviet regime, indicates a strong disposition to stress these favourable beginnings and to stimulate them. The planned preferential colonization of these areas is proof of these intentions. The emergence during recent years of a marked emphasis on strengthening the industrial areas indicates also that the Soviet Union intends to create in these territories a balanced economy in which all the natural resources will be equally well developed. The aim of Soviet economic planning to make each major region as independent as possible finds a particularly clear expression here, although it is, of course, true that the long distances and general remoteness from the main economic centres of the whole Union make this practice to some extent inevitable. The basic intention not only to populate these remote and somewhat specially situated areas, but also to make them economically as self-sufficient and as strong as possible, plays, of course, an important part in this. It is difficult to assess the potentialities which the Soviet Union possesses here, but they are undoubtedly great and time will be required to enable her to make full use of them.

In connexion with the foregoing remarks, the unique position which the Far Eastern network of communications occupies within the Soviet Union as a whole deserves special emphasis. A glance at the map shows that the whole of the manifold railway net of the Western Soviet Union becomes unified into one single railway line running towards the Far East. This single line crosses the Yenesei at Krasnoyarsk and continues as far as Ulan-Ude in Transbaikalia; only here does it start to divide and to develop again into a new net of rail lines (as far as it is possible to speak of such a thing in the Far East). The connexion of Transbaikalia and the Far Eastern territories with the rest of the Soviet Union depends on this single (double-tracked) railway line. Even the completion of the Baikal–Amur railway would not do away with the bottleneck of the narrow pass at Krasnoyarsk, so that the development of the railway net adds to the independence of the Far East.

Transbaikalia and the Far Eastern territories are the farthest outposts of the Soviet Union in East Asia, and symbolize the remote 'Far Eastern frontier' for the European part of the country. Coming from Leningrad in the Siberian Express, the traveller sees the sun rise and set eight times before reaching Chita, the capital of Transbaikalia, and another day and a half passes before he arrives at Vladivostok. As the crow flies, there are more than 5,000 miles between the western and the eastern frontiers of the Soviet Union. By railway, the distance between Moscow and Chita is 3,866 miles, while from Moscow to Vladivostok the distance is 5,787 miles, via Khabarovsk, and is still 5,153 miles by the more direct line of the Manchurian railway.

Even inside the Soviet Far East there are, according to European conceptions, tremendous distances to be overcome in travelling from one end to the other. There is a distance of about 1,550 miles between the south-west corner of Lake Baikal and the mouth

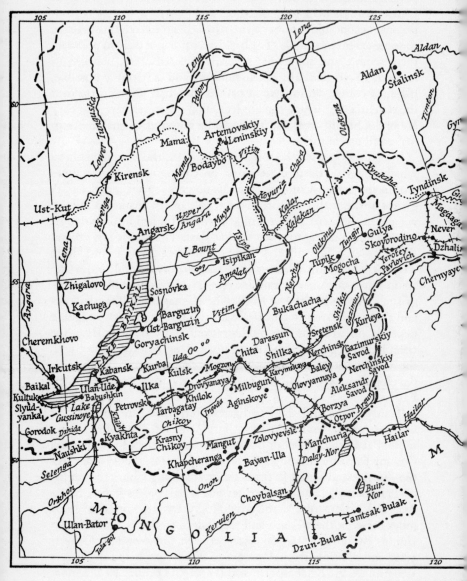

THE SOVIET FAR EAST AN

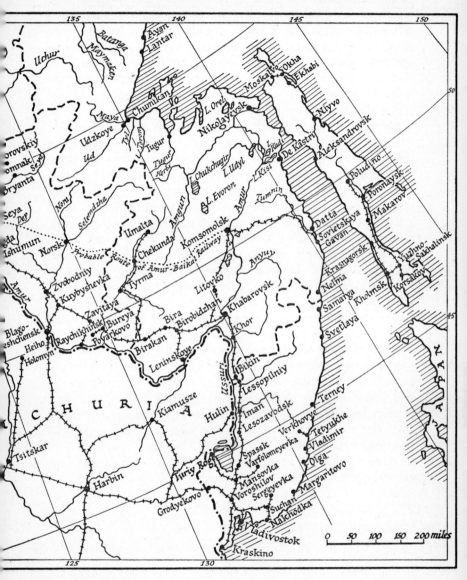

S SOUTHERN NEIGHBOURS

of the Amur, and a bee-line from the Posyet Bay south-west of Vladivostok to Cape Deshnev on the Bering Straits is nearly 3,100 miles long. The island of Sakhalin is almost 620 miles long from north to south, and the Kamchatka peninsula reaches out for about 990 miles from the mainland into the sea. These few examples should suffice to give an idea of the enormous distances and the vast area of the country. The latter amounts to 1,490,000 square miles, which is fifteen times as large as the combined areas of Great Britain and Northern Ireland, or seven times the area of France. These extensive territories are, in terms of European ideas, almost empty of people, because even if one takes the latest census figures of (1950) 6·3 millions total population as a basis, there are only just 4·2 inhabitants to the square mile as an overall average. This is an unusually low density, although it must be stated immediately that the actual distribution of population is, of course, quite different. There are areas in the south which are far more densely populated, while there are large expanses not served by existing communications (especially throughout the north) where there are many square miles for each human inhabitant.

The southern areas, including Transbaikalia, the Amur region, the coastal district, and the main part of Kamchatka and Sakhalin too, are naturally suitable for settlement, although even here the hard climate produces certain difficulties. However, the Russians in particular are more accustomed to enduring such conditions, and better able to overcome them than any other European people. Transbaikalia and the Far Eastern territories proper therefore offer good prospects for the resettlement of surplus population from other regions of the Soviet Union; the population of these territories has in fact been steadily and considerably increased by immigration as the following figures show:

| | | | | |
|---|---|---|---|---|
| 1911 | . | . | . | 1,723,754 |
| 1926 | . | . | . | 2,304,000 |
| 1939 | . | . | . | 4,039,000 |
| 1950 | . | . | . | 6,300,000 |
| 1955 | . | . | . | 7,100,000 |

The administrative areas of the 'Soviet Far East' correspond roughly with the natural regions. The boundaries do not always coincide exactly, but in order to make use of the available tables and statistics it will be necessary to treat the administrative area as though it were identical with the natural one. It is regrettable that for this purpose exact figures are available only for the time of the last census, taken on January 1st, 1939. The census figures for the Soviet Far East are as follows:

| Administrative Unit | Area (sq. m.) | Population |
|---|---|---|
| 1. Autonomous Socialist Soviet Republic of Buryato-Mongolia (ASSR) . . . . . . | 125,900 | 542,200 |
| 2. Chita District . . . . . . . | 273,600 | 1,159,500 |
| Transbaikalia . . . . . . . | 399,500 | 1,701,700 |
| 3. District of Khabarovsk . . . . . | 977,400 | 1,430,900 |
| 4. Coastal District . . . . . . | 78,500 | 907,200 |
| Far Eastern Territories . . . . . | 1,055,900 | 2,338,100 |
| Total for 'Soviet Far East' . . . . | 1,455,500 | 4,039,800 |

Taking the foregoing divisions as a basis for making comparisons, the following results are obtained. Transbaikalia comprises about one twentieth of the total area of the Soviet Union (which was 8,175,750 square miles in 1939), but contains less than one hundredth of its population. Within the Far Eastern territories the contrasts are even bigger, since their share of the total area amounts to one eighth, while their share of the population amounts to only one eighteenth of the total for the whole country. Thus this region shows, even in comparison with the Soviet Union as a whole, an extraordinary disproportion between area and population. This indicates that we are faced here with very special circumstances, for which there are geographical as well as historical reasons. These will be discussed at a later stage.

During recent years there have been several changes in the administrative divisions, which show how much importance the Soviet Union attaches to getting a tighter control over the Far Eastern territories. When occupation was taken of the whole of Sakhalin and the Kuriles on January 2, 1947, the Sakhalin Oblast was founded. On August 2 followed the Amur Oblast, which was formed from parts of the Chita Oblast and the District of Khabarovsk. In the farthest north-east a new Magadan Oblast was created from the Magadan District and the National District of the Chukches on December 3, 1953. Finally on January 23, 1956, the Kamchatka Oblast was separated off as an independent entity from the District of Khabarovsk.

The boundaries with the rest of the Soviet Union have remained

the same. Thus, under present arrangements the Far Eastern territories comprise the following administrative units:

| | | |
|---|---|---|
| 1. Buryato–Mongolian ASSR | 133,500 | sq. m. |
| 2. Chita District | 164,000 | ,, |
| 3. Amur District | 139,000 | ,, |
| 4. District of Khabarovsk | 327,000 | ,, |
| (which includes Nisniy Amur and the Jewish Autonomous District) | | |
| 5. Coastal Region | 62,000 | ,, |
| 6. Magadan District | 412,700 | ,, |
| (which includes the National District of the Chuckches) | | |
| 7. Kamchatka District | 212,800 | ,, |
| (which includes the National District of the Koryaks) | | |
| 8. Sakhalin District | 34,800 | ,, |

The two sketch maps which are included here show both the
old and the new administrative divisions. As a rule the old administrative units will be used as the basis for the numerical data
given throughout the remainder of this work.

Several re-arrangements of the administrative areas have been
carried out under Soviet rule, and it appears that a final form has
still not been achieved, either for purposes of settlement and economic development, or for purposes of the administrative organization of the Soviet Far East; everything is still fluid and in a
growing and formative state.

### Exploration and Settlement

The conquest of Siberia, which had been started in 1581 by
Yermak and his Cossacks, progressed very quickly towards the
east, unhampered by the sparse population. It followed the big
rivers, whose ample water-courses served the Cossacks as routes
and as guides into the wide open spaces where no European had
previously set foot. Thus they passed through river-basin after
river-basin, securing each through the establishment of permanent
bases. As early as 1632 the town of Yakutsk was founded midway
along the Lena in the country of the Yakutes, and from then on
Yakutsk served as the starting point for further advances. In 1638
a Cossack detachment under Atamans Koplov went up the River
Aldan and its tributary, the Maya. They wanted to reach 'Lamu',
the 'big sea' of which the Tungus had told them, but they got only
about 60 miles up the Maya and then had to spend the winter
there. A smaller group under the leadership of the Cossack Moskvitin continued on their way, dragging their boats from the upper

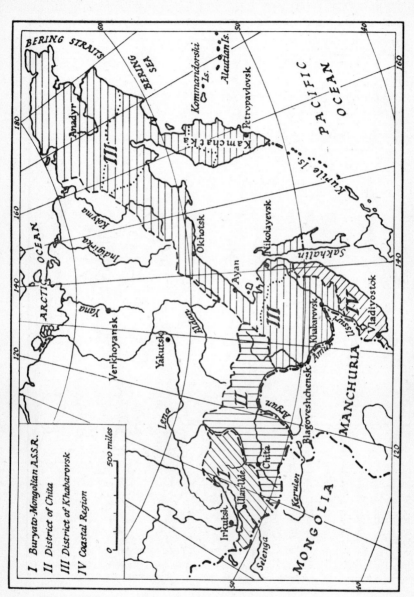

2. ADMINISTRATIVE DISTRICTS, 1947

I   Buryato-Mongolian A.S.S.R.
II  District of Chita
III District of Khabarovsk
IV  Coastal Region

0          500 miles

3. ADMINISTRATIVE DISTRICTS, 1956

BERING STRAITS

Chukchee Nat. Terr.

BERING SEA

Anadyr

Kommandorski Is.

Aleutian Is.

PACIFIC OCEAN

Petropavlovsk

VI

VII

Kamchatka

Kurile Is.

ARCTIC OCEAN

Kolyma

Indigirka

Magadan

Okhotsk

VIII

Nikolayevsk

Sakhalin

Yana

Verkhoyansk

Ayan

Aldan

IV

Khabarovsk

Amur

Ussuri

V

Vladivostok

Yakutsk

Lena

III

II

Blagoveshchensk

Argun

MANCHURIA

Irkutsk

I

Ulan-Ude

Chita

Kerulen

Selenga

MONGOLIA

I   Buryato-Mongolian A.S.S.R.
II  Oblast Chita
III Oblast Amur
IV  District Khabarovsk
V   Coastal Region
VI  Oblast Magadan
VII Oblast Kamchatka
VIII Oblast Sakhalin

0   100            500 miles

Maya across the watershed of the Dzhugdzhur to reach the Ulya, which they descended. These Cossacks reached the Sea of Okhotsk in 1639, and were the first Europeans to do so. Moskvitin built a base at the mouth of the Ulya, slightly to the south of the present town of Okhotsk. He explored the coast towards the north and the south, and got as far as the mouth of the Ud, but he did not find the Shantar Isles, which were not discovered until 1710. In 1649, near the small River Okhota, another Cossack by the name of Shelkovnikov founded the sea base of Okhotsk, which served the Russians for a long time as their principal harbour.

The penetration of north-eastern Siberia also commenced from Yakutsk. As early as 1633 Rebrov and Perfilyev went down the Lena into the distant unknown, and reached the Arctic, where they sailed eastwards along the coast to discover the mouth of the Yana. In 1641 Ivan Yerastov proceeded from the Yana to reach the Indigirka and the Alasseya, and in the same year Stadukhin started on his way farther towards the east and got as far as the Kolyma, where in 1644 he founded the base of Nizhne-Kolymsk. He could not get any farther to the east because the route was blocked by ice, so he returned to Yakutsk in 1645. Stadukhin brought with him the first reliable reports of the Chukchee. In 1646 Ignatyev got as far as the Bay of Chaun. The detachment of Stadukhin which reached the mouth of the Kolyma also included Semyon Deshnev, whose name is permanently linked with the history of discovery in northern Siberia. This daring Cossack seafarer, in spite of the previous failures, set out again with seven small boats from the mouth of the Kolyma towards the east. His aim was to reach the mouth of a big river (the Anadyr) which according to hearsay flowed into the open sea farther to the east. In 1648 he sailed round the cape which bears his name, thereby establishing the north-eastern end of the Asian continent, and thus becoming the first European to sail the Bering Straits. Because of dense fog he was unable to see the American coast beyond the Straits, but he reports having seen the two islands now known as the Diomedas. Deshnev must have travelled far to the south, for when his boats were stranded by a storm he had to march northwards, according to his records, for ten weeks in order to reach the mouth of the Anadyr. The possibility that Deshnev may have set foot on Kamchatka cannot be entirely rejected. It is known that Popov, one of his companions, sailed round Kamchatka and met in the Bay of Penzhina other Russian seafarers who had come from Okhotsk. Thus the opening up of north-east Siberia in the direction established by Moskvitin, and continued along the coast by Deshnev, was brought full circle. Later, Popov sailed along the River Tigil on Kamchatka, and died there. His companions were killed in an encounter with the natives. There exist several documents by Deshnev and his companions containing reports about the areas explored and about the inhabitants—the Chukchee, Koryaks, and Eskimos.

In 1647 Stadukhin started again from Yakutsk for the Kolyma area, where he stayed until 1649, and then, ignorant of the success of Deshnev's journey, took up anew his old plan to find the Anadyr. Forewarned by his first failure in 1643–44, he chose an overland route following the direction which an almost unknown Cossack named Mortora had taken before him. Stadukhin went up the Anyui (probably the Little Anyui), and in the face of great difficulties crossed the watershed of the Anadyr Mountains. This brought him to the river of the same name, which he followed to its mouth, to find Deshnev already there. Later he withdrew into the interior of the Anadyr region and founded a base there, the position of which is unknown. Stadukhin turned up again later in the Gulf of Penzhina, but it cannot be ascertained whether he arrived there by land or by sea. His last known deed was the founding of a settlement near the Bay of Tauyskaya, and it is to him that we owe our first accounts of the interior of north-east Siberia.

Although Kamchatka had already been entered several times by his countrymen, it was the Cossack leader Atlassov who finally succeeded in securing the peninsula for the Russians. In 1697 he was sent to the Anadyr as supreme commander, and in the same year invaded Kamchatka by land and built a base in the centre of the peninsula on the Kamchatka River. He was made the first Russian administrator of Kamchatka. Fights with the natives and also with his own Cossacks did not make his task an easy one. In 1707 the latter rose against him and made him a prisoner, accusing him of abuse of office and cruelty. It is presumed that he was murdered in 1711. The following years from 1711 to 1718 saw the exploration of the Kuriles, in which Kosyrevski particularly distinguished himself.

It is strange that until this time there had been no reference to Japan in the dispatches from the leaders of these expeditions. It is Atlassov in whose records we find the Japanese first mentioned. There is one reference to a Japanese who was shipwrecked and washed ashore on the west coast of Kamchatka, where he lived with the natives. In 1701 he was taken by the Russians to Mos-

cow, where his tales caused much excitement. He impressed even
Peter the Great, who had a school built for him in which he was to
teach the Japanese language to a group of selected Russian subjects. This school existed until 1739, and its pupils took part in the
Bering expedition as interpreters. In another of Atlassov's records
we find the remark that people from Japan are supposed to have
lived on the southern tip of Kamchatka. Apart from this his dispatches are filled with descriptions of the countryside, and he
draws particular attention to Kamchatka's wealth of fish and also
of furs—especially the sable and the 'Kamchatka Beaver'. (The
latter was a misnomer for the big sea otter, and accounts for the
Russian designation at that time of the Bering Sea as the Beaver
Sea.) Kosyrevski, the explorer of the Kuriles, was later to meet
Japanese people several times, and his reports about Japan so increased Peter the Great's interest in the Far East that he ordered
further journeys of exploration with the object of securing the un-
occupied land for Russia. By 1718 all the islands of the Kuriles had
been charted.

Among Deshnev's successors rumours had already become current that there was land farther to the east beyond the sea. These
rumours were founded on reports from the natives of the Chukchen peninsula, who maintained it was possible during the winter
to reach a continent which they called 'the big land'. Atlassov
attached special importance to these reports and had this still unknown land drawn in on his maps, but it was not until 1741 that
Bering and Chirikov entered Alaska for the first time and took
possession of it for Russia. There followed further advances by the
Russians, using the Aleutian Islands and the south coast of Alaska
as guides pointing the way forward. As early as 1812 Russian
settlers were to be found within 40 miles of San Francisco, and a
Russian base actually existed near this town. This was the most
distant point which the Russians reached in their quick and unmethodical eastern colonization, and it was followed by a definite
withdrawal. In 1867 Alaska, which was then considered of no
practical value, was sold to the United States for $7,200,000, and
Russia thereby limited herself to the western side of the Pacific.

The advance of the Russians into the still unknown territories
of the Far East was partly due to official orders, and the administrative posts in the hinterland helped to organize, equip, and provide guides for these generally rather small expeditions. Nevertheless there were also private enterprises, and in later years the Voye-
vodes were to follow the tracks of both. The principal aim of all

these expeditions was to take possession of the country by building bases, and to secure the collection of the 'Yassak', a sort of poll tax which had to be paid by the natives in the form of valuable furs. Private entrepreneurs known as the 'Promyshlenniki', who were mostly fur-dealers and hunters, also took part in the official expeditions. They distinguished themselves equally with the official administrators in cheating the natives, and it therefore happened quite frequently that the victims of this shameless exploitation turned against their invaders. Heavy fighting took place with the Chukchee, Koryaks, and the Kamchadals. The Russians, with their better arms, were inevitably the winners, but the attacks continued and the collectors of the 'Yassak' were frequently murdered. Not until the end of the eighteenth century were law and order established throughout the country.

The acquisition of Transbaikalia and the region of the Amur did not keep pace with the advance of the Russians in the north, because here they met a relatively denser population which was already organized as a state. When in 1648 the Cossacks invaded Transbaikalia from Irkutsk, they were at first beaten back by a tribe of Mongols—the Buryat nomads—and only step by step were they able to advance as far as the Argun and gain a foothold there. The exploration and first acquisitions of land in the Amur area were therefore launched from the north—from Yakutsk— since the direct route from the Lake of Baikal presented too many obstacles. Prompted by reports from the Tungus that there were vast rich lands south of the River Aldan, the Cossack Poyarkov set out in 1643, together with 132 men, to explore that area. From Yakutsk he pushed up the Aldan and followed its tributary the Uchur and then up the Gonam. They were caught by the winter on the broad watershed of the newly discovered Stanovoy range, where the lack of game on the unpopulated mountain ridges greatly endangered the expedition. They were all threatened by death from starvation, and had to feed themselves on bark and moss in order to keep up their strength. In spite of their desperate plight, Poyarkov succeeded in crossing the watershed on skis, and reached the Bryanka, a tributary of the Seya, just as the ice was breaking up with the spring thaw. On rafts and boats made by themselves they drifted down to the Amur and along to its mouth, where they spent the winter with a primitive fishing people, the Gilyaks. Then in the summer of 1645 they started northwards from here along the coast, in small boats without keels. After a journey of three months, during which they suffered incredible privations, they landed at the mouth of the Ulya, where they were saved by Russian settlers. From here Poyarkov followed the Maya as far as the Aldan and returned to Yakutsk in 1646. During the three years of this long and strenuous journey he lost eighty men, either through illness and exhaustion or through encounters with the natives. In his reports on the Amur region Poyarkov includes descriptions of the peoples settled there and, in addition to others, gives special mention to the Daures and the Gilyaks. Of the latter he says that they lived only on fish, whereas the Daures tilled the land and grew barley, buckwheat, millet, peas, and hemp. Cucumber, poppy-seeds, garlic, and beans were cultivated, and walnut trees were found growing wild in the woods. Cattle-breeding was also known to them, and horses, pigs, cows, and hens were kept. All these tribes paid tribute to the Emperor of China, who was called the Bogdo-Khan, and whose warriors were said by the natives to fight with fire and bow and arrow.

Three years after the return of Poyarkov, Khabarov started once more from Yakutsk with seventy men for another journey of exploration to the Amur. He chose a route farther to the west than that of Poyarkov, travelling up the Olekma and the Tungur, in order to reach the Amur by way of the Urka. However, he encountered a large, hostile population on his way, and his force proving inadequate returned to Yakutsk in 1650. In the following year he started along the same route with a bigger force. This time he reached the Amur, and founded the town of Albasin at its junction with a small tributary. Cultivation was begun and fortifications were provided. Numerous Russian peasants followed and settled here, but the restless Cossacks were lured on by distant unknown lands and the hope of rich booty. Khabarov undertook several expeditions along the Amur and also went up the Sungari and the Ussuri, fighting constantly with the Tungus tribe—the Daures, whose towns he plundered and destroyed. The winter of 1651–52 he had to spend at the junction of the Ussuri with the Amur, and had to defend himself there against heavy attacks by the Mandshus and other tribes. The town of Khabarovsk, which bears his name, was later founded on this same site.

The first Russians who invaded the country were mostly Cossacks of a rather footloose and martial nature, accompanied by Russian settlers and traders who built settlements at favourable centres of communication. Apart from hunting and fishing and tilling the land, they engaged in a lively and highly profitable trade

c

in furs, to which was added the usual *yassak* demanded from the natives. This levy was collected without any mercy whatsoever, and robbery and plunder of the native population were so much the order of the day that many natives, especially those who worked on the land, fled from this insecurity to settle on the right-hand side of the Amur in Manchuria.

By the middle of the seventeenth century there already existed along the Amur quite a number of Russian settlements, with Albasin (already mentioned above) as the principal town among them. The first Voyvode of Albasin was Tolbusin. Officially all these bases were placed under the Government at Moscow, and it was to Moscow that Khabarov was called to give a report on the area and to receive the title of Boyar. His successor, Stephanov, worked systematically to further the exploration and acquisition of this area, with the result that by 1681 Russia practically dominated not only the Amur region but also the basin of the lower Sungari and the lower Ussuri. Russian behaviour towards the natives was far from creditable; acts of violence and blackmail resulted in native revolts and eventually in fights with the Chinese. These hostilities caused the destruction of all settlements throughout the whole of the area during the 1680's and the death of most of the Russian settlers. Even Albasin, which by the constant immigration of fresh settlers had become the centre of Russian power in the Amur region, was taken and destroyed by Manchurian troops in 1684. However, after their withdrawal the town was rebuilt by the Cos-sacks, and they started once more to till their fields, although fights with the brigands continued along the frontier. In 1687 a Chinese army of 8,000 men with forty guns appeared outside Albasin, at a time when there were only 736 Russians in the town. In spite of this the Russians succeeded in repelling all attacks, although in the end they were left with only sixty-six men, the others having been killed either in the fighting or by scurvy.

To put an end to this terrible and pitiless fighting along the frontier, which had taken the form of a war of annihilation on both sides, Russia and China decided to negotiate a treaty, which was concluded at Nerchinsk on September 7th, 1689. It was agreed that Russia should retain the area west of the Argun, but she was to withdraw all Russian settlers from the east side of the river, and the basin of the Amur proper was to remain with China. A left-hand tributary of the Amur, the Gorbitsa, was fixed as the western frontier, while the northern frontier was to be the watershed be-tween the Lena and the Amur, running mainly along the Stanovoy ridge. All Russian settlers in the area of the Amur were required to leave, and Albasin was demolished and abandoned.

Following the Treaty of Nerchinsk the colonization of Transbaikalia was begun. To protect its frontiers the Cossack army of Transbaikalia was formed and settled in numerous *stanitses* (frontier posts) on the Argun, where they led an easy frontier life, half soldier, half peasant. They were soon on good terms with the Buryats, and many of the latter—who had at first strongly resisted the Russian invaders—were even accepted on terms of equality into the Cossack organization. But the Amur region, which had remained with China, was not forgotten, and many Russians were soon attracted once again by its wealth of furs. They advanced anew along the Amur, building settlements and starting to work on their own in this foreign country. Some of the more daring even went as far as Ussuriland.

The area of the Amur remained as unknown to the Chinese as it did to the Russians, and its northern frontier remained undetermined by any precise line of demarcation for more than 160 years. During this time and especially after 1800, many Russian scientific expeditions travelled through the country. In addition to the names of such well-known Russian explorers as Maksimovich, Venyukov, Nevelsky, and Ussoltsev, the records also contain numerous German names of Baltic origin, such as Middendorff, Schrenck, Radde, Schmidt, and Glehn. Middendorff in particular provides us with excellent descriptions of the country. During this same period the seafaring powers also began to show interest in the exploration of Asia's north-east coast, and we find Cook sailing the Bering Sea in 1778, La Pérouse exploring the Japanese islands and Sakhalin in 1787, and Broughton working in the same area in the years 1795–8. It is an interesting fact that the poet Adalbert von Chamisso was one of those taking part in the explorations of Kamchatka and the Aleutian Islands from 1815 to 1818.

In the region of the Amur geographical exploration was very much focused on the mouth of the river, because it was here that Russia hoped to find a favourable harbour and an exit to the Pacific. On the strength of reports about the unfavourable nature of the Sea of Okhotsk, the far-sighted Tsarina Katharina II as early as 1777 gave orders to explore the outlet of the Amur. Later La Pérouse, Broughton, and Krusenstern (1803–6) all reported that the Amur ended in a 'liman'[1] with only one shallow outlet to the

---

[1] The 'Amur-liman' is the former estuary of the river, now cut off by sedimentary deposits to form an inland lake with a narrow outlet. (Tr. N.)

sea in the north, unsuitable for sea-going vessels. Farther south
Sakhalin was reported to be connected as a peninsula to the mainland. As late as 1846 Gavrilov, who was ordered to explore this
part of the sea, confirmed these reports. For practical reasons,
however, a Russian marine officer named Nevelsko was of a different opinion; he could not and would not believe that such an
enormous river as the Amur, carrying such a tremendous volume
of water, should drain away into an almost completely enclosed
liman. It was a dramatic battle which he had to fight against the
authority of eminent explorers. He received support from Muravyev, the new Russian Governor of East Siberia, who was later
made a Count with the titled name of Amursky as a special honour. He secured for Nevelsko the command of a small ship, in
which he sailed from Kronstadt to the Far East, starting his explorations in 1849, even though he had not yet received permission
to do so. He discovered that sea-going vessels with a draught of
13 feet could use the northern outlet of the Amur Gulf all the year
round. He also discovered that Sakhalin was an island separated
from the mainland by the Tatar Straits, through which ships with
a draught of 18 feet could pass unhindered from the Amur Gulf to
the Sea of Japan during the warm season. This news created a
sensation in St Petersburg and aroused greatly renewed interest in
the Far East on the part of both the Government and the general
public. In the meantime, explorers such as Middendorff and
others, and later Nevelsko himself, had reported that the region
east of the Little Khingan and the Ussuri had never been taken
over by the Chinese administration, and were to all intents and
purposes free territories. They were consequently occupied by
Muravyev, together with the region of the Amur. (These developments are described in detail, albeit with a Chinese bias, in the
book by Aitchen K. Wu entitled *China and the Soviet Union* which
was published in 1950 (231).) In 1858 Russia and China concluded
the Treaty of Aigun, which declared that the Amur region was to
be Russian territory, and that the land of the Ussuri was to be
administered jointly by the two countries; yet only two years later,
by the Treaty of Peking, the Ussuri area was given to Russia, together with the island of Sakhalin. In this way all the territories
which belong to the Soviet Union today came under Russian
administration. The year 1860 saw the founding of Vladivostok,
in whose name is expressed the basic principle of Russian Far
Eastern policy: 'Dominate the East.'

## General Survey

*Transbaikalia*, together with all the other peripheral regions of the Soviet Far East, belongs to the East Siberian mountain system, but, in contrast to the other parts, it has in general a markedly regular structure. The numerous mountain ridges which cross Transbaikalia from south-west to north-east run in strikingly parallel lines, with elongated ridges and equally prolonged valleys as the main features, whereas in the regions of the Amur and the Ussuri and in the extreme north-east the landscape is characterized by irregularly spreading mountains interspersed with wide depressions. The Transbaikalian landscape forms the transition between the rich forests of humid Siberia and the dry belt of the High Asian steppes. The Mongolian steppes, which in some parts are semi-desert, spread over the border from the south and penetrate like long tongues along the wide valley floors between the mountain ridges; they even reach as far as Lake Baikal, and form islands in the middle of the wooded area (e.g. by the River Bargusin and in the valley of the upper Angara). At the other extreme the Siberian taiga pushes far southwards along the mountain ridges right into the upper reaches of the Onon and the Ingoda. In this way the steppes of Central Asia and the continental forests of North Asia intermingle in Transbaikalia, forming a large area of forest-steppe. In the south the steppe is prevalent, but the farther north one gets the farther the forests spread down the slopes from the rounded mountain ridges, until they finally fill the narrowing valleys. The valleys of the steppes change gradually into meadowlands, which in the north become boggy fields and sometimes swampy forests.

In general the relief of Transbaikalia is not quite so varied as a first glance at the map may suggest. The valley floors are mostly at altitudes between 2,000 and 3,000 feet, while the mountain ridges lie between 3,300 and 4,600 feet, resulting in relatively small differences in height. Moreover, the unbroken slopes rise only gradually, and as a rule have almost plateau-like rounded backs rather than pronounced crests, so that the differences in height become still less marked. The prevalent tree-cover also helps to mask the unevenness of the relief. There are some individual mountains which extend above the tree-line, and which are of a uniform and quite considerable height. These are mainly hard residuals which have put up a stronger resistance to weathering, and their bare round shapes stick out of the general thicket like naked skulls. This appearance earned them the Russian name of *golzy* (spelled *golez* in the singular) meaning 'bald heads'. These *golzy*, which appear only here and there in Transbaikalia, are very typical of all the mountain areas of the Far East.

In its culture, too, Transbaikalia shows a marked transitional character. The plains, valleys, and islands with steppe-vegetation have long been the home of nomadic cattle-breeders, in this case the Buryats, an intelligent and energetic Mongolian tribe which has kept to the steppes to which it is well adapted by nature and culture. It is interesting to note how even today their distribution is determined by the natural landscape. The Buryats have avoided the forest areas almost completely, leaving these to the Tungus, who were traditionally the forest people and who still inhabit these forests as hunters and reindeer-breeders. The Buryats were the first local people to put up a temporarily successful resistance against the conquering Cossack invaders, but as nomads they were forced to give way to the slow infiltration of Russian settlers who were tillers of the soil. They remedied the situation by voluntary assimilation, taking up agriculture themselves and acquiring the advantages of Russian culture. In this way, although intermingled with Russians, they have been able to stay on in their original territories and to reach a standard of culture which lifts them well above that of all the other Mongolian tribes beyond the Russian border. The result is the cultural equivalent of the transitional landscape, intruding into the pure forest areas in the north and into the pure steppes in the south, and taking the form of cultural islands rather than continuous zones. There remain, nevertheless, large areas near the southern border where the Buryat still leads his former nomadic life as a cattle-breeder.

Agriculture is favoured by the fact that most of the precipitation occurs in the summer season. Chita, situated in the middle of the region, has a yearly rainfall of only 12½ inches, but almost 11½ inches of this falls in the growing period, so that there is sufficient moisture available, together with the warmth of the continental summer, to make possible a relatively high yield of summer wheat. This has enabled Transbaikalia to become an important wheat producer and principal provider for the whole of East Siberia.

*The Amur Region* adjoins Transbaikalia, without any clearly defined boundary, to the north of the northern arch of the Amur. In its main morphological features it shows as much variety as Transbaikalia, but the differences in altitude have become bigger, since the valley floors have come down to between 650 and 1,650 feet, while the mountain ridges remain at altitudes between 3,300 and 4,900 feet. The number of plateau-like mountain ridges supporting numerous *golzy* has become fewer and the series of parallel ridges running towards the north-east which is so characteristic of Transbaikalia has disappeared. The principal mountain ranges of the Amur region run chiefly from west to east, and are crossed by others almost at right angles. Thus, in contrast to Transbaikalia, we find here an 'egg-crate' pattern with the individual mountain ridges separated by extensive low plateaux, which assume the character of lowland plains in the vicinity of the Amur River. The densely populated Seya–Bureya plain must be mentioned first. Here the characteristic box-like pattern of the mountains is reflected in the directions of the main rivers and valleys. The typically Baikalian south-west to north-east direction followed by the Argun, the Selemdzha, the Bureya, and the lower Amur intersects with the north-west to south-east direction which is most apparent in the middle Amur and the Gilyu. Some rivers—for example, the Seya—partly follow first the one and then the other direction.

The general appearance of the landscape presents a tremendous contrast with that of Transbaikalia, due to the pronounced influence of the Pacific Ocean—the Amur region being already within the area dominated by the East Asian monsoon. The proximity of the large continental land-mass still ensures a hard winter, but the summer is warm and the rainfall is more plentiful than in Transbaikalia. The yearly precipitation is generally more than 20 inches, and over half of it falls in the three summer months from June to August, producing a luxuriant vegetation. In contrast with Transbaikalia, where the valley floors remain free of forest because of the general aridity, in this region it is an excessive humidity which prevents forest growth in the valleys and plains. The character of the whole countryside is influenced by the overabundant summer rains, and the following features are typical of the entire Amur region: the rivers are lined by boggy thickets of reeds; the wide steppes are overgrown by tall grass on the more elevated plains, punctuated by small woods on the drier hills; the slopes and ridges of the mountains are covered by frequently impenetrable thickets of woods which here, in contrast to the Siberian taiga, are interspersed with oaks and other deciduous trees.

The excessive humidity during the growing period is an impediment to agriculture and makes an extension of the arable lands difficult, since as a rule new land for cultivation has to be wrested from nature by laborious drainage. Nevertheless the spacious Seya–Bureya plain and the banks of the Amur are fairly thickly populated, and a large part of the famous 'Amur-prairie' has been transformed into a cultivated landscape. The majority of the people who live here are Russians, the earlier Chinese immigrants having been pushed back, sometimes by force, beyond the Amur. Throughout the remainder of the Amur region nature reigns unchallenged, except perhaps for a few Tungus, or Russian hunters, who pass through it. The only exceptions are the upper courses of the left-hand tributaries of the Amur, where the occurrence of gold attracted many Russians and produced a lively local industry. The gold industry is now organized by the State, and these remote areas are thus linked with the economy of the whole country.

*The land of the Ussuri* is divided into two completely different parts: first, the large mountain massif of the Sikhota-Alin, occupying the whole area from the Bay of Peter the Great in the south to the mouth of the Amur in the north; second, the Ussuri–Khanka plain, which stretches in the same direction west of the Sikhota-Alin and continues south of Lake Khanka without any marked interruption as far as the Bay of Peter the Great.

The Sikhota-Alin is a mountain massif covered by woods and divided by many valleys. It divides up into several ridges running parallel with the coast. The outlines of the mountains are gentle without any marked crests or precipices, and plateau-like forms often prevail. The altitude is generally between 2,150 and 2,450 feet, but the valleys are deeply eroded. Rising gradually from the west, the mountain massif drops down steeply towards the sea, leaving only occasional narrow strips of coast where poor small fishing villages have sprung up. Cold ocean currents produce cool, foggy, unfriendly summers with plenty of rain along the whole of the coast as far north as Okhotsk and beyond. Boggy valleys, and forests of a more northern character, dripping with cool humidity, are the typical features of this eastern coastal area.

The western side of the Sikhota-Alin massif and the Ussuri–Khanka plain are both more like the Amur region. These areas are characterized by warm to hot summers with an abundance of rainfall, and a strong tendency to become swampy. The Sikhota-Alin, running parallel to the coast as it does, forms a shield against the cold and the sea-fog and allows the sun to be more effective. The more southerly location of these areas is evident everywhere. In the forests of the Sikhota-Alin more and more deciduous trees appear, increasing in number towards the south until they eventually form wonderful unmixed forests. In the cultivated zone, too, which spreads southwards over the whole plain, typically Manchurian–Chinese plants are to be found in ever-increasing abundance, with Kaoliang and other millets, soyabeans, and rice forming a characteristic feature of the landscape. The population changes, too: on the plain north of Lake Khanka, Russians and Ukrainians are in the majority, while in the farthest south, Chinese and Koreans are more predominant. The Ussuri–Khanka plain is relatively thickly populated, while, apart from some coal-mining districts in the south, the Sikhota-Alin is in large parts virtually uninhabited. As in former times, native Tungus pass through it in small numbers, and there are also Russian hunters and occasional Chinese collectors looking for strange and legendary plants.

*The island of Sakhalin* extends in a north–south direction for about 600 miles. Two parallel mountain ranges run through its southern part, separated by a comparatively wide depression. The eastern range is the shorter of the two, but is higher, and contains the highest point (6,600 feet) on the island. Towards the north both ranges flatten out to make room for a hilly lowland, where cool foggy air-masses move unhindered over the country. In the south the mountains cause a differentiation of climate, the eastern slopes being cool and unfriendly, with plenty of rain, while the western slopes are noticeably milder. On the whole the southern part of the island (which was in Japanese hands from 1905 to 1945 and has therefore only recently become Russian again) is the more favoured. Sakhalin can be described in general terms as a humid, cool, and wooded mountain country, although in many places there are treeless moss-steppes which remind one of the tundra of the north. The island, once feared as a Russian penal colony, is now playing an increasingly important part economically as a producer of mineral oil and coal.

*The Okhotsk coastal region* is a narrow coastal strip alongside the Sea of Okhotsk, beginning in the south-west at the Bay of Ud and continuing as far as the Gulf of Penzhina in the extreme northeast. In its more westerly part, which stretches roughly from the Bay of Ud to the port of Okhotsk, the Dzhugdzhur Mountains run parallel to the coast, forming abrupt precipices, which only rarely leave a small coastal ledge where the erection of a fishing village is possible. Passage from the coast into the interior is extremely difficult, since the only routes are along the deep valleys and narrow gorges eroded by the rivers in their brief tumble down from the crests of the mountain walls into the sea. Ayan, the only harbour on this part of the coast, has therefore little chance of being developed. Only at Okhotsk does the foreshore widen into a coastal plain offering more convenient routes into the interior. The eastern part of the coastal area, from Okhotsk to the Gulf of Penzhina, is heavily indented, with numerous peninsulas and coastal islands. Here the spurs of several mountain ranges push out to meet the coast almost at right angles, with long, gently rising valleys running between them into the interior. The diversity of the landscape is further intensified by a broken mountain range running parallel to the coast, which appears only in the peninsulas. The landscape of this coastal region is everywhere the same. Thick woods cover the slopes and fill the deeply carved valleys of the numerous (usually short) rivers and brooks that run into the sea. Only the higher slopes and mountain tops are devoid of trees, and are covered instead by stunted shrubs and moss banks, while the highest points jut out as naked *golzy* above the vegetation line.

From the north-east end of the Gulf of Penzhina a wide plain stretches farther towards the north-east into the interior of the country and continues (interrupted by the 'cross-bar' of a small watershed less than 1,650 feet high) into the Anadyr plain, which opens out in the east into the Bering Sea. Both the *Penzhina* and *Anadyr plains* are very much broken up by the numerous mountain ridges thrusting into them, and their landscapes are similar. In the higher areas between the rivers stretch extensive groves of poplars. The latter change into coniferous forests along the upper reaches of the rivers in the mountainous border districts. Generally speaking the area is part of the forest-tundra zone.

In the north adjacent to the Anadyr region lies the *Chukchen peninsula*. Its coast has been fairly thoroughly explored, but its interior is still almost unknown. There are two mountain ranges covered with scree which run from west to east, with spurs which in some parts reach the coast, where they break off steeply into the sea. There are also plains stretching along both sides of the rivers from the coast into the interior.

All these areas are only sparsely populated, if at all, and among the Russian coastal settlements only Okhotsk and Magadan are of any significance as ports. The breeding of reindeer by the Chukchee on the peninsula which bears their name is worth mentioning.

To the south of the Anadyr plain rise the Koryak Mountains, which cover the whole area as far as Korff Bay: a series of mountain chains, hardly separated one from the other, run through the country in a wide arc from the southern end of the Gulf of Anadyr towards the Kamchatka Mountains. In the vicinity of the coast the rivers have cut deep valleys in which some trees can grow, whereas the plateaux and ridges are covered by pure tundra.

Along the coast of the Bering Sea are sited numerous native and Russian fishing villages; the hinterland is inhabited by remnants of Palaeo-Asiatic peoples who are reindeer-breeders.

*The Kamchatka peninsula* must be counted as one of the most interesting regions of the Soviet Russian Far East. The relief, which (like Sakhalin) is characterized by two mountain ranges, is given added variety by the numerous volcanic cones which top the mountain ridges and which in some cases are still active. The Klyuchevskaya Sopka, which is the highest volcano of the peninsula, rises from the Kamchatka river valley to an altitude of 15,660 feet and makes with its glacial top an imposing picture. The mild climate and abundant rainfall of the peninsula produce a lush vegetation, with the tundra-like moss-steppes of the west coast forming the only large-scale exception. Deciduous forests predominate on the outer slopes of the mountains, while coniferous forests are to be found only in the interior. In addition to the numerous Russians who inhabit the coastal fishing settlements, there are still some Palaeo-Asiatic Koryaks and Kamchadals who have managed to survive in the interior.

The volcanic belt of Kamchatka is continued towards the south by the arc of the Kurile Islands, which, together with the southern half of Sakhalin, have belonged to the Soviet Union since the end of the Second World War.

## Geology and Morphology

The geological history of the whole of the Far Eastern territories is conditioned by the ancient Siberian Shield. The Angara region forms the nucleus of this rock-mass which solidified during the Archaean era. Around this ancient block, which solidified early and has since resisted every orogenetic movement, the earth's crust forms a series of wide folded zones which (with interruptions) belong to progressively younger periods as one moves farther away from the centre. Thus, the youngest Tertiary mountain formations appear only at the outer edges of the area, in Sakhalin and Kamchatka. With the accumulation of these folds a second process took place which profoundly affected the morphology of the whole area: every younger orogenesis, by its powerful tectonic pressure, shattered the rigid folds of the older zone, resulting in fault-formation and vertical shifting, and often leading to thrust-faulting in the peripheral folds. Since every new folding exerted its greatest effect towards the interior in the direction of the old central block, the result is that the degree of disturbance and fracturing of the old mountain masses into individual massifs, blocks, or horsts, diminishes towards the periphery, and the folded mountains are best preserved in the outer zones. These general characteristics of the geological structure can be recognized throughout the whole area, providing that local modifications are overlooked.

Transbaikalia is made up mainly of the oldest structures of the continent, which form the 'old shield of Asia', as Suess has called it. As early as Pre-Cambrian times a mountain range was formed here, with steep narrow folds whose strike-line in this area runs in a south-west to north-east direction, i.e. in the typical Baikalian direction. Powerful erosion reduced it to a peneplain which later was broken up into separate sections through a series of disruptive movements, particularly faulting. The resulting horst-and-trough formations are of decisive significance for the morphology and hydrography of the area. The mountain ranges which we find today in Transbaikalia are nothing but residual or uplifted horsts, the remnants of the old Pre-Cambrian mountain core. The shifting of these blocks, which recurred in several phases up to post-Tertiary times, did not disturb their predominant Baikalian line of strike, and all tectonic lines still run from south-west to north-east, following the old mountain folds. The result is a series of elongated horsts and troughs which it is often possible to follow up across the whole of Transbaikalia, and which are only occasionally intersected by small ridges and depressions. The Lake of Baikal owes its existence to one of the most recent periods of faulting in the area. It is certain that it already existed in the Miocene period, but it received its final form only in late Tertiary times by uplifting of the surrounding area. Its basin consists of four depressions, of which the strike-line of three lies in the Baikalian direction, while the most southerly of the four is aligned with the Sayan range. The Sayan Mountains (the folds of which lie along the south-western rim of the Angara massif) have in their oldest parts a structure similar to that of the Baikalian Mountains, but they are somewhat younger. The direction of their strike-line (generally known as the Sayan direction) is from north-west to south-east, thus running into the Baikalian strike-line almost at right angles.

Only the spurs of the Sayan range reach as far as Transbaikalia. It has not yet been ascertained whether the direction of strike of the Sayans changes here into that of the Baikals, or whether both, merging here, fade out together towards the south.

The denuded cores of the old original mountains are found exposed nearly everywhere in the horsts of Transbaikalia. They consist mainly of granite, syenite, and gabro, as well as numerous other metamorphic rocks of the Pre-Cambrian era, especially gneiss, crystalline slate, marble, and quartz. These rocks determine the prevailing gentle relief of the flat ridges, above which rise here and there the rounded tops of one or two residuals. The relief is livelier and more varied wherever igneous rock, especially porphyry or porphyrite, plays a part in the structure of the surface formations. This is the case with the peak of Sokhondo (8,230 feet), at the source of the Ingoda River, which consists of porphyry and porphyrous tuffs, and which shows an almost alpine formation cut by many valleys. Basalt occurs with greater frequency only in a few individual depressions, for example in the valley of the upper Vitim, in the Tugnuy depression between the Tsagan-Daban and the Saganski Mountains, and in the Zhilok depression. The usual occurrence was a flow of basalt, and only in the upper reaches of the Vitim (in the volcanoes Obruchev, Mushketov, and Lopatin) did the eruptions result in definite crater formations. However, these rise only 330–530 feet above their surroundings.

Towards the north-east there is a gradual transition from the horsts of the inner region of Transbaikalia to more plateau-like formations. The Vitim plateau, whose table-like character is accentuated by its superimposed layers of basalt, is the first of a series of further mountain ranges with similar surface formations. In general the Transbaikalian character is preserved, with Pre-Cambrian rocks forming the basis of extensive horsts, but the wide troughs are missing. Instead, the results of the more recent formative forces—water, ice, and frost—are much more noticeable. Deeply carved valleys are typical, often following the faultlines, but just as often finding their own way. In spite of the general plateau-like character, it is still possible to trace the Baikalian strike-line. In the Patom plateau, however, north of the lower Vitim, this uniformity of character is less clearly maintained. The core of the plateau still consists mainly of metamorphic rock series of the Pre-Cambrian era, and the main folds are also Pre-Cambrian, but the Baikalian direction of strike now disappears.

In a well-defined arc (convex towards the north) the folds turn towards the east and then east-south-east, forced in that direction by the Aldan massif which belongs, like the Angara region, to the hard Archaean core of the old Siberian Shield. The folds then run along the south-western and southern edges of the Aldan massif, until they are violently shattered in the Stanovoy Mountain area east of the Olekma River.

The horsts of the plateau region are generally more pronounced than in Transbaikalia proper. They lie mostly at altitudes between 3,300 and 4,900 feet, with numerous hard residuals composed mainly of intrusive rocks rising above them to altitudes of over 7,500 feet. These old Proterozoic masses contain numerous mineral deposits which are of economic importance, including the richest gold deposits of the USSR, which are found in the regions of the Vitim and the Patom. Apart from the gold quartz seams which are still to be found, gold also appears in the permanently frozen diluvial gravel and the sands of the river valleys.

The Stanovoy mountain system begins to the east of the Olekma River, and to the north of the outlet of its tributary, the Nyukzha. This Proterozoic structure forms the southern edge of the Aldan mass, and represents the continuation of the denuded Transbaikalian body of rock which has been somewhat deflected towards the south by the resistant Aldan mass. At many places, though, the old folds which form the main body of the formation run in a south-east to north-west direction, so that the tectonic and orographic lines do not always conform. A similar south-east to north-west line of Pre-Cambrian folds can be found in the region of the upper Olekma, to the north of the main bend of the Amur. The Olekma depression and the course of the middle Vitim also indicate tectonic lines running in this same direction. It is thus apparent that the Stanovoy Mountains were built up independently of the old fold lines, and are the result of subsequent faulting into horst-and-trough formations, with the old buttresses of the Aldan mass acting as the main determinants of the system's surface relief. The contour lines stretch from west to east in an arc slightly convex to the south. Eruptions of igneous rock are associated with the faulting, and are found in considerable quantity along the northern edge of the area where they have produced steep localized mountain formations. The range proper has the character of a plateau, with an average altitude of 3,900 feet above sea level. The highest point in the area, to the north of the headwaters of the Seya, reaches a height of 8,140 feet. It is typical of large parts of the Stanovoy mountain system that it descends towards the south in shallow steps.

In the east the Stanovoy Mountains stretch as far as the Maya River, a tributary of the Ud, where they adjoin the Dzhugdzhur mountain range. The latter extends north-eastwards along the coast of the Sea of Okhotsk as far as the Okhota River, and is the principal range of a series of three parallel mountain chains. It consists mainly of gneiss, granite, and porphyry, with slate and limestone folds, the fossils of which belong to the Upper Devonian series. This explains the Variscian origin of the Dzhugdzhur Mountains in the west, where they join the older zones forming the eastern edge of the Aldan massif.

Towards the south and south-east the apparently homogeneous block of Pre-Cambrian folds of the Transbaikalian and Stanovoy regions gives way to a series of Mesozoic folds extending as far as the Sea of Japan. These vary considerably in their state of development and degree of preservation as between one individual region and another. The limited extent of knowledge about this part of the country has made it impossible to classify all of the tectonic movements in relation to the date of occurrence, and only a general and rather synoptic view can therefore be given.

The Pre-Cambrian region adjoins a large zone of Caledonian and Variscian folding, which stretches from Mongolia to the Sea of Okhotsk and is aligned with the direction of strike of the older zone. The eastern parts, including the middle region of the Amur into which the Triassic and Jurassic seas were still able to penetrate, belong to the Cimmeric orogenesis, which can be regarded as the most powerful affecting the Far Eastern regions. Its influence was felt far into the interior, where, to a greater or lesser extent, it overwhelmed earlier formations, breaking them up into elevated blocks with intervening depressions. The Cimmerian zone is replaced by that of the Tertiary Alpine orogenesis in the peripheral areas, particularly in Sakhalin and Kamchatka, and in the Koryak mountain area, which is situated in the middle of the Penzhina–Anadyr depression. On the mainland, the effects of the Tertiary movements can be recognized in the warping and the shifting of blocks in the Amur region.

In south-east Transbaikalia, as in other parts of this region, the characteristic horst formations are predominant, but the regular trough formation is less evident here, and the individual mountain ridges owe their form mainly to simple faulting. The greater intensity of the tectonic influence in these areas can be attributed to the Mesozoic orogenesis which is already in evidence here. North-east of Nerchinsk, in the Shikal Mountains, it is known that the Cimmerian mountain formation is prevalent. Farther south again, in the Nerchinsk Mountains, to the north and east of the railway station of Borsya, the existence of pre- and post-Jurassic folds with north-east strike-lines has been proved, while along the upper Ingoda there appear old north-west folds underlying more recent folds, the strike-lines of which run in the Baikalian direction. The outer limit of the old Baikalian peneplain which remained un-influenced by the Mesozoic orogenesis must therefore be located to the west of a line from Nerchinsk to Borsya.

The Yablonovy range (which belongs entirely to the Pre-Cam-brian horst region) is situated south of the upper Vitim and its tributary, the Kalakarn, and pushes north-east almost as far as the Olekma River. To the north-west are the Kalar Mountains, which contain several lofty summits, including Golez Skalisty (9,184 feet) and Golez Snezhny (8,249 feet). These regions, to which the Olekminsk Stanovik (in the hinterland of the upper Olekma) also belong, have not yet been completely explored and at present there is little that can be said about them.

Towards the south, at the foot of the Stanovoy Mountains, lies the upper Seya plain and its western continuation, the Gilyuy val-ley, forming a wide trough covered with river deposits containing gold. The centre of the trough is at an altitude of 1,079 feet. To the south this trough is terminated by an elongated mountain range which, like the Stanovoy range, runs in an east–west direc-tion; these are the Tukuringra–Dzhagdy Mountains. The Yankan ridge forms the connexion towards the west with Olekminsk Stanovik. The whole mountain range consists mainly of gneiss, granite, and mica, but some folds of Palaeozoic rock have been found as well, so that an earlier presumption that the whole range is of Pre-Cambrian age does not hold good. Lines of local fractur-ing occur throughout the mountain mass, and are especially pro-nounced along its southern foot. The wave-like surface is strongly eroded and is surmounted by numerous groups of residuals which rise up to 4,248 feet. The average altitude of the passes is between 2,952 and 3,280 feet. Towards the south the Tukuringra Moun-tains are cut by the Seya River, the only outlet of the enclosed trough bearing the same name. Terrace formations indicate more recent vertical movements. Beyond the River Dep, a left-hand tributary of the lower Seya, the mountain range is known as the Dzhagdy Mountains—a wide high ridge which terminates the upper Seya plain in the east and forms the link with the Stanovoy Mountains. The two principal directions of strike (towards the north-east and towards the north-west) are both found in the Dzhagdy mountain range, which is the explanation for its winding course. Its ridge forms the watershed between the River Ud, which flows into the Sea of Okhotsk, and the Selemdzha River, which flows into the Seya. The head-waters of the Selemdzha are almost completely encircled by high mountain ridges which form the northern part of the Bureya mountain area.

The Bureya mountain area includes the whole of the Bureya river-basin, and its flanks extend as far as the lower Amur and the Amgun. Here again the north-east strike-line is clearly visible, both in the Turana ridge west of the River Bureya, and particularly in the Bureya range which forms the spine of this whole mountain region. This latter range is a continuation of the Little Chingan, which lies in Manchurian territory, and it therefore often carries this name even in Russian territory. The Amur River, running between high rocky banks, cuts through this mountain range in a valley more than 93 miles long and often only half a mile in width. Here by the Amur the Bureya Mountains are only from 650 to 1,650 feet high, but they rise towards the north, where, between the sources of the Selemdzha and the Bureya rivers, there are the highest peaks of the region, with altitudes of 7,070 and 6,950 feet. In this area various parts of the mountain range have special local names, e.g. the Dusse-Alin, which surrounds the head-waters of the Bureya, and the Yam-Alin. The latter attains a height of 6,560 feet. Scattered throughout the area there are frequent occurrences of porphyry and diabase (in addition to the usual gneiss, granite, and metamorphic slate), while in the south Jurassic sediments predominate. The valley of the Bureya contains large deposits of severely fractured Jurassic coal. The ridges frequently show the character of intensely dissected plateaux.

The course of the lower Seya divides the wide plain of the middle Amur into two parts: the Amur–Seya plateau to the west, and the Seya–Bureya plain to the east. The former is a plateau about 800 feet high, sloping down gently from north-west to south-east, with flat watershed areas and deeply incised valleys. It is composed of evenly deposited Jurassic and Tertiary beds, the latter containing lignite. Along the steep river-banks of the Seya the Tertiary deposits are 500 feet thick measuring up from the river-bed. Below these beds granite and gneiss are sometimes to be found, and occasionally porphyry, melaphyry, and basalt. The

D

area between the Seya and the Bureya is higher in the north, where it shows a hilly relief. On the left-hand side of the Seya, and along the Amur towards the east as far as the mouth of the Bureya and beyond, it forms a pronounced peneplain which is filled mainly with young Tertiary deposits, although in the gullies between individual hills there are older rocks to be found. The whole region of the middle Amur owes its present form to an extensive warping of the peneplain in the Tertiary era. However, there were also subsequent vertical movements which are shown by four clearly defined terraces along both the Seya and the Amur, the highest lying 330–390 feet above the present level of the lower Seya.

The region of the lower Amur, which starts at Khabarovsk, can best be regarded as an elongated trough running between the Little Chingan and Bureya Mountains on the one hand, and the Sikhota-Alin Mountains on the other. The northern part of the lower Amur region is very broken up and has not yet been much explored. Here also, as in the Bureya Mountains, the folds run predominantly towards the north-east, but there has been extreme disruption of the structure which can be traced back to two successive Variscian disturbances. The inlets between the southern Shantar Isles can be regarded as fault troughs, and the islands themselves (which consist of slate and granite) as residual horsts.

The lower Amur River comes close to the sea at the lakes of Kisi and Kada, but then turns away again towards the north to be joined by the Argun before turning sharply eastwards to drain into the sea. This strange course is due firstly to eruptions of andesite and basalt which occurred during the formation of the Sikhota-Alin Mountains, and secondly to later crustal movements.

The Sikhota-Alin is a mountain massif surrounded on all sides by faults, with sedimentary deposits occurring only in the south. The main folding took place in the Lower Cretaceous period, with the folds lying in a direction varying between north-east and east-north-east, with thrust-faults towards the north-west. The steep faults which occurred later (with the main fault lines running parallel to the strike-lines of the folds) disrupted the Sikhota-Alin and Ussuri areas by resulting in both uplifting and subsidence. The latter was responsible for creating both the Ussuri depression and the coast-line of the area. Farther north opposite Sakhalin the coastal fault-line turns northwards and converges with the strike-line of the folds. In the south the Sikhota-Alin is terminated by a transverse fault. The following facts concerning the composition of the rock in this area are of the greatest significance in relation to present surface features. In both the central and peripheral areas granite forms the oldest layers, appearing on the old surfaces and on the lower slopes as pronounced blocks. The flanks are covered chiefly by younger rocks which have been strongly folded and disturbed. These are composed mainly of crystalline slate, gneiss, mica, and quartzites in the west, with phyllites, clay and gravel slates, and sandstone predominating in the centre. Of the erupted igneous rocks, the porphyries generally form numerous round domes, while the basalt has spread out as thin sheets over extensive areas. The southern part of the Sikhota-Alin is distinguished from the northern area by the appearance of overfolds.

Thick layers of Carboniferous and Permian marble blocks are found at numerous places, particularly on the high mountains. North-westerly inversions of the Jurassic and Triassic beds are indicative of thrust-faulting which must have taken place during the time between the Upper Jurassic and Miocene periods, with the thrusts coming from the direction of the Sea of Japan. The surface features are uniform on the whole. Long deeply divided ridges capped by round domes are characteristic, as are the winding, unevenly developed valleys with slopes which are often convex. The rivers have worn deep canyons into the layers of basalt. Vertical movements, which started in the Pleistocene period and which have not yet come to an end, are important in relation to the younger features of the relief. Near Vladivostok there are abrasion terraces which are 35, 100, 160, 390, and at some places nearly 1,000 feet high. At present the south coast is a submergent coast, while the east coast is probably emergent. The tilted position of the whole of the Sikhota-Alin block, which slopes down towards the interior, is a consequence of the early and later Pleistocene uplifts.

The Alpine zone of folds is limited to the outermost peripheral regions and is preserved only in fragments, which nevertheless give recognizable indications of two large arcs of folds. The more western of these appears on Sakhalin and probably reappears at the north coast of the Sea of Okhotsk in the Chutnavar Mountains, west of Magadan, and on the peninsula of Koni Pyagina and Taygonos, thence circling in a wide arc around the Penzhina depression in the west and the Anadyr plain in the north. Kamchatka, together with the Koryak Mountains to the north-east, forms the centre of the second arc, with the Kuriles forming a continuation southwards to the Japanese islands, where the two arcs of folds meet on the island of Jesso. The western arc differs from the eastern in having none of the active volcanoes which are characteristic of Kamchatka and the Kuriles.

On Sakhalin the presence of several alternate marine and continental formations in the Upper Cretaceous and Tertiary sedimentary deposits proves that the island is situated at the edge of a geosyncline. The two mountain ranges, which are separated by the longitudinal depression of the Tym and the Poronay (filled with young Tertiary marine deposits), are essentially different from each other. The eastern range rises up to 6,600 feet and displays an older (probably Variscian) folding with pronounced intrusions, together with faults and block formations. The western range consists only of younger rocks, mainly Upper Cretaceous and early Tertiary deposits. Here the meridional strike-line of the Tertiary folds repeats the direction followed by the Variscian folds of the eastern range. The folding has many individual irregularities and is less pronounced towards the north. Of the three Tertiary periods which are discernible, the youngest is characterized mainly by longitudinal faults with intrusions which are in evidence at both coasts. The vertical movements which accompany these have lasted up to the present time; and although the northern tip of the island is in a state of submergence, the Quaternary marine deposits in the centre of the island have been lifted up to as much as 490 feet, and five raised beaches are visible along the shore.

Kamchatka is structurally similar to Sakhalin. The Kamchatka River from the south and the Yelovka River from the north meet in a depression separating the two mountain ranges, which both run parallel with the trough in a north-north-easterly direction. Kamchatka also has an eastern section containing remnants of an old Caledonian or Variscian folded zone, but its folds run towards the north-west to meet the Tertiary folds at right angles, thus partially accounting for the considerable fracturing which is such a pronounced feature in the east. The western range is a chain of hills of medium height (3,300–3,900 feet), consisting basically of crystalline slates and phyllites covered with layers of sandstone and slate (probably of Palaeozoic age) together with Upper Cretaceous and Tertiary deposits (the latter from the Oligocene to the Pliocene periods), with powerful igneous intrusions.

The formation has been repeatedly folded towards the southeast producing overfolds and a general north-north-easterly direction of strike. West of this mountain range stretches a dissected coastal plateau, uplifted to 2,000–2,500 feet, which consists partly of dislocated Pliocene marine deposits and partly of Upper Cretaceous deposits. The plateau drops down to the Sea of Okhotsk in a series of raised beaches. This coastal zone shows slight undulations and is interrupted by isolated elevations, composed of igneous intrusions. The western chain contains numerous dead and shattered volcanoes. In the centre of the chain rises the only active volcano in the western half of Kamchatka—the Ichinskaya Sopka (11,830 feet), with its enormous dome and several hanging glaciers, whose crater produces a constant cloud of smoke. The eastern side of Kamchatka, in contrast to the unbroken emergent west coast, is characterized by numerous bays resulting from subsidence. The eastern mountain range is very broken up, and is covered by volcanic deposits which leave only fragments of the original structure visible. The granite and crystalline slate in this area are thought to be Proterozoic. Tectonic movements have penetrated the structure so completely that even the Pliocene formations are overfolded. The disruption here is associated with the intensive volcanic activity along the eastern side of the peninsula. The eruptions generally occur along large faults which run at right angles to the folding. Seventy-four of the 127 known volcanoes belong to young volcanic formations, and eighteen of these are still active today. The most important is the gigantic symmetrical andesite cone of the Klyuchevskaya Sopka (15,660 feet), which is covered with glacial snows down to an altitude of 4,900 feet. The Commander (Kommandorskii) Islands, too, are young volcanic areas, where Tertiary deposits are also to be found.

In the north the Kamchatka peninsula is connected with the mainland by only a narrow plateau (rising up to 510 feet) called the Parapolsky-Dol, which was uplifted only in recent times. The Koryak Mountains stretch northwards from this narrow strip, forming a wide mountainous zone in which the ridges continue the strike-line of the Kamchatka folds. The three known principal ranges—the Palpal, the Tingeney, and the Rarytkin—consist, as far as is known today, of Cretaceous and Tertiary deposits with basalt intrusions. The present formation of the area is apparently due to comparatively recent block-faulting, which was most intensive in the Pleistocene period and gave rise to overthrusts and even overfolding of beds. At present the coast is emergent in these areas, and two elevated raised beaches can be seen. However, the whole of the Koryak mountain region has been little explored, and the structure of this area awaits further clarification in the future.

The southern tip of Kamchatka is adjoined by the Arc of the

Kuriles. Twenty-eight of these islands have volcanoes, eighteen of which are still active.

Information about the Anadyr region and the Chukchen peninsula is also still very limited, and only the coastal areas have been more fully explored. The strike-line of the mountains appears to differ and to be influenced by an older nucleus—the 'Chukchen mass'—in the north, around which the mountains are arranged much as they are around the old Angara mass. A main 'fold-track' runs in a roughly west to east direction across the Chukchen peninsula, consisting probably of two mountain chains. Farther south, in the vicinity of the Kolyma River, the mountain ranges (which belong to the Mesozoic orogenesis) seem to have a south-east to north-west direction of strike.

## The Ice Age and its Effects

The greater part of Transbaikalia and the Far East was spared the Quaternary Glaciation. It is possible that over large parts of the country the proximity of the high-pressure system of Central Asia, with its outflowing currents of air in winter and the resulting moderate amount of precipitation, was an important contributory factor, while in other areas a more southern position may be taken as an additional factor of importance. In those areas where it proved possible for glaciation to occur, special local conditions must have prevailed to bring it about, but research has not yet gone far enough to provide the final explanation for its occurrence. Only three areas were affected to any large extent by glaciation: the extreme north-east, the peninsula of Kamchatka, and the area to the east and north-east of Lake Baikal. Even in these areas the glaciation was limited mainly to the mountains and the higher parts of the country, while the lower-lying plains remained free of it. Consequently, however large the area affected by glaciation, it was always of a purely local character and not to be compared with the immense ice-cover experienced by Europe.

The glaciation of the extreme north-east is closely connected with the glaciation throughout the whole of north-east Siberia, resulting in a complex system of glaciated mountains with ice-free plateaux and plains in between. The glaciated areas are distributed over the whole of the region from the lower Lena in the west to the Chukchen peninsula in the east, forming a marked contrast with the conditions in middle Siberia, the larger part of which remained free from ice. The next areas of glaciation are not to be

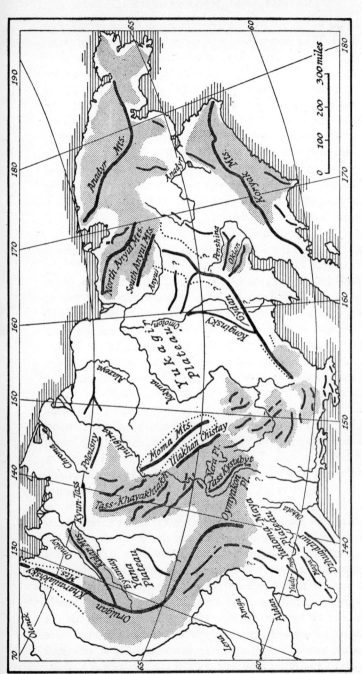

4. THE GLACIATION OF NORTH-EAST SIBERIA

The tinted areas indicate the glaciated regions. Apart from the areas around the Kolyma mouth, the Chukchen coast and the Koryak peninsula, this glaciation is of an alpine type and the areas shown on this map therefore are somewhat too extensive. The dotted lines around some of the mountain chains indicate areas not yet fully explored.

found until far to the west of the lower Lena, in the river valley of
the Khatanga. The north-east Siberian area of glaciation thus
forms one large area throughout which similar conditions were
prevalent. The Far Eastern territories form only part of North-East
Siberia, but in order to avoid taking them out of their setting it
seems advisable to deal with the whole of the area in our consideration of Ice-Age conditions, so as to give a better impression of the overall situation. Certain limitations will still remain,
however, since the extremely tentative nature of research into the
subject permits exact information to be provided for only a few
individual areas, while for the rest only a general picture can be
given. (In this connexion, the reader's attention is drawn to the
author's essay 'Die Eiszeit in Sibirien'—'The Ice Age in Siberia'—
published in the periodical *Erdkunde*, Vol. V, Bonn, 1951.)

Glaciation east of the River Lena begins at the Verkhoyansk
mountain range. This arc-shaped range starts in the north with the
Kharaulakhskiye Mountains (4,000–5,000 feet), whose spurs extend as far as the Lena delta, but whether these particular mountains have been subject to glaciation or not has not yet been
generally confirmed. Some scientists, such as Parkhomenko (149)
and Saks (170), believe that they have, but others, such as Romanov (166) and Vollossovich, think not, even though these mountains still carry glaciers today. The picture is much clearer in the
Orulgan Mountains (heights up to 6,560 feet), which are found
immediately to the south, since there are unmistakable signs here
of extensive valley glaciation (84). To the west the glaciers
emerged from the valleys and coalesced to form a piedmont
glacier which advanced almost as far as the present line of the
Lena. To the east they advanced as far as the Bytantay, a left-hand
tributary of the Yana (170). According to Saks, the Kular Mountains (on the left side of the Bytantay), which extend north-east
from the Orulgan Mountains to the lower Yana, have also under-
gone glaciation. The Verkhoyansk Mountains proper, which begin at the source of the Bytantay and rise as high as 6,600 feet towards the west and 8,200 feet towards the south-east, underwent
glaciation similar to that which affected the Orulgans. Again it
was the valley glaciation which prevailed, but in this case it was
more powerful and extensive. The glaciers emerged towards the
south-west and the south, creating a uniform piedmont ice-sheet
which pushed forward as far as the Lena and the Aldan, reaching
distances up to 125 miles from the foot of the mountains and descending to altitudes of 6,000 feet (64, 137). At the time of their

greatest expansion they reached as far as a line from Okhotsk to the lower reaches of the Aldan. According to Saks, traces of an old glaciation have also been found in the Dzhugdzhur Mountains, which run along the coast of the Sea of Okhotsk, but no exact information about the nature and extent of the glaciation is yet available.

The spread of the Verkhoyansk glaciers towards the north has not yet been explored systematically enough to allow any final conclusions to be drawn, but Khmysnikov (45) has not found any moraines on the high Yana plateau (Yanskoye Ploskogorye). The south-eastern part in the area of the upper Indirka, however, is better known. Here, between the Verkhoyansk Mountains and the Cherski range, are two plateaux: the Oymyakon plateau (source of the Indirka) in the south, and the Nerskye plateau (from which the Nera drains into the Indirka) in the north. The two plateaux are separated from each other by the Tass-Kystabyt Mountains. The Cherski Mountains (which, apart from Kamchatka, possess the highest elevations of north-east Siberia, including Mount Chen at 9,990 feet) were covered by a considerable depth of ice to which S. V. Obruchev ascribes the character of a continental glaciation. Even today these mountains still have glaciers whose full extent remains unknown. The ice-cap spread over the Nera plateau (altitude 3,300–3,900 feet), over the Tass-Kystabyt Mountains (which through their own glacier formations added to the total thickness of the ice-mass), and over the Oymyakon plateau (altitude 4,900 feet), where it met with the north-flowing glaciers of the Verkhoyansk Mountains. Thus the whole area between the two principal mountain ranges had an unbroken cover of ice. According to Obruchev, the ice-cap over the Oymyakon plateau was as much as 1,300 feet thick.

Strangely enough, the very substantial glaciation of the Cherski Mountains developed only slightly towards the north, and the north-flowing ice-masses did not even reach the Momskiye Mountains which run parallel to the Cherski range beyond the Moma river valley. Some scientists believe that the Momskiye Mountains (whose highest peaks rise to altitudes of more than 6,500 feet) were untouched by glaciation, but others disagree with this view, and the matter remains unsettled. Further north, between the Yana and the Indigirka rivers, it is known that the Tass-Khayakhtakh Mountains were glaciated, and that from here the glaciers advanced as far as the Indigirka, at a latitude of about 68° N. In the extreme north there was no glaciation of the Polousny

Mountains, according to the latest information, although they attain heights up to 3,900 feet (170).

The mountain ranges along the upper Kolyma (including the Garmychan, the Arga Tas, and others) show numerous clear traces of glaciation, but these are never found below altitudes of 1,600 feet, and it is therefore presumed that there was only local glaciation in these areas. The Kolyma plateau, which adjoins these mountains to the north, also has only local centres of glaciation of moderate size. More detailed information about these areas does not exist.

Between the upper drainage area of the Kolyma and the coast of the Sea of Okhotsk, and also in the southern part of the Gydan Mountains (often called the Kolyma Mountains), glaciation was again more extensive and attained the unbroken form of an ice-cap. This mainly affected the slopes running down towards the Sea of Okhotsk, on which were superimposed extensive masses of ice. At the time of their greatest expansion these resembled the Norwegian type, with glaciers flowing from the height of the Gydan range (altitude 6,600 feet) down to the coast (74, 137). The northern Gydan, lying in the interior of the country, is also presumed to have been completely glaciated, and this glaciation continued as far as the Chukchen peninsula.

In contrast to the relatively intense glaciation of the mountains, the plains lying inside the arcs of the Verkhoyansk and Gydan mountain ranges were completely free from any ice-cover. This applies to the higher plateaux as well as to the coastal plains and hinterland, which are morphologically very different units, and includes the lowlands of the Omoloy, Yana, Indigirka, and Kolyma rivers, the Alasseya plateau (altitude 650–2,300 feet) on the eastern side of the Indigirka, and the Yukagir plateau (Yukagirskoye Ploskogorye: altitude 1,000–1,300 feet, with local elevations of 3,300–3,900 feet) on the east side of the Kolyma. Research into these areas, including the early work by Vollossovich and later studies such as those of S. V. Obruchev (74) and Waker (224), has not led to the discovery of any traces of glaciation. Only Vollossovich found some sandy deposits and erratics in the river valley of the Omolon (a right-hand tributary of the Kolyma), which he thought might be of fluvio-glacial origin, but which could have been transported there by river ice. The modest extent of these finds certainly makes the latter explanation quite possible.

The region between the lower Kolyma and the Chukchen peninsula is considered, according to present knowledge, to have been completely glaciated. Numerous reports are available to confirm this, but the nature of the glaciation has not been clearly established. S. V. Obruchev (136) is of the opinion that the ice-cap did not completely cover the whole area. The principal area of glaciation was the Anadyr Mountains, together with the northern Anyuy Mountains in the west and the Chukchen peninsula in the east. The boundaries of the whole area of glaciation have not yet been fixed in detail, but there are numerous reports indicating that the glaciers stretched locally as far as the coast, that is, to Chaun Bay in the north, and to Cape Chaplin and Providenya Bay in the east. Towards the south, in the direction of the Anadyr depression, they passed beyond the foot of the mountains to only a small extent. From the northern Anyuy Mountains the zone of glaciation continues south towards the Gydan Mountains, but there is no information as to how far it extends in this direction. According to Saks (170), new research has been carried out in the region of these glaciated areas and also on the Chukchen peninsula, but nothing has yet been published.

The glaciation of the Koryak peninsula was almost as extensive and unbroken as that in the north. The ice-masses originated in the Koryak Mountains (altitudes 4,300–7,200 feet), and flowed from here on a wide front towards the sea, covering the mountain slopes with their gentle south-easterly gradient, and even reaching the coast in some places. In contrast to this, the opposite north-westerly flow of ice, towards the lowlands of the Anadyr and Penzhina rivers, was only slight.

Apart from the northern and southern edges, the Anadyr lowlands themselves are free of all traces of ice, as Polevoy (155), Sostsava (195), and S. V. Obruchev (136) have all confirmed. In the western hinterland, too, between the upper Anadyr and the Penzhina, glacial traces are very rare and are to be found only locally in the mountain ridges, starting at heights not less than 3,300 feet. The transition area from the Anadyr lowlands to Penzhina Bay was also untouched by any sort of glaciation. However, to the north of this latter area the Kameny and Ichigemsky mountains were once the home of glaciers whose presence is proved by glacial deposits along the Oklan, a right-hand tributary of the Penzhina. Some individual glaciers even pushed forward as far as the Penzhina and carried some erratics close to the mouth of the river.

During the Ice Age the Anadyr lowlands were doubtless separated by areas of heavy mountain glaciation from the basin of the

Kolyma, much as the latter was isolated from the Yana and the Indigirka. The Anadyr lowlands were thus able to play a special part as a refuge for arctic flora; here plants could survive, to take possession of the liberated country once again after the disappearance of the ice. Tolmachev (217, 218) and the Swede, Hultén (81), have done some detailed research on this subject. The latter has ascertained that conditions similar to those of the Anadyr lowlands must also have been prevalent across the straits in Alaska, and because of the similarity of plants and their distribution on both sides of the Bering Sea, he draws the conclusion that during the Ice Age a continental link must have existed between the two continents. Antevs and Daly (48) have estimated that the eustatic sinking of the water level during the period of maximum glaciation was between 300 and 330 feet. On the basis of the existing underwater configuration of land in the vicinity of the Bering Straits, a drop in the sea level of 160 feet would produce a continental link 190 miles wide, while a drop of 330 feet would result in a link 750 miles wide. On the basis of his research into the geographical distribution of the flora, Hultén maintains that a continental link at least 750 miles wide must once have existed.

If a continental link of this width did exist, the climatic conditions in 'Beringia' (as Hultén calls the whole of this continental connexion) must have differed greatly from those of today. The warm water of the Pacific must have washed against its south coast, and its mitigating influence must have penetrated to the north, making itself felt at least in the lower-lying regions in the south of the Chukchen and Alaskan peninsulas. This is the only explanation for the fact that relics of a Tertiary flora (including different kinds of timber such as the *Chosenia macropolis* and the *Betula cajandri*) have been preserved up to present times in the Anadyr and Penzhina lowlands, surrounded as they are by glaciated mountains.

As it may well be that isostatic forces played a part over a considerable period in both building and preserving this continental link, the possibility that such a bridge existed right into postglacial times cannot be completely discounted. The Quaternary marine deposits in the Bering Straits are considered to be deposits of an inner basin. The marine transgression into the Anadyr basin must have been a very late one; the basin consists exclusively of recent formations in an excellent state of preservation which are obviously very young, indicating a late appearance of the sea. The recognition that a continental link had continued to exist until some time in the post-glacial period would explain in a plausible way the migration of mankind from Asia to America, although the establishment of the exact proof must remain a task for the future.

On Kamchatka even today the high volcanic peaks—Klyuchevskaya Sopka (15,660 feet), Sopka Tolbachin (12,080 feet), Koryatskaya Sopka (11,340 feet), and others—are covered with glaciers which descend to altitudes of about 4,000 feet. Abundant proof of a former glaciation is available, particularly along the south-east coast. A fully developed U-shaped glaciated valley more than 30 miles long has been found, which almost reached the coast at Avachinskaya Bay, near the town of Petropavlovsk, and there are moraines 650–800 feet above sea level at the foot of the Kameny volcano (103). Several research scholars believe that this was a case of a foreland glaciation which in some places reached as far as the coast (101). In contrast to these conditions, the glaciation of areas near the west coast was less extensive and powerful than along the east coast, and the glaciers advanced only very little beyond the foot of the mountains into the flat coastal plain, getting no closer to the coast than 40–50 miles at the latitude of Petropavlovsk (101). Farther to the north, in the region of the River Byeyala, the old moraines are at heights of 2,060–2,250 feet above sea level, again proving that glaciation was less in the west than in the east. The glaciation of Kamchatka originated in both the eastern and western mountains, and the ice-masses amalgamated in the south, where the two mountain ranges meet. Thus the Kamchatka valley was bounded on three sides by glaciated mountains, but in spite of this the valley proper was never glaciated. In the middle of the elongated valley (which is no more than 50 miles wide) only river and marine deposits can be found, and it is only at the edges that there appear first fluvio-glacial formations and then moraines as well (113). The glaciation thus reflects the same conditions of precipitation which prevail today. During the Ice Age the snow-line lay at about 2,300 feet, while today it is at heights of 4,900–5,900 feet.

Finally, among the regions of extensive glaciation, the environs of Lake Baikal have still to be mentioned. These are primarily the mountainous areas to the north-east of the lake, stretching from its north-eastern end right across the Vitim to the Olekma, and including the North Baikalian Mountains and the Patom plateau. According to the printed works of numerous scholars (Krapotkin, V. Obruchev, A. Gerassimov, and others), the fact that an

extensive glaciation of these regions took place has been ascertained beyond doubt, but there is a difference of opinion about the
character of the glaciation which is being only slowly resolved.
V. Obruchev was the first to maintain that there had once existed

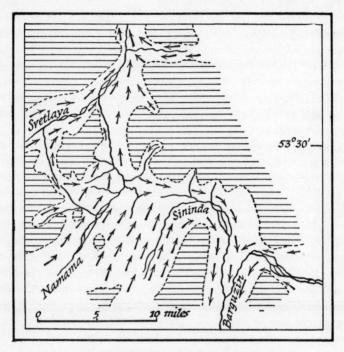

5. THE GLACIATION OF TRANSBAIKALIA
(*After* Eskola, *Bibliog.* 58)

This sketch map indicates the distribution of the glaciers in
the region of the watershed between the Barguzin River and
the Namama River, which flows via the Svetlaya into the
Upper Angara. The white areas show the glaciers and the
arrows indicate the direction of the flow of the ice. The
glaciers followed the valleys, the intervening heights remaining untouched. The type of glaciation shown on this map can
be taken as typical for the whole of Transbaikalia.

a continental glaciation, and from this he derived the concept of a
large-scale glaciation over the whole of northern Siberia which
later proved to be erroneous. As proof of the continental character of the glaciation north-east of Lake Baikal, Obruchev mentions the following main characteristics: rounded valley slopes,

roches moutonées, corries and corrie-lakes, U-shaped valleys, shoreline terraces, eskers, &c., as well as erratic blocks found on the watersheds. Meister (128) proved later that the 'erratic blocks' on the watersheds are of local origin and are composed of rock similar to the local sub-strata usually found covered by other deposits. In these areas, where the subsoil is permanently frozen, the rounded slopes may well be the result of solifluction. Meister says, 'At the Vaga I saw clayey masses of an enormous extent whose movement carried away trees hundreds of years old as if a hurricane had passed over them; embedded in the clay were pieces of nearby rock formations also being carried away; in short, it was a young clay glacier!' (123, pp. 22–23). On the strength of these and other proofs, V. Obruchev altered his opinion and adopted the idea of a gradually decreasing glaciation, changing from a continental ice-cap in the north (in the Vitim–Olekma mountain region) to an alpine type of glaciation in the south. However, the results of further research show that in fact we are dealing here with an example of a general alpine-type glaciation. East of Lake Baikal, between the Vitim, upper Angara, and Barguzin rivers, Eskola (58) has done some research which clearly establishes the alpine character of these areas. The valleys of most of the rivers (including the Barguzin, Svetlaya, Sininda, Namama, Oktokitan, and others) were filled with ice-masses of the large valley glaciers, which were 1,300–1,600 feet thick. The higher areas rose above the ice-level of the valleys, but they themselves gave rise to small glaciers which flowed down to join the valley glaciers below. The Barguzin mountain area, whose remarkable similarity with the Alps is specially mentioned by all students of this area, can well serve as an example of the whole region.

Strangely enough, the valley of the upper Angara, which runs a long way to the east between the glaciated mountains (that is, between the upper Angara Mountains in the north and the Barguzin Mountains in the south) was completely untouched by glaciation.

To the south of Lake Baikal the mountains also carried glaciers which in the valleys of the Slyudyanka and Pokhabkha rivers reached as far as the lake in the form of valley glaciers. Here, within an area of 23 square miles, more than twenty-five glaciers have been counted, but they were all insignificant and less than 30 miles in length. The region is rich in corries, which are to be found at widely different heights, varying between 160 and 2,000 feet above the present level of the lake (altitude 1,490 feet above sea level).

The snow-line in the Ice Age must therefore have been very low here, as compared with the nearby Sayan Mountains, where it was roughly at 6,500 feet, or the north-eastern Baikalian Mountains, where it was at least as high as 3,900 feet. An explanation for this striking phenomenon could be found in the influence of Lake Baikal, which may have affected the climate of the surrounding area even in the Ice Age, particularly towards the south, where there is even today a high amount of precipitation. The slopes of the Khamar-Daban which face towards the lake receive a larger amount of precipitation than any other area in Transbaikalia. An additional factor which must be considered is the recent subsidence south of Lake Baikal which is still continuing, and which could account for some subsequent dislocation of the glacial traces.

Apart from the areas of glaciation described above, there are additional areas of local glaciation to be found in Transbaikalia, the best-known being those of the Sokhono (altitude 8,200 feet) and neighbouring mountains on whose slopes corries, U-shaped valleys, and even moraines appear.

Traces of an old glaciation have also been found in the Dzhugd-zhur Mountains, as well as in the Stanovoy (8,140 feet) and the Yam-Alin (7,265 feet), and in the higher parts of the Tukuringra Mountains on both sides of the Seya gap. However, these characteristics are not to be found anywhere to any great extent, and their appearance in only a few limited areas suggests that they were due solely to local, patch-like glacier formations.

### Regions of Permanently Frozen Subsoil and their Significance

The greater part of Soviet Russia's Far Eastern territories lie in the zone of permanently frozen subsoil or 'permafrost', as this phenomenon of nature has been called. It therefore deserves to be dealt with in considerable detail within the framework of this book. The Soviet authorities have taken a special interest in the research work on this phenomenon which is so typical of the greater part of Siberia, and also of some parts of the European North. B. Shostakovich and M. Sumgin are both distinguished names associated with research in this field. Eight permanent research stations have been built, of which four lie within the area under discussion. These are Petrovsk in Transbaikalia, Skovorodino on the railway line north of the northern arc of the Amur, Bomnak in the basin of the upper Seya, and a fourth in the Anadyr region. The sketch map on page 67, which is based on Russian sources, indicates the extent of permafrost in Transbaikalia and the Far East. It can be seen that in these regions the only parts which are completely free from permafrost are the areas adjacent to the rivers Seya and Bureya, including the whole of the area between them, and the areas to the east of the Bureya Mountains, including the whole of the Ussuri region and the coastal region. No areas of permafrost have been found in the greater part of South Kamchatka, or on the island of Sakhalin.

In the regions which are dominated by permafrost the ground thaws only on the surface, to a depth varying with the locality, while below lies a layer of permanently frozen subsoil which also varies in thickness from place to place. The upper layer, which thaws in the summer, is called the 'active layer' (Deyatelyny Sloy) by the Russians, and only this layer sustains any organic life. In the majority of cases the small particles of soil in the 'perennial ice-floor' are so firmly cemented together by the ice that the ground can be broken up only by the use of a crowbar. This cementing together by ice is not sufficient, by itself, to indicate the areas of permafrost; since it is solid, the subsoil temperature is the overriding determinant. Rocks can also carry the perennial ice-floor, although no external changes may be evident.

In winter the ground starts to freeze from the surface down. In some cases the winter frost zone and the perennial frost zone knit together to form a uniform mass, but in most cases a horizon of unfrozen soil remains between the two, from which water breaks through the frozen upper layer either in special morphological circumstances, particularly at the foot of slopes, or by the pressure exerted from above by the frozen surface of the ground. This produces ice formations (called Naledy) superimposed on the frozen ground, which may cover large areas and reach thicknesses of 3–6 feet in cases where several waves of upwelling water are frozen superimposed on each other. Under other conditions nodules of ice are formed beneath the surface, which grow and force the overlying ground upwards to form hillocks. These subside again during the warm season, when they are often replaced by hollows filled with pools of water.

As a rule, since precipitation has to run away mainly on the surface, the existence of the perennial ice-floor prevents moisture from sinking in to more than a certain limited depth. This is a common reason for the irregular flow of water in the rivers of these regions, which all show such a marked difference between

E

high and low water levels. At the confluence of the Shilka and the Argun, the Amur has a yearly average flow of 42,000 cubic feet per second, with a minimum for the year of only 4,400 cubic feet per second. Any increase in the amount of rainfall immediately produces a flood-like rise in the water levels of the rivers. The thawing of the surface layers of the ground provides the best possible conditions for solifluction, particularly in areas of varied morphological formation, and the permafrost zone is thus the classical area for soil creep and landslides.

Apart from these numerous and very interesting natural phenomena, we must consider the effects of permafrost on the people and their economy, since these effects are noticeable everywhere throughout these regions and are the cause of unexpected difficulties. The expansion of the moisture in the ground as it freezes causes local upheavals of the surface which seriously damage lines of communication. Deep cracks appear in the roads, through which mud and water often well up from the lower (still unfrozen) layers of the ground to the surface, where they freeze, forcing the cracks open still further and forming large humps which gradually render the roads unusable. Then with the thaw the surface subsides and disintegrates into a morass of mud and slush. Moreover, the roads, and particularly the bridges, apparently encourage such destructive ice formations. As an example of this tendency, Sumgin mentions the road leading from Bolshoy Never on the Amur railway, via Tyndinsk and the gold-mining region of the Aldan Mountains, to Yakutsk on the Lena River, a total distance of about 800 miles. This road was intended to be usable by lorries all the year round. However, in the winter of 1927–28, 117 major ice-formations were counted on the southern part of the road alone, over a distance of 450 miles between Bolshoy Never and Tammot. These formations caused a great deal of destruction, especially to bridges, which were lifted and tilted so that they eventually became unusable. Bridges damaged in this way often break down completely when the ice thaws in the spring. According to information gathered from the local population, such ice formations occurred only very rarely in this same area in former times. It must therefore be assumed that the building of the roads has encouraged these ice formations, an assumption which Sumgin has proved to be correct. Research and experience have contributed to the evolution of new methods of road construction designed to prevent damage of this kind, but none has yet proved entirely successful. In general, it can be said that in the areas of permanently

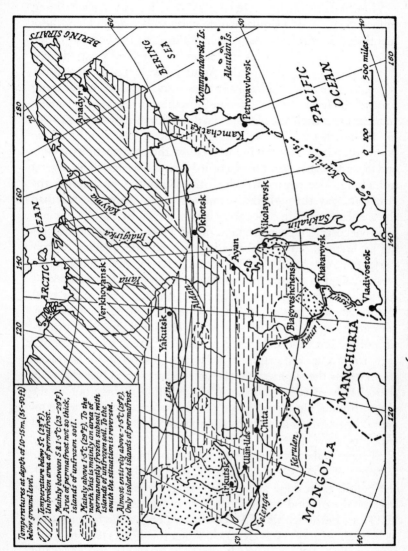

6. REGIONS OF PERMAFROST

frozen subsoil these difficulties make the building of roads much slower and costlier than in other areas.

The difficulties encountered both in building and in maintaining railway lines are of a similar nature, with soil-creep and landslides mentioned as particular dangers in addition to the heaving of the ground. All these obstacles and difficulties were fully experienced during the construction of the Amur railway. There were times when, in spite of the additional cost, the track had to be laid along a route which was totally different from the one originally planned. In these areas there are also special difficulties involved in providing the railway with water during the winter. The water must be pumped up from layers lying well below the permanent frost-line, and in some places water has to be led through heated pipes several miles long. The degree to which the difficulties of building the Amur railway through the permafrost areas were greater than those encountered in other areas is best shown by a study of comparative costs. The construction of the Trans-Siberian railway (as far as Sretensk in Transbaikalia) cost on the average 67,737 rubles per verst,[1] including all the preparatory work, whereas the western section of the Amur railway (from Kuenga to Kerak—a distance of 597 versts) cost an average of 158,000 rubles per verst in construction costs alone. The maintenance of the Amur railway is more expensive, too, because of the continual thorough inspection of the lines and bridges (especially the latter) which is necessary to enable adequate precautionary measures to be taken promptly at the slightest sign of any disturbance. Over the years there has been some shifting in the position of fifty out of the eighty bridges along the Amur railway, which have had to be repaired by means of alterations and the use of additional props and supports.

The perennial frost also has important repercussions on the building of houses. Apart from the direct influence of the cold, the buildings in these areas are in danger of slow disintegration because the ground under the buildings freezes only a little, if at all. Thus, in the words of V. G. Petrov (154), 'The house stands as if on the rim of a frozen bowl. When this bowl starts to thaw, its retreating rim causes the house to be stretched sideways, and the damage has started.' This damage leads to a general distortion of the house, which causes it to sink slowly into the ground. Sumgin points out that this danger is due primarily to the fluid masses which form underneath the house as the result of the variations in

[1] 1 verst equals ⅔ mile. (Tr. N.)

ground temperature. The mere pressure of large multi-storey houses can cause the formation of these masses. In some cases it happens that the ground-water, trapped between the winter frost and the perennial ice-floor, forces its way up to the surface underneath the houses. It then penetrates into the cellars and even into the rooms, forcing the people out of their houses. Sometimes this happens so quickly that the inhabitants have no time to remove their belongings. The areas of permanently frozen subsoil thus demand methods of building designed to counteract these dangers. As a rule the foundations are laid deep enough to secure a firm footing in the perennial ice-floor, by ramming wooden or corrugated-iron piles into deeply cut holes in the ground. The question of safe foundations receives careful consideration in the building of new towns and industrial premises, and is an important factor in the estimate of costs. When the town of Magadan was built, with blocks of flats as much as six storeys high, thick layers of earth had to be removed in order to let the foundations freeze into the ground. The sides of the foundation were then protected by 'insulating walls', and often the foundation was completely embedded in layers of insulation. To overcome these difficulties, M. M. Kryllov (who is quoted by Sumgin) has devised a method, using modern techniques of low temperature control, by which the ground within the actual construction area is kept permanently at a certain desired temperature. The aim is to keep the perennial ice-floor constantly fixed at its existing depth, or even to raise it somewhat higher. This method has been tried very little in practice.

Apart from the general difficulties of water supply, the provision of drinking-water in the winter is a specially difficult and often worrying problem in these areas, particularly for larger settlements. Many rivers freeze right down to the bottom, in which case the water has often to be brought from far away. In some areas the smaller settlements have met the problem by producing water artificially from the surface ice-formations. However, it would lead us too far afield to go into all the details regarding the various and often unique methods of providing water under these conditions.

The perennial ice-floor is also of great significance in relation to mining and the extraction of raw materials, since its tremendous hardness is a great obstacle to the sinking of shafts. Sometimes even diamond drills are unsuccessful, and if the motor stops even for only a minute the drill freezes in the water of the drill-hole. On the other hand, the tunnels and shafts usually hold firm without the use of props; there is little danger of fire-damp or of ground-water, and flooding occurs only rarely. For surface mining the frozen ground has to be dynamited, and then the loosened blocks turn into slushy mud. There are particular difficulties to be over-come in gold-mining, as the alluvial gold is found mainly in the permanently frozen subsoil. However the over-burden is an un-frozen layer of medium thickness which is fairly easily removed. In the more important gold-mining areas the most modern machi-nery has been installed, through which the gold-bearing sand moves from the grab to the washer in one single continuous pro-cess. All these technically perfect installations have a hard struggle contending with the perennial ice-floor, which is so hard that it offers tremendous resistance. The natural summer thaw is so slow that man commonly intervenes to hasten the process. Flooding with hot water is not sufficient in these areas, and the primitive method of using log and coal fires has been replaced by the use of steam. According to recent information it is likely that electricity will be used in the future.

The influence of the perennial ice-floor on the vegetation is a many-sided one, and the inter-relations have not yet been clarified to any great extent. As a reservoir of moisture the frozen subsoil is of considerable benefit to agriculture, especially in the regions of the interior which depend on these moisture reserves in the ground to make up for the lack of summer rainfall. By making favourable use of the natural conditions in this way, the Soviet Russians have succeeded in bringing agriculture within the Arctic Circle, al-though not yet very extensively. For instance, beyond Magadan towards the north there are small fields (and even occasional larger ones) to be found in the vicinity of all the settlements, which are sufficient at least to provide for local needs.

## The Climate

The climatic conditions in the Soviet Far East are determined by the changing balance, according to the season, between the continental and oceanic pressure systems. Dry air-masses flow to-wards the ocean in winter, while humid winds blow inland from the sea in summer. The influence of the ocean is limited to the Far Eastern territories proper, that is, to the lands whose waters flow into the Pacific. These form one climatic region, in which the regu-lar seasonal rhythm of the East Asian monsoon area prevails. The typical character of the latter is clearly evident throughout the region, extending even beyond the 6oth parallel. Only Transbaikalia lies outside this region. Its more inland situation results in much more pronounced continental characteristics, although even here the summer monsoon is noticeable as far as the Yablonovy Mountains.

Apart from Transbaikalia, the following climatic sub-regions can be distinguished: the Amur–Ussuri region, the southern Coastal Region (including Sakhalin), the northern Coastal Region (including Kamchatka), and the Anadyr region. The different essential characteristics of each are summarized in the following table:

| Region | Annual Rainfall in Inches | Number of Months with an Average of more than: | | Annual Range of Variations in Tempera- ture (° F.) |
| | | 5° C. (41° F.) | 10° C. (50° F.) | |
| --- | --- | --- | --- | --- |
| Transbaikalia . . . | 7·9–11·8 | 5 | 3 | 76–94 |
| Amur–Ussuri . . . | 20·7–24·4 | 5 | 5 | 76–86 |
| Southern Coast . . . | 21·3–29·9 | 6 | 4 | 54–61 |
| Sakhalin . . . . | 19·7–29·6 | 5 | 4 | 50–63 |
| Northern Coast . . . | 11·8–35·5 | 4 | 2 | 59–67 |
| Kamchatka . . . | 19·7–39·4 | 4 | 2 | 41–58 |
| Anadyr . . . . | 7·5– 7·9 | 3 | 3 | 72–81 |

Transbaikalia has a very small annual precipitation and is subject to a wide range of temperature variation. The Amur–Ussuri region has almost double the precipitation with the same large variations in temperature. The whole of the Coastal Region has even higher precipitation, with a smaller range of variation in temperature, while the Anadyr region is again an area of low precipitation with higher yearly variations in temperature.

Of all the regions, the Amur–Ussuri region has the greatest number of months with an average temperature of more than 50° F. Within the Coastal Region the number of warm months decreases towards the north, until one reaches the Anadyr region, where the number of months with average temperatures above 50° F. exceeds the number in either the northern Coastal Region or Kamchatka.

*Transbaikalia,* as is the case with its other characteristics, is also an area of transition climatically, exhibiting characteristics of the Siberian forest climate as well as those of the Mongolian steppes. In addition, an important climatic factor of local significance is the marked influence of Lake Baikal. The annual rainfall is seldom higher than 12 inches. Strangely enough, among the driest areas are some near Lake Baikal, as well as those found near the Mongolian border, where the annual precipitation is as low as 6·4 inches at Selenginsk. On the island of Olkhon the yearly precipitation is only 6·7 inches, and in the valley of Barguzin the Buryat settlers are forced to use artificial irrigation. The northern slopes of the Khamar-Daban are an exception (as shown by the 20·3 inches annual precipitation at Myssovaya), and the thicker snow cover and more extensive forest cover on these northern slopes indicate that Transbaikalia's moisture comes mainly from the north-west. An essentially Mongolian characteristic is the great variation in the quantities of precipitation during the course of the year: as a rule 75 per cent or more of the annual precipitation falls during the six summer months, while the winter months of December, January, and February receive no more than 3–10 per cent.

The winter is extremely cold, with the lowest temperature to be found at Nerchinsk, where it averages minus 24·5° F. in January. Because of the thin, sometimes non-existent snow cover, the frost penetrates very deeply into the ground, with the result that the whole region lies within the area of permanently frozen subsoil. The perennial ice-floor is found at its greatest depth to the west of Chita, at the station of Mogson, where its depth of 187 feet is the lowest yet discovered in Transbaikalia. The general absence of snow means that the roads can be freely used by cars even in the winter, while sledges can use the frozen rivers. The roads are so dry that they are just as dusty as in the summer. Transbaikalia has the advantages which are generally characteristic of the East Siberian winter: its impressive quietness, its clean air, and a constantly cloudless blue sky. The air is so dry that the snow often evaporates straight away without passing into the liquid state; thus, in small brooks which sometimes freeze right to the bottom, the ice often disappears completely, leaving only the bare river-bed. The spring is short, with practically no period of melting snow, so that the ground warms very quickly and there is a noticeable absence of spring flooding. The river levels therefore depend almost wholly on the amount of rainfall, and are highest in the summer. Summer temperatures are very high, with the unreduced average for July reaching 64–68°, and the whole of the country suffers from a blazing heat, especially on the valley floors. It is therefore a great advantage economically that the summer months are the rainiest and the cloudiest of the year. Taking the year as a

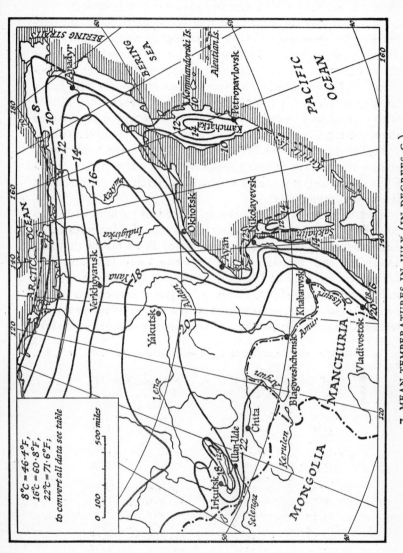

7. MEAN TEMPERATURES IN JULY (IN DEGREES C.)

(See p. 74 for fuller conversion table.)

whole, however, clear sunny days are the rule, and during the year Transbaikalia has an average of 100–140 completely cloudless days, closely resembling the climate of the desert in this respect.

A. A. Borissov (39) draws our attention in particular to the temperature inversions which are a characteristic phenomenon of the Transbaikalian climate. During the winter Transbaikalia is near the centre of the Asian anticyclone which builds up over the continent, and consequently is subject to accumulations of cold heavy air-masses which get trapped in the valleys, where they remain with extraordinary persistence. This explains why it is usual for the low-lying places to have lower winter temperatures than places at higher elevations. At Perevalnaya (altitude 3,360 feet), for instance, the average January temperature is minus 10°, while at Chita (2,240 feet) it is minus 17·3° and at Nerchinsk (1,590 feet) it is as low as minus 24·5°.

The influence of Lake Baikal is limited to its immediate surroundings, and therefore produces some remarkable contrasts. At Listvenichnoye, where the Angara River flows out of the lake, December and January are 18° warmer, and June and July are 13° cooler, than at Ulan-Ude, although the latter is only 56 miles from the lake shore. The range of yearly temperatures at the former is only 53·3°, as compared with a range of 89·8° at the latter. Furthermore, the slowness of temperature changes in the lake

The following tables of equivalents can be used in conjunction with Figs. 7, 8, 9, 10, 11 and 12.

| | | | | | | |
|---|---|---|---|---|---|---|
| −46° C. | equals | −50·8° F. | | 8° C. | equals | 46·4° F. |
| −44° C. | ,, | −47·2° F. | | 10° C. | ,, | 50·0° F. |
| −42° C. | ,, | −43·6° F. | | 12° C. | ,, | 53·6° F. |
| −40° C. | ,, | −40·0° F. | | 14° C. | ,, | 57·2° F. |
| −38° C. | ,, | −36·4° F. | | 16° C. | ,, | 60·8° F. |
| −36° C. | ,, | −32·8° F. | | 18° C. | ,, | 64·4° F. |
| −34° C. | ,, | −29·2° F. | | 20° C. | ,, | 68·0° F. |
| −32° C. | ,, | −25·6° F. | | 22° C. | ,, | 71·6° F. |
| −30° C. | ,, | −22·0° F. | | | | |
| −28° C. | ,, | −18·4° F. | | 150 mm. | equals | 5·9″ |
| −26° C. | ,, | −14·8° F. | | 200 mm. | ,, | 7·9″ |
| −24° C. | ,, | −11·2° F. | | 250 mm. | ,, | 9·8″ |
| −22° C. | ,, | −7·6° F. | | 300 mm. | ,, | 11·8″ |
| −20° C. | ,, | −4·0° F. | | 350 mm. | ,, | 13·8″ |
| −18° C. | ,, | −0·4° F. | | 400 mm. | ,, | 15·7″ |
| −16° C. | ,, | 3·2° F. | | 450 mm. | ,, | 17·7″ |
| −14° C. | ,, | 6·8° F. | | 500 mm. | ,, | 19·7″ |
| −12° C. | ,, | 10·4° F. | | 550 mm. | ,, | 21·6″ |
| | | | | 600 mm. | ,, | 23·6″ |
| | | | | 650 mm. | ,, | 25·6″ |
| | | | | 700 mm. | ,, | 27·6″ |
| | | | | 750 mm. | ,, | 29·5″ |

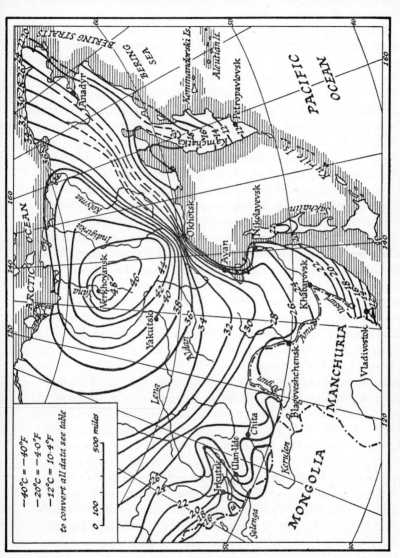

8. MEAN TEMPERATURES IN JANUARY (IN DEGREES C.)

(See p. 74 for a fuller conversion table.)

causes a shifting of the yearly extremes away from their customary places in the calendar. All these characteristics are strangely suggestive of an oceanic climate.

Within Transbaikalia, the Yablonovy Mountains form a climatic divide which finds less expression in meteorological data than in the flora—a far better indicator of climatic conditions than the best instruments. For example, deciduous trees are found in much greater numbers east of the Yablonovy ridge, thus showing the influence of the East Asian monsoon. The fact that it reaches this far is also confirmed by the frequent changes in the direction of the wind. North-westerly and northerly winds prevail throughout the year at Ulan-Ude, while at Nerchinsk these winds frequently give way in the summer to winds from the north-east and east.

As already mentioned, climatic conditions in the remaining Far Eastern territories are almost completely dependant on the seasonal changes in the major air currents. The continental winds of the winter, which reach as far as the coast, are very cold and dry, while the winds from the sea in summer are also comparatively cool. In this respect the eastern coastal waters have a very disadvantageous influence on the whole of the Far Eastern coast. Most important of all is the Sea of Okhotsk, which is an enormous reservoir of cold water, and is called quite rightly 'the ice-box of East Siberia'. The barrier of the Kuriles hinders the exchange of water with the open ocean, so that the cooling influence of the surrounding land-masses during the winter is retained in the water throughout the rest of the year. Thus the Sea of Okhotsk remains disproportionately cool in summer, at a temperature of roughly 50°. In addition to the Sea of Okhotsk, there is a cold ocean current which flows along the coast from the north and carries large ice-floes towards the south even in the summer. The result is that in the region of the Chantar Islands accumulations of ice can still be found in July and August. In the Bering Sea and in the Sea of Japan there are also cold currents flowing southwards along the coast. These lower the air temperatures in summer not only directly by their coolness, but also indirectly by the fogs they produce, which are typical of long stretches of the Far Eastern coast. Thus in the Soviet Russian Far East the general disadvantages which are common to the eastern sides of all the northern continents are particularly pronounced. For example, Vladivostok has the same July temperature as Moscow (latitude 55° 56′ N.), although it is on the same latitude as Nice (latitude 43° 7′ N.). It has an average temperature in January of 4·8°, as compared with 46·4°

in Nice, and in July it reaches an average temperature of only 68·0° as compared with 73·8° in Nice. These disadvantages suffered by the Soviet Russian Far Eastern coast are particularly obvious when its climatic conditions are compared with those on the opposite side of the Pacific, on the west coast of America.

*Average temperatures of the Soviet Far Eastern coast and the North American west coast*
(in degrees Fahrenheit)

| Place | Latitude | Mean Yearly Temp. | Coldest Month | Warmest Month | Yearly Range of Temp. |
|---|---|---|---|---|---|
| Ayan . . . | 56° 3′ | 25·0 | − 4·7 | 54·3 | 59·0 |
| Sitka . . . | 57° 1′ | 41·5 | +30·2 | 54·7 | 24·5 |
| Nikolayevsk . . | 53° 2′ | 27·9 | −10·1 | 62·2 | 72·3 |
| Tongas . . . | 54° 8′ | 46·6 | +34·0 | 59·2 | 25·2 |
| Vladivostok . . | 43° 2′ | 39·7 | + 4·8 | 69·4 | 64·6 |
| Umgua . . . | 43° 7′ | 52·5 | +44·2 | 59·9 | 33·7 |

Fortunately the unfriendly influence of the Sea of Okhotsk is limited mainly to the coastal strip because of the mountain chains running parallel to the coast. This mountain barrier enables the warm summer sun to make its influence felt more strongly, and explains the distinction made between the Coastal Region and the other climatic regions.

*The Amur–Ussuri climatic region* is situated farther inland, and comprises the region of the middle and lower Amur and the valley of the Ussuri. The Sikhota-Alin and Bureya Mountains protect these regions in the summer from the cool, foggy air-streams from the sea. In their place come warm, humid winds from the southeast and the south, blowing across the wide plains of Manchuria and beyond the Amur to the north, thus producing a warm and humid summer in contrast to the hard, dry continental winter.

The favourable conditions of this climatic region are clearly demonstrated in the vegetation, which is characterized by the appearance of deciduous trees, such as oaks, elms, lime trees, &c., which are absent from the whole of the Siberian area as well as from Transbaikalia and the coastal area.

The total yearly precipitation exceeds 20 inches over the whole of the region, but diminishes towards the interior, as would be expected. Thus there is a fall of 24·3 inches in Bikin, which is situated in the middle of the Ussuri region, 22·2 inches in Khabarovsk, where the Ussuri flows into the Amur, and 20·7 inches in Blagoveshchensk, which is situated still farther to the north-west. It is of the greatest importance that this precipitation occurs mainly in the summer months. Throughout almost the entire region 85–95 per cent of the yearly total falls between April and November, and of this amount 50–60 per cent falls in the three summer months of June, July, and August. Thus this region receives more rain in these three months than most of Transbaikalia receives throughout the whole year. Blagoveshchensk normally receives 25 per cent of its annual precipitation in July and a further 25 per cent in August, recording half of its yearly total in these two summer months. The course of precipitation during the year is shown in the following figures, which represent the average of observations taken at six stations in the region (79, p. 292):

*Precipitation expressed as a percentage of the yearly amount*

| Jan. | Feb. | March | April | May | June | July | Aug. | Sept. | Oct. | Nov. | Dec. |
|------|------|-------|-------|-----|------|------|------|-------|------|------|------|
| 1 | 1 | 1 | 4 | 10 | 15 | 23 | 24 | 13 | 4 | 2 | 2 |

The contrasts in temperature during the course of the year are just as marked as the extremes in precipitation, and the severity of the winter is particularly pronounced. With an average temperature for January between minus 8 and minus 11·6°, this region has winters almost as cold as those in Transbaikalia. The summers here are warmer, with a mean temperature for July of 68·4–70·2°. The sudden rapid jump in average monthly temperature from April (between 36·3° and 38·7°) to May (50·7–53·4°) is remarkable, and is matched by an equally sharp decline from September (53·8–56·5°) to October (34·5–40·5°). The growing season thus has only four to five months with an average temperature of more than 50°. The abnormally cold winters of the Amur region are the result of the heavy cold air-masses drifting from the higher inland regions towards the coast, following the valley of the Amur and filling all the depressions. The river-basins of the Seya and the Bureya are characterized by particularly hard winters, and in spite of its relatively southern position the Amur freezes just like the rivers of northern Eurasia. At Blagoveshchensk, which is 122 miles above the mouth of the Amur, the river is blocked by ice for 178 days of the year, and this is still true at Nikolayevsk, which is only 24 miles from its mouth. Thus at Nikolayevsk, at a latitude of 53° 8′ N., the Amur is covered with ice just as long as is the Dvina

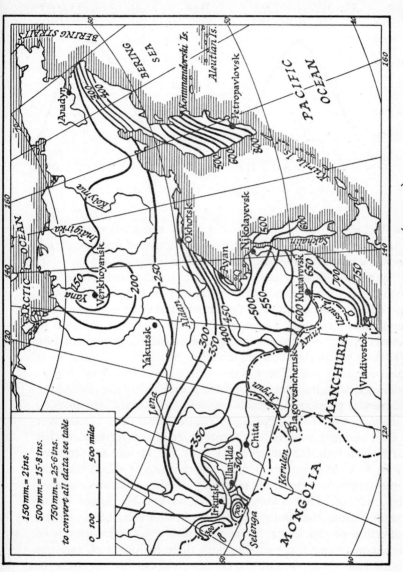

9. MEAN ANNUAL RAINFALL (IN MM.)
(See p. 74 for a fuller conversion table.)

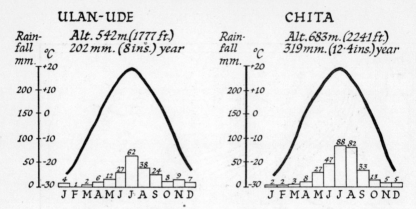

10. CLIMATE DIAGRAMS FOR ULAN-UDE AND CHITA

at Archangel, at a latitude of 64° 33′ N. Large areas north of the Amur have permanently frozen subsoil, because of the general lack of snow resulting from the meagre winter precipitation.

Summer follows winter quickly, after a very short spring. The country is then filled with the warm humid air of a greenhouse, produced by the combination of intense heat and the heaviest precipitation of the year. The relative humidity of the air (which is so characteristic of the monsoon type of climate) is greatest in July (88 per cent) and smallest in December (68 per cent). September is also relatively dry. There is much less cloud in winter than in summer, with the hours of sunshine reaching 75 per cent of the maximum possible in December (90–95 per cent in Khabarovsk), dropping to a low of 34 per cent in June. The heavier cloud cover of the summer reduces the diurnal range of temperature, so that at Khabarovsk, for example, it is only 8·1° in July as compared with 13·1° in February. Severe (though usually short) thunderstorms start to occur at the beginning of June, often accompanied by cyclones. They approach the Amur and the lower Ussuri regions from the south or south-west, and then recede in the direction of the lower Amur towards the sea. The fringes of typhoons sometimes penetrate into these regions, too, carrying humid air-masses far into the country, and causing heavy downpours of rain which may lead to dangerous flooding. This was the case in July 1928 in the Seya and Ussuri regions, when the major part of the harvest was destroyed (63). In 1872 the Amur rose and flooded the town of Blagoveshchensk (situated on the flat banks of the river) to such a depth that small river steamers could sail

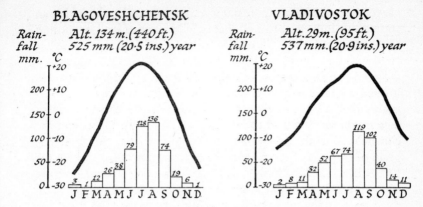

II. CLIMATE DIAGRAMS FOR BLAGOVESHCHENSK AND
VLADIVOSTOK

along the main street (132, p. 445). Borissov reports that on such
an occasion more than 4 inches might fall in a twenty-four-hour
period. These conditions, and the routes of the cyclones in particular, have not yet been analysed in detail. The rainy season proper starts only at the beginning of July and lasts until the end of
August. During this time there is rarely a week with even one day
free of rain.

In addition to the sudden thunderstorms already mentioned
above, rain also comes down in the form of steady downpours, a
typical form of which has been described by Arsenyev as 'the sub-
sequential rains'. These occur when the day following a storm has
been sunny and without wind, in which case the condensation of
the intense humidity which rises during the day causes another fall
of rain in the evening.

The abundance of the summer rainfall swells the rivers, and the
rising waters occasionally flood the banks and interrupt communications. At many places, where the water cannot drain away
immediately, it remains on the flat fields and makes bogs out of
the meadows. On the low-lying plains to the left of the Amur,
above Khabarovsk, which were to be developed for agriculture to
feed the quickly growing town, a large-scale system of drainage
canals had to be created, not only to drain the soil but also to facilitate disposal of the excess precipitation. The considerable humidity and intense heat are hazards to European varieties of grain,
and diminish their yields. The grain shoots up in a luxurious
growth, but the yield is small. During the early growing period
the plants suffer from drought, while later the ripening and

F

harvesting coincide with the rainy period. Ground moisture has an appreciable influence, too, so that in hilly tracts of land, according to many reports, the fields on the hill-tops and slopes give a higher yield than those in the valleys. The ground is often so soggy from the summer rain that it is difficult to use machines. This has formed a considerable obstacle in organizing the system of *kol-khozes* and MTS (machine-tractor stations), and to some extent new machines have had to be designed and built. Moreover, the climate favours the development of fungi and other parasites. The grain often suffers from a spore-fungi (*Fusareum roseum*) which the Russians say makes the bread 'pyany' (meaning drunk), because eating it produces intoxicating effects and sickness. Fruit grown in this area contains plenty of water but little sugar. On the other hand, the indigenous plants and those of Manchurian–Chinese culture grow extremely well. It is characteristic for the forests to have an abundance of undergrowth, but the trees themselves (especially the deciduous ones) are rather delicate. They often suffer from internal decay and are generally short-lived. Ordinary leather boots are of little use when penetrating these woods full of summer humidity, since they get soaked through from the soggy ground and soon rot away.

The most beautiful season is the autumn, which lasts through September and October. The rains have ceased and a clear sun shines from a blue sky, spreading an agreeable warmth in the absence of any wind. Once the frosts begin, this sky remains unchanged throughout the winter, and there is rarely a break for a thaw. The intense dryness of the air is remarkable, and here, too, the snow often evaporates without having previously melted.

*The Coast Climate* dominates the whole of the coastal strip running from Vladivostok in the south to beyond Okhotsk in the north. Although there is a considerable change in latitude over the length of this coastal area, the changes from one part to another are only gradual. For practical reasons, however, it is advisable to divide the area into two parts, so as to treat the southern and northern coastal strips separately.

*The Southern Coastal Region* covers the area between Vladivostok and the mouth of the Amur. The whole of the hinterland is taken up by the Sikhota-Alin range, the principal ridge of which acts as a distinct climatic divide both in winter and in summer. In spite of the proximity of the ocean, the winter in this region is of the hard continental type. This is more pronounced towards the north,

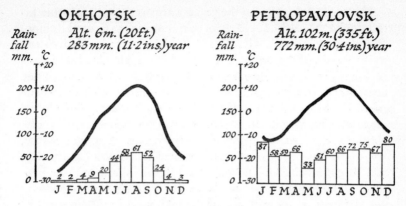

12. CLIMATE DIAGRAMS FOR OKHOTSK AND PETROPAVLOVSK

where a firm ice-cover forms between the mainland and the island of Sakhalin, than it is in the south, where only a wide belt of floating ice appears. The whole of the coastal strip is under the influence of the cold continental air-masses flowing towards the sea, but the winter temperatures at the coast are not as low as those to the west of the Sikhota-Alin. One reason for this more moderate temperature is that the air-masses increase somewhat in temperature as they lose height on approaching the coast. The other reason is the influence of the winds which blow in from the open sea even in the winter, and help to raise the average temperature. In contrast to the winter, the coastal region in summer exhibits all the characteristics of a maritime climate. The cool air-masses which move towards the mainland from the sea, and which cool down still further while passing over the cold coastal current, help substantially to lower the temperatures in the coastal areas, while west of the Sikhota-Alin the influence of the sea on air temperatures is hardly noticeable. The strong influence of the Sikhota-Alin as a climatic divide in relation to temperature is well illus-

|  | | | | Olga | Voroshilov |
|---|---|---|---|---|---|
| January | . | . | . | . | +10·9° F. | − 3·1° F. |
| July . | . | . | . | . | +66·2° F. | +70·0° F. |

trated by the contrast between the two places, Olga and Voroshilov (formerly Nikolsk Ussuriski) which lie on the same latitude only 170 miles apart.

The marked delaying of the year's warmest period is another indication of the maritime character of summer in the Coastal Region.
The warmest month at all places along the coast from Vladivostok
to the mouth of the Amur is August, while at all inland stations it
is July. The longer duration of the transitional seasons in the
coastal area is attributable to the same cause, which makes the
transition less abrupt than in the Amur and Ussuri regions in the
interior. This results in a longer growing season, which gets
shorter as the distance from the coast increases. Olga, for instance,
has a growing season of 185 days, while Khabarovsk has 172 days
and Blagoveshchensk has only 164. On the other hand, the raw-
ness and humidity of the summer retard the growth of vegetation,
and the trees on the east side of the Sikhota-Alin do not grow to
the same height as those on the west. North of the 44th parallel,
the mountains at heights over 3,900–4,300 feet are generally treeless, although there is insufficient precipitation to cause the formation of glaciers.

As a rule the annual precipitation is higher in the Coastal Region
than in the Amur–Ussuri region, and its distribution throughout
the year differs considerably from that in the interior of the country. In particular, the concentration of the precipitation in the
summer months is not so marked, and the spring and autumn
have a larger share. These characteristics show up clearly in the
following tables giving the monthly precipitation in inches at
Olga and Blagoveshchensk.

| | Jan. | Feb. | Mar. | Apr. | May | June | July | Aug. | Sep. | Oct. | Nov. | Dec. | Total |
|---|---|---|---|---|---|---|---|---|---|---|---|---|---|
| Blagoveshchensk. | 0·1 | 0·04 | 0·5 | 1·0 | 1·5 | 3·1 | 5·0 | 5·4 | 2·9 | 0·7 | 0·2 | 0·04 | 20·6 |
| Olga . . . | 0·6 | 0·5 | 0·8 | 1·5 | 3·3 | 3·5 | 4·1 | 5·2 | 5·4 | 2·4 | 1·6 | 0·7 | 29·6 |

The contrast is still more striking when the comparison is made
between the total precipitations for the various seasons.

| | Winter | Spring | Summer | Autumn | Year |
|---|---|---|---|---|---|
| Blagoveshchensk . | 0·2 | 3·0 | 13·5 | 3·9 | 20·6 |
| Olga . . . | 1·7 | 5·7 | 12·8 | 9·4 | 29·6 |

The difference in precipitation can be explained by reference to
the regular tracks followed by the cyclones in East Asia. As the
warm season progresses, these tracks shift towards the north, so
that cyclones reach the Coastal Region in the spring, but do not
reach the Amur–Ussuri region until the summer. When they with-

draw again to the south in the autumn, the Coastal Region is again afflicted by frequent cyclonic disturbances. Thus in the Coastal Region the cyclones are less active in the summer than in the spring or autumn, and most of the summer precipitation is attributable to the monsoon winds. In the late summer in particular, Vladivostok and the southern Sikhota-Alin are frequently afflicted by heavy storms which quite often assume the destructive character of a typhoon. In the absence of more research into the phenomena of cyclonic activity and the appearance of typhoon 'tails' in the Soviet Russian Far Eastern territories, it is impossible to give any more exact and definite information.

Frequent fogs are a further characteristic of the coastal climate. These occur wherever the surface temperature of the water is lower than that of the rest of the sea, as is the case, for example, with the cold currents along the coast. During the summer the predominant south-easterly winds from the ocean carry warm air-masses, saturated with humidity, towards the mainland. These air-masses cool down quickly as they approach the coast, partly by contact with the cold coastal currents, and partly by mixing with the relatively cold local air-masses. It is the condensation of surplus moisture resulting from this cooling process that forms the coastal fogs. These often hang over the coastal strip for days at a time, and frequently push inland with their cool humidity. The contrast between the fog-bound coastal strip and the interiors of the bays, which are generally free of it, is particularly noticeable. Cape 'Nismenny Myss', encircling the south-west of Olga Bay, is regularly enveloped in fog for twenty-six days in June and July, while Olga itself, which is situated inside the bay, separated from the entrance by only a low wooded hill, has only nine to eleven foggy days as a rule during the same period (although in some years it has been known to have twenty-one or twenty-two foggy days in the month of July).

*The Northern Coastal Region* stretches from Nikolayevsk at the mouth of the Amur in the south, to Shelekhova Bay in the north, and has a much more rigorous character than the southern region. In Okhotsk the mean temperature for January is minus 13·4°, while in Leningrad at roughly the same latitude it is only 18·3°. Added to its northern position, the cooling influence of the Sea of Okhotsk becomes very noticeable during the raw summers. The ice-masses in the sea, which remain near the coast until the beginning of the summer, have an important effect, together with the cold ocean currents flowing along the coast from north to south, and the up-welling channels of cold water (see the description of the Sea of Okhotsk). Fog produced over these cold waters is driven into the coastal region by the constant on-shore wind, and occasionally succeeds in reaching up the Amur as far as the Bureya, since there are no morphological obstacles to prevent the penetration of these air-masses from the sea.

The winds have a clearly pronounced monsoon character. In winter they blow from the cold mainland to the sea, and in summer the other way round, but with a remarkable difference in the force of the wind. The winter monsoon, produced by a difference in barometric pressure of 22 mm. (0·87 inch) between land and sea, is much more pronounced than the summer monsoon, which is the result of a barometric pressure gradient of only 6–7 mm. (0·24–0·28 inch). Strong off-shore winds, sometimes very stormy in character, predominate from October until March. During this time Okhotsk has 83 per cent north and north-west winds with a velocity of 16 ft./sec. or more, and only 5 per cent calm weather. Nikolayevsk, situated 24 miles above the mouth of the Amur and thus at some distance from the coast, still has 64 per cent winds blowing towards the sea with a velocity of 12·5 feet/second, and only 14 per cent calm weather. In the summer Okhotsk has only 50–52 per cent winds with velocities from 9·8 to 11·5 feet/second.

Although summer temperatures are very much lowered by the cooling effect of the Sea of Okhotsk, its influence does not reach very far inland. Along the coast from Uda Bay to Okhotsk, it extends as a rule only as far as the nearby watershed, and it therefore influences only the mountain slopes facing the sea. Beyond the ridge warm continental summers prevail. The traveller finds an amazing contrast as he moves from Yakutsk to the coast in summer. Until quite close to the coast there is an oppressive heat of 86° or more with a completely clear sky, while at the coast itself it is cool, humid, and foggy, with cloudy or overcast skies. Every breeze from the interior brings welcome warmth and sometimes even heat to the coast, but these warm winds also carry with them unbearable swarms of mosquitoes which are generally unknown in the Coastal Region with its prevailing wind from the sea. The average temperature for June is remarkably low (41·4° at Ayan, 41·7° at Okhotsk), and even in August, which is the warmest month of the year, the average is only 54–56° (54·5° at Ayan, 56·3° at Okhotsk). Winter temperatures are very low, because of the solid belt of ice which forms along the coast, and the floating ice which covers all the northern part of the Sea of Okhotsk, acting as a barrier to the moderating influence of the sea. The average temperatures in January are minus 12·1° at Nikolayevsk on the Amur, and minus 13·4° at Okhotsk, but only 4·5° at Ayan.

The annual precipitation decreases generally from south to north. Nikolayevsk has a total of 17·6 inches, while Okhotsk has only 11·1 inches. The exceptionally high amount at Ayan (35 inches) is caused by local conditions, which also account for its appreciably higher average winter temperature. The total annual precipitation varies considerably from year to year along the whole of the coastal region. In years with abundant rainfall Nikolayevsk has as much as 27·6 inches, while in dry years it may receive only 7·8 inches. Most of the yearly precipitation falls in the summer and early autumn; during this period Okhotsk receives 87 per cent, and Ayan 91 per cent of their yearly totals.

Corresponding to the precipitation, there is more cloudy weather in summer than in winter. The average percentage of cloud cover is:

|  | Winter | Spring | Summer | Autumn |
|---|---|---|---|---|
| Okhotsk . . . . | 37 | 58 | 76 | 48 |
| Nikolayevsk . . . | 42 | 56 | 60 | 55 |

The number of overcast days is greatest in June, which has an average of only one to four clear sunny days, and the highest relative humidity (85 per cent) of the year.

Vegetation starts to flower after the thawing of the snow cover, in late May and early June. During the summer cool and humid days are prevalent, with the steady winds from the sea often bringing fog and fine misty rains. Later, as autumn approaches, the winds abate, there is less rainy weather, and it seems to be warmer. By the end of September, however, it starts to snow and the cold winter begins. The growing season is appreciably longer in the south, lasting 138 days in Nikolayevsk (from May 22nd to October 8th) but only 109 days in Okhotsk (from June 6th to September 24th).

*The Northern Region*, including mainly the Anadyr region and the Chukchen peninsula, has a different climate from that of the other regions of the Far East because of the less pronounced influence of the monsoon air movements, resulting in a long hard winter and a short but comparatively warm summer. The average temperatures in the warmest month surpass those of the northern Coastal Region, and some of those in Kamchatka as well. The farther one gets away from the coast, the smaller becomes the influence of the monsoon; the yearly temperature range increases and the climate generally shows more continental characteristics.

Near the coast the winter is milder and the summer is cool. Novo Marinsk, on the estuary of the Anadyr, has an average July temperature of 50·7°, compared with 57·4° at Markovo, which is situated 190 miles inland on the same latitude. The latter has three months with an average temperature of more than 50°, while the former has only one. In the winter, however, Novo Marinsk is the warmer, with an average January temperature of minus 9·9° compared with minus 19·7° at Markovo. The precipitation is generally small and is nowhere more than 8 inches, except in the south-east, where the coast of the Koryak peninsula receives 10 inches. During the six summer months the prevalent east winds bring overcast weather and frequent fogs to the coastal region, while inland at the same time the weather is dry and calm with clear skies and sunshine. The warmer weather and summer precipitation have encouraged the growth of woods in the river valleys and the protected plains of the interior. These woods consist of alders, willows, aspens, and birches, while along the coastal strip there are only occasional shrubs to be found apart from the prevalent tundra. The warm summers do not last long, however, and a cool wet autumn with snow in September is quickly followed by the winter. North and north-east winds of great force then predominate, and often develop into blizzards which are very much feared. Some areas, especially in the mountains, are swept clear of snow, while in other places it piles up so high that it often remains until the beginning of June and occasionally even until August.

## Sakhalin

The climate of the island of Sakhalin, which extends southwards a distance roughly equal to that between Hamburg and Trieste, fits perfectly into the general outlines of the coastal climate. The fact that the island has such harsh climatic conditions in these latitudes is due partly to the proximity of the mainland, with its East Asian monsoon climate, and partly to the proximity of the Sea of Okhotsk, with its cold-water zones and the cold currents which carry drifting ice along the east coast until well into the first half of the warm season. Only in the south-western part of the island is the climate more moderate, thanks to a branch of the warm ocean current coming from south of the Sea of Japan. The west coast is milder here than the east coast for this reason.

The differences in climatic conditions and in the character of the landscape on the island are due firstly to Sakhalin's great length of 590 miles from north to south, and secondly to the two mountain ranges which run down the length of the island, protecting the valley of the Tym and the Poronay, situated between them. As the distance south from the northern tip of the island increases, the winters become progressively warmer and the range of temperature fluctuation in summer becomes smaller. The average temperature of the coldest month changes from minus 10° at Kirovskoye in the valley of the Tym, to 17·6° above, at Cape Krilon, the southern tip of the island. The change in average summer temperatures is much smaller, from 59° in the centre to 63° in the south. The absolute minimum yearly temperature varies from minus 54° in the north to minus 24° in the south. There is also a very considerable difference between north and south in the length of the growing season. At Okha, on the northern end of the island, it extends over only ninety-seven days, while at Korivskoye in the valley of the Tym it is 146 days, and at Korsakovo, on the southern tip of the island, it is 167 days.

In winter there are great differences in temperature between the protected central valley and the open coastal plains which are exposed to the influence of the sea and constant fogs. In summer, on the other hand, the temperatures are almost the same. The average temperatures for January are 2° along the west coast and minus 10° in the central depression, while for the warmest month the average temperatures are 61·2° along the west coast (in August) and also 61·2° in the central depression (in July). The shift in the date of the warmest month indicates the more continental character of the climate in the central depression, from which the influence of the sea is largely excluded. In summer the thermometer may register as much as 90°, while the reading in winter may drop as low as minus 54°. The mean annual range of temperature is 71·3° in the central valley, but along the west coast it is only 63·5° and at the east coast only 59°. The central valley also has fewer and weaker winds than the coast. Fogs from the coast which are driven inland by the wind appear above the valley as grey clouds and cause at most a slight drizzle.

The ocean waters influencing the two coasts are of different temperatures. The south-west coast is affected by a branch of the warm current coming from the Straits of Korea. This current runs along the coast for a short stretch, until it meets a cool weak current coming from the La Pérouse Straits; it flows over this cooler current for a while and is then pushed away from the coast by it. The northern part of the west coast and the whole of the east coast are affected by the mass of cold water which wells up near the west coast and passes along the east coast as a cold current. The cold surface of the Sea of Okhotsk causes summer fogs, which often hang over the adjacent coast for weeks on end.

The southern part of the Sea of Okhotsk is not frozen in winter, and its moderating influence is transmitted to the island by the north-eastern and northerly winds which blow across the sea, bringing considerable falls of snow and occasional blizzards (known as 'buran'). The summer is cool because of the prevalent east winds and their attendant fogs, and the highest average temperature for July is only 21°. Annual precipitation on the west coast is 23–31 inches, of which roughly half is snow. Rain is plentiful in the summer, with hardly a rainless day in July and August, and the sky is usually covered with dense low clouds. In the central depression the yearly precipitation is less (22–30 inches), with the maximum monthly precipitation falling in September and the minimum in February. Relative humidity is high during the whole year, averaging 77–89 per cent. The climatic differentiation caused by the mountain ranges is more marked in the south, and disappears where the ridges flatten out in the north.

Winter lasts for seven months in the north, and five to six months in the south. March still has a wintry character everywhere on the island, and snowstorms are especially frequent. Average March temperatures are 22·5° in the south and 11·8° in the north. Snow remains on the ground for at least 200 days during the main part of the winter, but its distribution varies a good deal because of the strong stormy winds. Some areas are swept clear, while in the bottoms of the valleys and depressions the snow piles up, often to the point of burying houses completely. Along the east coast solid ice is rarely formed, but floating ice is common and is sometimes found in the sea even in June. The Straits of Tartary, on the other hand, are closed regularly every year from December to March by a firm bridge of ice stretching across to the mainland. Along the south-west coast and in the Straits of La Pérouse floating ice forms in mid-winter.

The spring season is unpleasant, and there are frosts until the beginning of June. Summer lasts for only two to two and a half months in the north, and only July and August are free of frost.

The summer precipitation comes as light but continuous rain. In the central depression and at the south-west coast the frost-free period begins earlier, so that June is already warm, and July brings summer into full bloom. The autumn lasts for two months and is warmer than the spring, but, at least in the north of the island, the first frosts appear already in September.

The climatic conditions, especially in the north, are not very favourable for agriculture. Along the flat coastal strip we find tundra vegetation with arctic flora, which is quite extensive in some localities. Reindeer still graze there even today, along a stretch of about the same latitude as that between Hamburg and Hanover. In the central depression and along the south-west coast where conditions are more favourable, summer wheat, summer rye, oats, and barley can be grown.

## Kamchatka

The climate of Kamchatka is more rigorous than would be expected from its latitude. This is the result of its position between continent and ocean, and the proximity of two cool seas and various cold sea currents. Nevertheless the coasts are very much milder than those of the neighbouring mainland. The winds have a monsoon character, blowing from the Asiatic mainland to the ocean in winter, and blowing in from the ocean in summer. Thus the prevailing winds are north-westerly in winter, and easterly or north-easterly in summer. The summer monsoon appears only in June and July, and is surpassed in both duration and strength by its winter counterpart. In Petropavlovsk the winter monsoon has an average velocity of 26·6 feet per second, while the summer monsoon averages only 13·8 feet per second. However, it must be borne in mind that in the winter the northern half of the Sea of Okhotsk is largely covered with ice, so that the climate of the peninsula becomes an extension of the continental climate.

Within the general atmospheric circulation there is a second regular movement of air caused by local conditions which partly counteract the monsoon circulation and is an important element determining the climatic conditions of the peninsula. In the winter a small 'tongue' of high pressure (decreasing from north to south) is formed, stretching from the mainland in the north-east right into the centre of Kamchatka. This high-pressure area coincides with the Kamchatka valley, sheltered by its mountains to east and west. The air-masses flowing outwards from this local high-pressure area reinforce the general circulation of the

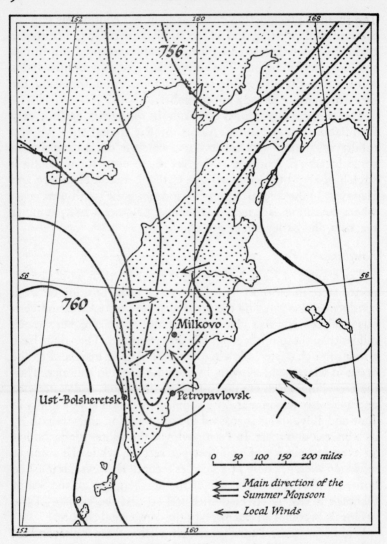

13. KAMCHATKA: PRESSURE AND WIND DIRECTIONS IN SUMMER

monsoon in the east, but counteract it in the west. For this reason the winter monsoon is stronger on the east coast (at Petropavlovsk, for instance) than on the west. In summer the opposite development occurs inside the peninsula, and above the protected Kamchatka valley a low pressure system is formed. The local winds which are thereby produced again reinforce the general circula-

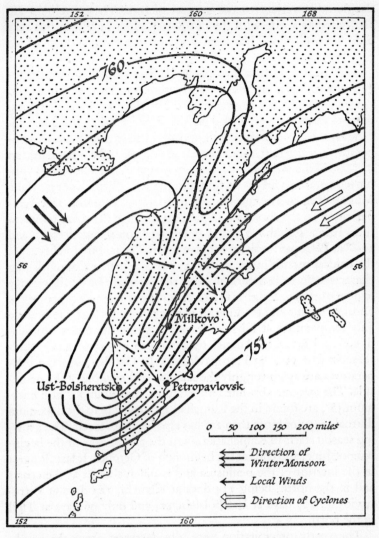

14. KAMCHATKA: PRESSURE AND WIND DIRECTIONS IN WINTER

tion of the monsoon in the east and counteract it in the west. These local conditions account for the fact that both in winter and summer the monsoon winds appear as typical phenomena only along the coastal fringes, strengthened by local influences on the eastern side of the peninsula, while in the interior local variations predominate. The intrusion of cyclones from the

Pacific adds variety to the general picture. These cyclones are associated as a rule with the north-east winds in winter, but very little research work has been done on the irregularities which they cause.

The great length of the peninsula from north to south, together with its morphological structure, produces differences in the general climatic character of the various regions. A typical general characteristic is that as the distance from the coast increases, there is a corresponding drop in the average winter temperatures, a rise in the summer temperatures, and consequently an increase in the mean annual range of temperature. The lowest winter temperatures are to be found in the Kamchatka valley, where Milkovo has an average January temperature of minus 13°. Temperatures on the coasts are higher, the average February temperatures being 4·8° above at Ust-Bolsheretsk on the west coast, and 11·8° at Petropavlovsk on the east coast. The fact that February is the coldest month in the coastal zones is a further distinguishing characteristic in comparison with the interior. In April average temperatures are roughly the same for the whole of the peninsula. During the summer the interior becomes warmer (e.g. the average July temperature at Klyuchi is 58·5°), while the coasts are relatively cool (average August temperatures are 53·6° at Ust-Bolsheretsk and 53·4° at Petropavlovsk). In October, average temperatures are again roughly the same over the whole of the peninsula. The extreme absolute temperatures, maximum 82° and minimum 58°, are found in the Kamchatka valley, where the maximum diurnal range of more than 27° has also been observed. The growing season starts in Kamchatka about the end of May or the beginning of June, and ends at the beginning of October. It lasts longest in the interior of the peninsula and is much shorter at the coasts and in the north, being 134 days at Klyuchi, 127 days at Petropavlovsk, 107 days at Ust-Bolsheretsk, and only 96 days at Tigil in the north.

The yearly precipitation generally decreases from the south-east of the peninsula, where it is more than 31·5 inches, towards the north-west, where it is only 13·8 inches or less. The coasts receive the largest amount, while the Kamchatka valley is noted for the small amount of precipitation falling there. There is precipitation on between 120 and 200 days of the year, including snow on between seventy and ninety-six days. It is characteristic of Kamchatka that the snow-cover lasts a very long time—occasionally almost until the end of May, and even into June in the mountains

—but the first snow falls rather later in comparison with the adjacent Far Eastern regions. As a rule there is no snow in September. There are two maxima in the yearly distribution of precipitation: these occur in the summer and the winter, while there is less precipitation in the spring and the autumn. The relative humidity is higher in summer and winter than in the transitional seasons, and is higher in the coastal zones than in the interior. The maximum humidity which has been measured is 87 per cent on the coast at Petropavlovsk in August.

The summer is cloudier than the winter, but the difference is less marked in Kamchatka than in the other regions of the Far East. The coastal regions of the peninsula are naturally the cloudiest. On the west coast (at Ust-Bolsheretsk) the cloud-cover is as much as 89 per cent in July and 67 per cent in December, while in the Kamchatka valley (at Milkovo) it is only 69 per cent in July and 49 per cent in December. The difference between the coasts and the interior is thus very pronounced:

*Relative figures for clear, overcast and foggy days*

|  | January | | | July | | |
|---|---|---|---|---|---|---|
|  | Clear | Over-cast | Foggy | Clear | Over-cast | Foggy |
| Ust-Bolsheretsk . . | 2 | 14 | 1 | 0 | 25 | 25 |
| Milkovo . . . | 18 | 6 | 3 | 3 | 16 | 0 |

Dense summer fogs are particularly characteristic of the coastal regions of Kamchatka, giving the traveller a drab impression of the whole country. In Petropavlovsk almost every second day is foggy, and on the west coast fog is still more frequent. In the interior, however, there is hardly any fog in summer.

Kamchatka can be divided according to its climatic differences into three regions: east coast, west coast, and interior.

The east coast is under the influence of the oceanic monsoon in summer, and under the influence of northerly winds and the Pacific cyclones from the north-east in winter. It is also generally influenced by the cold current of the sea, although this lessens towards the south, where the moderating effect of the Pacific is more noticeable. Along the south-east coast the change in average temperature during the year is only 41·6°. The winter is generally mild along the east coast, with average February temperatures of 7–11·6°, while the summer is cool, with average temperatures for

August of 53·4–54·5°. The delay of the coldest and warmest
months until February and August reflects the proximity of the
ocean. In winter the ground freezes to a depth of only 4 inches. In
contrast to the rest of the monsoon areas of the Far East the difference in the amount of precipitation between summer and winter is small. However, compared with the other parts of the peninsula, particularly the interior, the east coast has a relatively large
amount of precipitation in the winter. This is brought by the
north-east winds and their attendant cyclones, which can produce
considerable falls of moisture in a short time. In Petropavlovsk
there was once a fall of 7·4 inches during a single day in October
(205/371). In particularly warm winters there has sometimes been
even more precipitation during the six winter months than in the
six months of summer. As a result the east coast has a very thick
snow-cover which averages 51 inches, and has been as much as
10 feet (e.g. in March 1916). The south-east coast is notorious
for its snow-storms and blizzards, and at Petropavlovsk it happens quite frequently that houses are buried in snow up to the
roof. The thaw occurs during May and the beginning of June,
and is sometimes accelerated by falls of volcanic ash. Summer
on the east coast is characterized by thick clouds, and fogs are
so numerous that it is usual for half the days in July to be
foggy.

The western coastal area of Kamchatka is generally under the
influence of the Sea of Okhotsk. In winter it is dominated by the
cold dry monsoon, and by the north-easterly and easterly winds
coming from the centre of the peninsula. The latter are also dry
and cold, in contrast to those blowing over the east coast, with the
result that winter precipitation is comparatively limited and only a
quarter to a third of the amount which falls in summer. The snow-
cover on the west coast is therefore thin, generally no more than
16 inches. Its distribution is uneven, however, because of the
winds which often sweep the mountains clear and build up deposits in the hollows and valleys. In contrast to the east coast, blizzards are rare. The summer is cool, with plentiful cloud and fog.
The local winds, which often blow steadily into the coastal hinterland for days on end, carry the fogs and cool humid weather inland with them to the detriment of the vegetation. An additional
adverse feature is that the growing season is considerably shorter
here than it is on the east coast.

The central depression of the peninsula, composed mainly of the
Kamchatka River valley, is well protected from the influence of

## Average air temperatures in degrees Fahrenheit

| | Jan. | Feb. | March | April | May | June | July | Aug. | Sept. | Oct. | Nov. | Dec. | Year |
|---|---|---|---|---|---|---|---|---|---|---|---|---|---|
| *Transbaikalia* | | | | | | | | | | | | | |
| Barguzin | −16·6 | −10·1 | 10·2 | 31·5 | 45·7 | 59·0 | 64·8 | 60·4 | 47·5 | 30·9 | 9·0 | −10·8 | 37·2 |
| Ulan-Ude | −16·1 | −7·1 | 10·6 | 32·9 | 46·6 | 61·2 | 66·6 | 61·5 | 47·1 | 30·4 | 8·6 | −8·5 | 28·0 |
| Troitskossavsk | −9·6 | −2·2 | 14·4 | 34·9 | 48·9 | 62·1 | 66·6 | 61·7 | 48·2 | 32·2 | 12·6 | −2·4 | 30·6 |
| Chita | −17·3 | −8·1 | 9·7 | 32·0 | 46·2 | 60·3 | 65·7 | 59·7 | 46·8 | 28·9 | 5·9 | −11·4 | 26·6 |
| Nerchinsk | −24·5 | −13·9 | 5·0 | 31·6 | 49·1 | 63·0 | 68·9 | 62·6 | 49·3 | 28·8 | 1·4 | −20·0 | 25·2 |
| *Amur–Ussuri Region* | | | | | | | | | | | | | |
| Blagoveshchensk | −11·6 | 0·6 | 14·9 | 36·3 | 50·7 | 63·3 | 70·2 | 65·7 | 53·8 | 34·5 | 11·5 | −6·9 | 31·8 |
| Khabarovsk | −9·6 | 0·7 | 16·2 | 37·0 | 51·6 | 62·1 | 68·4 | 67·3 | 56·5 | 39·6 | 17·1 | −2·9 | 33·6 |
| Bikin | −8·0 | 0·7 | 16·3 | 38·7 | 53·4 | 62·6 | 68·7 | 68·5 | 54·7 | 40·5 | 17·6 | −2·7 | 29·8 |
| *Coastal Region* | | | | | | | | | | | | | |
| Vladivostok | 7·3 | 13·8 | 25·3 | 39·9 | 49·1 | 56·5 | 64·6 | 69·1 | 61·7 | 48·7 | 31·1 | 14·7 | 40·3 |
| Olga Bukht | 10·9 | 16·2 | 27·0 | 24·4 | 47·5 | 54·3 | 62·4 | 66·4 | 58·1 | 44·8 | 28·8 | 14·5 | 39·2 |
| Nikolayevsk | −12·1 | 3·6 | 9·1 | 27·3 | 38·5 | 52·5 | 62·1 | 61·0 | 52·5 | 35·6 | 14·2 | 4·2 | 28·2 |
| Ayan | 4·5 | 3·7 | 13·8 | 27·0 | 35·1 | 41·4 | 54·0 | 56·3 | 50·2 | 32·4 | 12·9 | 0·3 | 26·8 |
| Okhotsk | −13·4 | −4·9 | 5·9 | 21·2 | 32·5 | 41·7 | 53·1 | 54·5 | 46·6 | 27·9 | 4·3 | −7·4 | 21·7 |
| *Kamchatka* | | | | | | | | | | | | | |
| Petropavlovsk | 12·2 | 11·8 | 19·0 | 28·4 | 36·0 | 44·1 | 51·1 | 53·4 | 48·6 | 39·0 | 27·5 | 18·3 | 32·4 |
| Bolsheretsk | 7·5 | 4·8 | 13·8 | 27·5 | 35·8 | 41·0 | 51·8 | 53·6 | 46·0 | 36·3 | 25·7 | 13·6 | 29·8 |
| *Sakhalin* | | | | | | | | | | | | | |
| Aleksandrovsk | −2·4 | 3·9 | 14·7 | 31·6 | 41·4 | 51·4 | 59·9 | 61·2 | 53·6 | 39·4 | 21·9 | 7·0 | 32·0 |
| Korsakovsk (Otomari) | 11·8 | 14·2 | 22·5 | 34·2 | 41·5 | 49·3 | 58·1 | 62·2 | 56·7 | 45·0 | 30·9 | 19·0 | 37·0 |
| *Far North* | | | | | | | | | | | | | |
| Markovo | −19·7 | −14·3 | −9·9 | 4·6 | 27·7 | 50·0 | 57·4 | 50·2 | 37·4 | 16·5 | −3·5 | −15·3 | 15·1 |
| Novo Marinsk | −9·9 | −6·3 | −3·8 | 5·2 | 25·2 | 40·8 | 50·7 | 48·9 | 38·7 | 23·4 | 4·8 | −6·7 | 17·4 |

G

the sea by the two mountain ridges lying to the east and west. The climatic conditions here therefore show distinct continental features. The summer is warmer and drier than on the coasts, while the winter is severe, with less snow than on the east coast but more than on the west coast. The quick transition from winter to summer,

*Annual and seasonal precipitation*

(in inches)

| Place | Altitude (feet) | Yearly Total | Summer Half Year | Winter Half Year | June, July, Aug. | Dec., Jan., Feb. |
|---|---|---|---|---|---|---|
| *Transbaikalia* | | | | | | |
| Barguzin . . | 1,640 | 10·2 | 7·9 | 2·4 | 5·2 | 1·1 |
| Ulan-Ude . . | 1,777 | 8·0 | 7·0 | 0·9 | 5·0 | 0·5 |
| Troitskossavsk . | 2,493 | 11·0 | 10·1 | 0·9 | 6·3 | 0·4 |
| Chita . . | 2,240 | 12·6 | 11·2 | 1·3 | 8·5 | 0·4 |
| Nerchinsk . . | 1,588 | 11·1 | 9·8 | 1·3 | 7·1 | 0·4 |
| *Amur–Ussuri Region* | | | | | | |
| Blagoveshchensk . | 440 | 20·6 | 18·9 | 1·6 | 13·5 | 0·2 |
| Khabarovsk . . | 164 | 22·2 | 19·2 | 3·0 | 13·7 | 0·7 |
| Bikin . . . | 239 | 24·3 | 19·5 | 4·7 | 12·1 | 1·1 |
| *Coastal Region* | | | | | | |
| Vladivostok . . | 95 | 21·1 | 17·6 | 3·6 | 10·2 | 0·9 |
| Olga Bukht . . | 148 | 29·6 | 23·1 | 6·5 | 12·8 | 1·7 |
| Nikolayevsk . . | 69 | 17·6 | 11·8 | 5·8 | 6·6 | 1·9 |
| Ayan . . . | 33 | 35·0 | 26·2 | 8·8 | 17·4 | 1·4 |
| Okhotsk . . | 20 | 11·1 | 9·6 | 1·5 | 6·4 | 0·3 |
| *Kamchatka* | | | | | | |
| Petropavlovsk . . | 335 | 30·4 | 13·7 | 16·7 | 7·0 | 8·5 |
| Bolsheretsk . . | 33 | 20·7 | 15·3 | 5·4 | 8·1 | 2·0 |
| *Sakhalin* | | | | | | |
| Aleksandrovsk . . | 52 | 23·6 | 13·2 | 10·4 | 6·9 | 4·1 |
| Korsakovsk (Otomari) | 121 | 19·4 | 12·0 | 7·5 | 12·8 | 3·0 |
| *Far North* | | | | | | |
| Markovo . . . | 85 | 7·9 | 5·6 | 2·3 | 4·1 | 1·0 |
| Novo Marinsk . . | 16 | 7·4 | 5·4 | 2·0 | 3·7 | 1·0 |

and the warm autumn, give the central depression the longest growing season of the peninsula. The stone birch develops buds here by the middle of May, in contrast to the coastal regions, where the buds do not appear until about the middle of June. The generally more favourable conditions of the central depression make this the most suitable area for arable farming, which has been developed extensively, whereas the coastal areas offer better conditions for cattle-breeding.

## The Eastern Coastal Seas

By acquiring possession of the Kuriles and South Sakhalin as a result of the Second World War, the Russians made the Sea of Okhotsk virtually an inland sea. It is separated from the Pacific by the island chain of the Kuriles, which forms a barrier broken by numerous but shallow gaps which allow the interchange of only the surface water. There exist two natural connexions with the Sea of Japan, one through the Straits of La Pérouse and the other through the Straits of Tartary, but the latter has been blocked since 1952 by a dam connecting Sakhalin with the mainland. The Sea of Okhotsk washes up against the shores of western Kamchatka, the coastal mainland, and northern and eastern Sakhalin.

### The Sea of Okhotsk

The northern coast of the Sea is more noticeably indented than the other coasts. The peninsula of Taigonos divides the large Bay of Shelekhova into Gizhiga and Penzhina Bays. West of Cape Koni the Bay of Tauyskaya penetrates inland, and in one part of this bay, known as Nagayeva Bay, lies the port of Magadan, which has become very well known during the last few years. In the extreme west, where the mountain ridges run into the sea, the interpenetration of land and water produces a coastal formation of long promontories and deep estuaries, extending offshore as the islands of Shantar. The Sea of Okhotsk is poor in islands, and apart from those just mentioned there are only a few coastal islands in the north, and rocky St John's Island in a lonely position in the western waters. The remainder of the coastline appears remarkably straight. In the west the coast runs parallel with the mountains, which fall steeply to the sea, so that flat approaches to the sea are to be found only at the mouths of the rivers and at the backs of the bays. The coasts of Kamchatka and Sakhalin, on the other hand, are mainly flat.

The Sea of Okhotsk is deepest in the south, where a channel more than 1,600 fathoms deep (maximum depth 1,843 fathoms) runs parallel with the Kuriles, the floor of the sea rising steeply from this deep sea-valley up to the island chain. Beyond the islands the bottom slopes down again still more steeply to the elongated deep sea-trough of the Kuriles, which reaches a depth of 5,672 fathoms. In the north on the other hand, the floor of the Sea rises only slowly. The contour line at 200 m. (109 fathoms) below sea level is always at a distance of 90–120 miles from the coast.

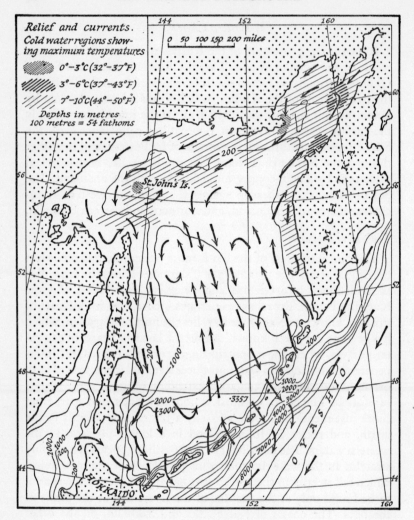

15. THE SEA OF OKHOTSK

There is a slight interchange of waters between the Sea of Okhotsk and the Sea of Japan through the Straits of La Pérouse, but
the main movement of waters is the continual interchange with
the Pacific. Through several of the gaps between the Kuriles there
is an inflow of surface waters from the ocean into the Sea of Okhotsk, while through others the surface waters flow out into the
ocean. At lower levels the flow is in the reverse direction from that
at the surface. Only two of the straits between the Kuriles are

deeper than 1,000 m. (546 fathoms), and only two others are deeper than 500 m. (273 fathoms), and as these are all rather narrow, the interchange of deep sea-water is very limited and the temperature balance between the sea and the ocean remains relatively unaffected. The bulk of the waters of the Sea of Okhotsk lie at depths greater than 500 fathoms, where they cannot take part in the interchange with the waters of the ocean.

In spite of the confusingly varied circulation of currents through the numerous gaps in the Kuriles, it is possible to recognize a regular circulation of currents within the Sea of Okhotsk moving along the coasts in an anti-clockwise direction. The main current enters the Sea past the southern tip of the Kamchatka peninsula and moves along its west coast towards the north, until it meets a cold current from the north which pushes the ocean current slightly away from the coast. The current undergoes a major change of direction in Shelekhova Bay, from which it proceeds to follow the coast towards the west. This turning in the bay, and consequent diagonal change of movement along the coast, is the cause of an upwelling of cold water which is drawn into the main current, which then continues to follow the coast to the west, where it washes around St John's Island. Strengthened by the outflow of the waters of the Amur, the current then runs along the east coast of Sakhalin towards the south, where it joins the current coming from the Straits of La Pérouse, and then emerges through the southern gaps of the Kuriles to rejoin the Pacific. The currents in the middle of the sea follow the general pattern established by the main current.

The whole of the Sea of Okhotsk is tidal, with the tide coming in from the Pacific through the gaps between the Kuriles. The tidal movement is strongest through the central gaps, from which it spreads out evenly inside the island chain. The average tidal range along the open coastal areas is 13 feet, but inside the large bays it increases considerably, and reaches 37 feet, for instance, in the Bay of Gizhiga.

The long cold winter with its harsh winds blowing from the mainland has a strong cooling effect on the water, and the short cool summer with its prevalent clouds and frequent fogs brings very little warmth. The temperature of the surface water seldom rises above 50° F., and this modest seasonal rise affects only the top layer (maximum depth 16–26 fathoms), while the lower layers have a temperature constantly below freezing point. Research has revealed that at first the temperature of the water falls slowly in proportion to the depth, and then suddenly drops to 32° at a depth of 8 fathoms. Below this point the temperature falls only very slowly until it reaches 29·3° at a depth between 40 and 80 fathoms. From here on down to the bottom of the sea the temperature rises slowly, reaching 34·2° F. in the north and 36·5° in the south. It is possible that the surface-water increases in density through the processes of ice-formation and salt crystallization to such an extent that it sinks down to the bottom.

Definite zones of cold water are characteristic of the Sea of Okhotsk, and in certain regions are a permanent feature, giving these parts of the sea a special character. These cold-water zones are derived from the circulation of the ocean currents, and can be considered as zones of upwelling water. The three most important zones are: (1) in front of Yama Bay around the islands of Yamsk, (2) around St John's Island, and (3) in the open water lying roughly between the northern tip of Sakhalin and the Shantar Islands. Within the first two cold-water zones the temperature of the water never rises above 34°, and in a wide area surrounding these two zones it remains constantly 5–9° lower than the average temperature of the sea. Even at the height of summer the temperature of the water just outside Penzhina Bay never rises above 41–43°. When the main current flowing into Shelekhova Bay turns back inside the bay towards its exit, it causes the upwelling of cold water within the smaller bays. This is particularly noticeable in front of Yama and Penzhina bays. From Yama Bay the cold water spreads out towards the south-west, following the direction of the main current, partly becoming warmer on the surface and partly sinking, but always presenting recognizable cold-water fronts. It is assumed that the elevated ground of the massif surrounding St John's Island is responsible for raising the layers of cold water which are so characteristic of the waters surrounding the island. Near the island the water is never warmer than 34°, and somewhat farther out it is only 34–37°. The cold-water zone then extends southwards from St John's Island, and cools down still more between the Shantar Islands and the northern tip of Sakhalin. This further cooling has been ascribed to an upwelling of cold water in the vicinity of the Shantar Islands, said to be due to the strengthening of the main current by the addition of the large quantities of water from the Amur.

In the summer these cold-water zones are marked by the formation of dense fogs which become more intense the greater the contrast in temperature between the air and the water. Dense fog-banks lie over these areas for weeks on end during the summer, clearing only when the sky is overcast. Nowhere over the Sea of Okhotsk is the fog as constant as in the areas near Yama Bay and St John's Island. Winds help to spread the fog, so that it also appears over areas of relatively warm water, but the source of the fog over the areas of cold water is inexhaustible and new fog-banks are always being formed. These fogs are characteristic of the whole of the northern part of the Sea of Okhotsk, where they are a frequent hindrance to navigation.

Because of its deep penetration into the continental mainland (where the low winter temperatures are common knowledge), there is a firm cover of ice all along the coast of the Sea of Okhotsk as early as December, stretching from the Straits of Tartary in the south to the Bay of Penzhina in the north. In February the whole northern half of the sea is covered with floating blocks of ice which often come close enough together to form a continuous ice-cover, until broken apart again by a storm. Not until the middle of June is the main part of the sea completely free from ice. (Further details about the ice-cover and its significance for the population are given in the chapter on maritime traffic.)

The proportion of salt in the Sea of Okhotsk is lower than in other seas in the vicinity, and varies between 32 and 32·5 parts per thousand. It is even lower in the bays at the mouths of the big rivers, as for example in the Amur Liman, where it is 31 parts per thousand. The proportion of salt increases with the depth, reaching 33·5–34·5 parts per thousand at the bottom of the sea.

## The Bering Sea

The Bering Sea is the most northerly of the seas bordering the Pacific Ocean, from which it is separated by the island chain of the Aleutians. Compared with the Sea of Okhotsk, the Bering Sea is less completely enclosed, since between the Kommandorskie (Commander) Islands and the beginning of the Aleutian chain, there is a connexion with the Pacific which is 212 miles wide and more than 1,600 fathoms deep, allowing an interchange of water down to this depth without any obstruction.

The connexion with the Arctic Ocean through the Bering Straits is much more restricted, being only 22 miles wide and no-where deeper than 32 fathoms. The influence of cold Arctic waters (flowing from the Chukchen Sea) is thus kept to a minimum, with the result that the characteristics of the Bering Sea are on the whole more akin to those of the northern Pacific, although modified according to the structure of the sea-basin.

The Bering Sea can be divided into two parts, based on the changing relief of the sea-floor. In the north-east, up to a line drawn roughly from Cape Navaron on the Russian side to Unimak Island just off the western tip of the Alaskan peninsula, the bottom of the sea is formed by the continental shelf, and is nowhere deeper than 116 fathoms. This part of the Sea is about 44 per cent of the whole. Beyond the continental shelf is a deep sea-basin with depths between 1,160 and 2,160 fathoms. This basin underlies 43 per cent of the total area of the Sea, the remaining 13 per cent being accounted for by the continental slope leading steeply down from 110 to 550 fathoms. The greatest depth of the Bering Sea is 2,230 fathoms (205/226).

The varied relief of the sea-bottom, with its steep incline from the deep sea-basin to the continental shelf, produces a very complicated circulation of currents. The main current from the Pacific enters the sea through the channel between the Kommandorskie and Aleutian Islands, and flows north-eastwards towards the Bering Straits until it meets the edge of the continental shelf, where it partially divides into two branches. The eastern branch remains within the deep sea-basin as a clockwise circular current. Part of the western branch also remains in the deep sea-basin, as an anticlockwise circular current in the centre, but the other part reaches the mainland coast. Here while passing Olyutorskaya Bay it causes an upwelling of cold water, which then moves south along the coast of Kamchatka and leaves the Bering Sea as a strong current flowing between the peninsula and the Kommandorskie Islands. This cold current joins the equally cold water coming from the Sea of Okhotsk to form the Oya-Shio current. Part of the main current which flows into the Bering Sea continues north over the continental shelf and travels with moderate speed through the Bering Straits into the Chuckchen Sea. This current is strengthened by another current from the Pacific which enters the Bering Sea through the Straits of Unimak (west of the island of the same name). This second Pacific current flows over the continental shelf along the west coast of Alaska until it passes, together with the central current, through the Bering Straits into the Arctic Ocean. (Reference should be made to the sketch map on the opposite page for further details about the currents in the Bering Sea.)

The surface temperature of the water depends in the first place on the general climatic conditions. In general, the Bering Sea can

16. THE BERING SEA

Relief and currents
Depths in metres
100 metres = 54 fathoms

0   100   200   300 miles

be considered as being very cool, the natural result of its situation in high latitudes, wedged between the continental masses of northern Siberia and north-western America with their long severe winters. Even during the summer the surface water over the continental shelf, away from the warm currents, becomes only moderately warmer, reaching temperatures of 44–48°. As a rule the surface water over the deep sea-basin is warmer and reaches 50–52°. It is a remarkable fact of special significance that throughout the year the surface water of the Bering Sea is warmer than the air above it, because of the continual inflow of warm water from the Pacific. A. A. Borissov (39/122) publishes the following table:

| Month | | | | Water temperature (° C.) | Air temperature (° C.) |
|---|---|---|---|---|---|
| January | . | . | . | −1·0 | −3·8 |
| April . | . | . | . | 1·6 | −0·9 |
| June | . | . | . | 10·3 | 8·5 |
| October | . | . | . | 6·9 | 4·3 |
| Year . | . | . | . | 4·7 | 2·1 |

As a result of the interchange of deep sea-water with the Pacific Ocean, the deep-sea temperatures of the Bering Sea are completely different from those of the Sea of Okhotsk. In the summer the temperature falls gradually with increasing depth from 50° at the surface to 39–43° at 16–20 fathoms. The coldest layer of water is found at 55–81 fathoms with a temperature of 33–34°. The temperature rises again to 38·3° at 116–266 fathoms, and then falls slowly to 34–36° at a depth of 1,200–1,600 fathoms. The coldest surface water is found in Olyutorskaya Bay and Anadyr Bay, where upwelling deep sea-water and particularly dense fog are characteristic. Fog-banks are also characteristic of the east coast of Kamchatka, where they are produced by the cold current which flows southwards along this coast.

The salinity of the water is the same on the whole for all parts of the Bering Sea. It is generally 32 parts per thousand on the surface, and increases to 34·5 parts per thousand at a depth of 1,600 fathoms. Only in the extreme north is the sea less salty, because of the influx of fresh water from the two big rivers—the Anadyr and the Yukon, which reduces the proportion of salt to 27 parts per thousand.

In the winter a solid sheet of ice forms along the northern coasts of the Bering Sea, while in front of the solid ice a large expanse of the Sea is covered with floating blocks of ice, which extend as far as the east coast of Kamchatka. The boundary of this floating mass of ice runs parallel to the edge of the continental shelf, and slightly to the south of it. At the entrances to Anadyr Bay and the Bering Straits this floating ice accumulates as a powerful mass of pack-ice. The warm-water currents cause the ice to melt early, so that by the middle of May it is to be found only along the Asian coast, and in June only in Anadyr Bay. In July the ice-line recedes beyond the Bering Straits into the Arctic, and the Bering Sea is completely ice-free.

## The Sea of Japan

The Sea of Japan extends from the Asian mainland in the west to the islands of Sakhalin, Hokkaido, and Hondo in the east. It is linked by the Straits of Korea (depth 61 fathoms) with the East China Sea, by the Straits of Tsuguru (58 fathoms) and Shimonoseki (16 fathoms) with the Pacific Ocean, and by the Straits of La Pérouse (30 fathoms) and Tartary (only 4–6 fathoms and now completely closed) with the Sea of Okhotsk. Because of these relatively shallow connexions with the neighbouring seas, the Sea of Japan forms a clearly-defined separate sea-basin. More than half of the Sea has a depth of 1,160 fathoms, and a quarter is deeper than 1,600 fathoms. The sea-floor drops rapidly to 1,160 fathoms from the Asian continental shore, but the drop is somewhat less rapid in the east. Towards the Straits of Korea in the south and the Gulf of Tartary in the north the change in depth is much more gradual.

Although the Sea of Japan forms an almost separate sea-basin, it shows in its surface currents all the characteristics of a marginal sea. From the south a branch of the Kuro-Shio (a warm current coming from tropical latitudes) enters through the Straits of Korea. While still in the Straits this warm current (known as the Tsushima River by the Japanese) divides into two tributaries. The eastern current, which is the wider and more swift-flowing of the two, runs along the Japanese islands towards the north, while the weaker western current runs roughly parallel to the Korean coast. This latter current soon meets a cold current moving along the coast towards it from the north. It partially mixes with this cold current, but its main stream is pushed away from the coast towards the east. After moving slowly to the east and later to the south-east, it joins the still relatively warm current of the retrograde former Tsushima River and forms a circular current running in an anti-clockwise direction.

The warm main stream of the Tsushima current gradually loses its force as it runs northwards along the coast of the Japanese islands. One part flows out through the Straits of Tsuguru, another part flows out into the Sea of Okhotsk through the Straits of La Pérouse, while the remainder of the current pushes farther north in the direction of the Gulf of Tartary. There it passes over a cold current which has come from the Sea of Okhotsk through the Straits of La Pérouse, and pushes as far as the south-west coast of Sakhalin, where its moderating influence is still noticeable. Here it has to leave the coast, since the moderate depth of the Gulf of Tartary acts as a barrier to any further movement towards the north. The relatively warm current therefore turns west, and later south-west, pulling along with it a cold stream which is recognizable as upwelling water because of its greater salinity. This cold-water stream runs along the coast to Vladivostok, where it has an appreciable effect in lowering the temperature of the water and the air in the vicinity. It then moves to the south along the coast of Korea, where it meets the western branch of the Tsushima current (as mentioned above), and thus comes to an end. As it proceeds the cold-water current is strengthened by upwelling water, which is evident along the coast of the Sikhota-Alin, particularly south of the Bay of Olga, and is characterized (apart from its lower temperature) by a higher salinity. Where the cold current meets the warmer current, a cold-water front is formed, which changes its position during the course of the year. During the winter the cold front shifts to the south because of an apparent strengthening of the cold current, while during the summer it moves back to the north (116/118). The great length of the Sea of Japan from north to south—the Gulf of Tartary is just below latitude 50° N. while the Straits of Korea are just below latitude 35° N.—results in large variations in the surface temperature of the water between different parts of the sea and different times of the year. Surface temperatures vary between 79° and 57° in the vicinity of the Straits of Korea, between 75° and 41° in the Straits of Tsuguru, between 72° and 34·5° in the Straits of La Pérouse, and between 63° and 28° in the northern part of the Gulf of Tartary.

The temperature of the water decreases rapidly as the depth increases. In the middle of the sea in July 1928, the temperature was found to be 68·7° at the surface, but only 38·1° at a depth of 50 m. (27 fathoms) and only 33·4° at a depth of 100 m. (54 fathoms). The latter temperature persisted to depths of 260

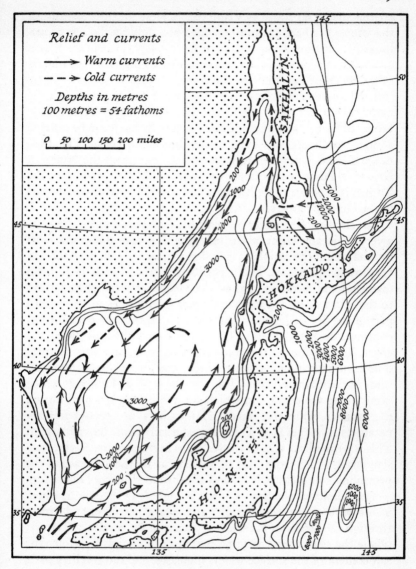

17. THE SEA OF JAPAN

fathoms or more, and nowhere, even at greater depths, has a lower temperature been ascertained (205).

In winter the Gulf of Tartary is regularly covered by a solid sheet of ice as far south as latitude 50°. The only other areas which are frozen solid on the surface like this are the bays of the Soviet coastal area as far south as Vladivostok. Here for three months of the winter the harbour can be kept open only by the use of ice-breakers. Floating ice is regularly found every winter in the northern part of the Sea of Japan, as far south as a line from the middle of the island of Hokkaido to the Bay of Korea.

Tidal movements affect the whole of the Sea of Japan, but the amplitude is not very great. The high tide enters by the wide Straits of Korea, and then spreads so quickly that it can be noticed almost simultaneously everywhere along the coast. The tidal range decreases in proportion to the distance from the Straits of Korea. In Pusan it is as much as 7 feet, while at the mouth of the Tumen it is only 1 foot; it rises again to 9 feet in the narrow part of the Gulf of Tartary.

The circulation of water-currents with different temperatures has a very noticeable effect on the neighbouring coastal regions. During the winter the mainland is under continental influence and has very low temperatures. This is particularly true of both the Russian mainland and Sakhalin, and as a consequence ice appears farther to the south along the mainland coast than it does in the eastern part of the Sea of Japan. Even in the late spring the cold current continues to carry floating blocks of ice southwards along the coast. In the summer the cold coastal current, aided by the predominant east and south-east winds, moderates the air temperatures of the mainland coast. It is also the source of the fogs which occur along the coast, and which are particularly frequent during the summer, when the greater contrast between sea and air temperatures results in fogs which are especially dense and persistent. This is particularly true of the sea areas in front of the Soviet Russian coast, which from May to July are under the influence of the prevailing south-east winds, and are shrouded by cool dense fog.

The salinity of the Sea of Japan is highest in the south, where water with a salt content of 34·56 parts per thousand enters through the Straits of Korea. It is lowest in the Straits of Tartary, where the salt content is 31·96 parts per thousand. In winter the salt content of the surface waters increases, and can reach 35 parts per thousand, owing to the low precipitation during the winter and the consequently reduced inflow of fresh water from the rivers.

The frequent storms, which are particularly numerous in the spring and autumn, have important effects on shipping on the Sea of Japan. These storms appear in the wake of cyclones which come from the mainland or from the East China Sea and use the Sea of

Japan as their route to the north-east. In the summer they are less frequent than in the transitional seasons, but they are more violent, especially during the later summer, when equatorial typhoons penetrate as far as this area with winds of great velocity. During the winter the continental cold front forces the cyclones to the south and south-east, thus restricting their activity more to Korea and the eastern part of the Sea of Japan where they hardly touch the Soviet regions.

## Flora

Although it is normally possible to divide up the vegetation of a large area into zones roughly corresponding to the climatic zones, in this area the vegetation has not created any individual formations of its own and shows generally a transitional character. In Transbaikalia the Siberian taiga merges into the Mongolian vegetation of the steppe. Along the Amur and the Ussuri typical Manchurian plants spread beyond these rivers to mingle with representatives of the Siberian conifers. Only in the coastal climatic region have special plant types developed which are characteristic only of this area.

In Transbaikalia the steppe vegetation penetrates far to the north, where it often appears as islands in the midst of otherwise unbroken forest. In the valley of the upper Angara, feather grass (*Stipa pennata*) and sheeps fescue grass (*Festuca Ovina*) are typical of the southern slopes, while the northern slopes are covered with dense larch and pine-woods. In the valley of the Barguzin, *Stipa pennata* and *Steppe Artemis* are to be found in close proximity. The well-known steppe of Nerchinsk, better known as the forest steppe, forms a well-defined island about 60 miles long and the same in width. Here a prairie character is predominant, with salt-pans and numerous xerophilous plants in the lower-lying places. The largest, and in this case completely unbroken, expanse of steppe occurs in the south-east between the upper courses of the Argun and Onon. This steppe of Argun starts in the north as a prairie, but changes towards the south into an Artemis steppe which gives the impression of a semi-desert. West of the Onon pure steppe is to be found only occasionally, and only in the Selenga region does it spread to any great extent. Here between Selenginsk and Troitskossavsk are found alluvial sands which frequently have been laid bare, giving rise to a desert-like landscape of drifting dunes and salt-pans in scattered depressions.

The relief is of decisive importance in relation to the distribution of the different forms of vegetation. As a rule, the steppes keep to the valley floors, at altitudes from 1,600 to 3,000 feet. Then comes the forest steppe up to about 3,900 feet, composed mainly of birch trees, above which come the unbroken forests of conifers. In South Transbaikalia the upper tree-line lies at an altitude of 5,600–6,200 feet, but in the bitter north it is considerably lower. There the tree-line is sometimes as low as 3,900 feet, with the forest extending below this and descending on the north-facing slopes down to the shores of Lake Baikal.

West of the Yablonovy ridge, the forests are composed of the same species as are found throughout the whole of East Siberia, mainly Dauric larches (*Larix dahurica*). In addition there is the Siberian cedar or Cembra pine (*Pinus cembra*), which occurs even more frequently than the larch at higher altitudes, and the pine (*Pinus silvestris*), which is found on drier, more sandy soil. The Siberian pine (*Picea obovata*) and the Siberian fir (*Abies sibirica*) are comparatively much more rare. West of the Selenga River only a small number of Siberian larches are to be found. The Sokhondo Mountain (8,227 feet) near the Mongolian frontier demonstrates clearly the influence of altitude on the vegetation. Here the forests start at an altitude of 3,900 feet, rising to 6,200 feet, and are composed of the various Siberian species mentioned above. One important point of difference between the Transbaikalian forests and those of Siberia is their dense undergrowth, composed mainly of rhododendrons and dwarf birches (*Betula Middendorffi*).

Above the tree-line there begins a strange kind of dwarf-timber vegetation which is very characteristic of these altitudes, not only in Transbaikalia but in all the other regions as well. It includes the dwarf pine (*Pinus Pumila*), the dwarf birch (*Betula Middendorffe alpina*), the Cassiope (*Cassiope ericoides*), the rhododendron (R. *chrysanthum*), and a dwarf type of the Dauric larch (*Larix Daurica* var. *pumila*). This shrub-like formation, which can grow to a height of 10 feet, is such a dense and tangled growth that it appears to be impenetrable.

There is no meadow-land region in Transbaikalia, and as a rule moss and lichen lead straight from the shrub vegetation to the bare rocks of the *golzy*.

East of the Yablonovy ridge the forests are generally of the same type as in the west, but in addition we find here the first deciduous trees such as oaks, elms, and apple trees, which are the forerunners of the more temperate zones of East Asia. On their way to the east the Russians must have missed the deciduous trees from beyond the Urals, and on seeing them again here for the first time were apparently so delighted that they called the ridge where they found the first wild apple trees the Yablonovy Khrebet, meaning the 'apple mountains'.

The forests of the Far Eastern territories proper consist of three main elements: the East Siberian, the Okhotsk, and the Manchurian. The Dauric larch represents the East Siberian element; the Ayan pine (*Picea ayaninsis*), the stone birch (*Betula ermani*) and the white-barked fir (*Abies nephrolepis*) are characteristic of the Okhotsk type, and are limited to the cool and humid coastal area; the Manchurian type is characterized by its wealth of deciduous trees, with an abundance of different species—oaks, maples, ashes, limes, and others—which are found mainly in the valleys of the middle Amur and the Ussuri, and in the southern Sikhota-Alin.

It is the mild climate of the Amur–Ussuri region which causes the large-leaved deciduous trees to appear as part of the general vegetation picture of this region, where they even become predominant over wide areas.

Eastwards from the northern arc of the Amur, the spreading East Siberian taiga changes its character and becomes a mixed forest, and in the vicinity of Blagoveshchensk deciduous trees become predominant.

The most characteristic tree is the oak (*Quercus mongolica*), followed closely by the lime (*Tilia Amurensis* and *T. Manchurica*), the ash (*Acer ginala*), and elms and numerous other deciduous trees. A similar change occurs south of the Stanovoy ridge in the direction of the Amur. The Scotch pine (*Pinus silvestris*), the most loyal tree of North Eurasia, which survives in spite of all climatic differences from Europe to the Sea of Okhotsk, is found no more beyond the lower Amur, and the Siberian fir (*Picea excelsa obovata*, a variety of the European *Picea excelsis*) finds its eastern limit here too.

The Lespedeza (*Lespedeza bicolor*) is characteristic of the deciduous-tree areas of the Amur region, and in clearings or areas which have been burned over it often covers the ground completely. Although not as nourishing as lucerne, it nevertheless provides excellent cattle-food. Along the Amur, and especially in the Seya–Bureya plain, are to be found extensive grasslands known as the Amur prairie. Next to the rivers, reed bent-grass (*Calamagrostis Langsdorffi*) is predominant. But with regard to both plants and animals these plains also contain elements of the steppes, e.g.

H

the typical steppe grass (*Stipa Capillata*) and the rodent Ssusslik
(*Citellus Eversmanni jacuntensis*). In boggy river valleys, particularly
along the Bureya, there is bog-forest composed of poplars (*Populus
suaveolens*), limes (*Tilia cordata amurensis*), Manchurian nut trees
(*Juglans Manchurica*), and others. These swampy forests are characterized by a particularly dense and strange undergrowth with
numerous climbing plants, among which the enormous Manchurian vine (*Vitis amurensis*) requires special mention. It grows in
the Amur region as far north as the 51st latitude, and as far as the
Seya towards the west. Its trunk achieves a diameter of 4 inches,
and its sweet black grapes are gathered by the inhabitants to be
made into wine or jam.

In the Ussuri region the vegetation becomes entirely Manchurian. Here, in comparison with the dearth of species of the
Siberian taiga, the explorer is surprised by the extraordinarily
great variety of flora. Komarov points out sixty-four different
types of trees, seventy-nine of shrubs and fifteen of lianas. It
may be of decisive importance that these regions were not
touched by the Ice Age, which allowed specimens of Tertiary flora
to be preserved until today. In the Ussuri depression and in the
valleys of the southern Sikhota-Alin deciduous trees are completely predominant. In the south the Manchurian species become
interspersed with Korean and Japanese types. Besides the deciduous trees mentioned above, the following may be pointed out
as characteristic: the different species of ash (*Acer barbinerve*, *A.
mono*, *A. tegmentosum*, and *A. ukurenduense*), alders (*Alnus fruticosa*,
*A. japonica*, *A. incana*), pears (*Pirus ussuriensis* and *P. sineneis*),
mountain ash (*Sorbus aucuparia*, *S. sambucifolia*), and the Amur lilac
(*Syringa amurensis*). Also worth noting are the East Asian cork tree
(*Phellodendron amurensis*) with its strange soft bark, the white walnut (*Aralia manchurica*) and the palm-like Dimorphant (*Dimor-
phantus manchuricus*).

In the higher regions of the Sikhota-Alin it is the conifers which
are again the more characteristic, and the Dauric larch can be seen
everywhere. New additions are the Manchurian cedar (*Pinus manchurica*) which keeps mainly to the coast, the pine (*P. funebris*), and
at the east coast the Olga larch. The yew tree (*Taxus cuspidata*),
which grows up to a height of 65 feet, is to be found occasionally,
while the juniper tree is found everywhere, often covering large
areas at higher altitudes with a creeping species (*Juniperus daurica*).
In the Sikhota-Alin the three types of Far Eastern forest are all to
be met within a narrow compass. The Manchurian type fills the

valley floors and the slopes, but is never found above an altitude
of 2,500–3,300 feet. Above it is found the Okhotsk taiga, and beyond that is the Siberian type—mainly *Larix dahurica*. The abundance of precipitation and the considerable warmth in the south of
the Ussuri region create particularly good conditions for the development of aquatic plants. Here grow the lotus flower (*Nelumbo
speciosa*), the Brasenia (*Brasenia purpurea*) which in pre-Quaternary
times was also to be found in Europe, the water-nut (*Trapa incisa*),
and in certain localities the water-lily (*Euryale ferox*), whose enormous leaves reach a diameter of up to 51 inches.

In contrast to the Amur–Ussuri region the vegetation of the
coastal areas presents a different and more clearly defined picture.
The hardy perennial Dauric larch, which extends into north-east
Siberia as far as the Arctic tree-line and towards the south as far as
the Sikhota-Alin, oddly enough avoids the eastern sea-coast, with
its cool and humid winds, and appears only at some distance inland. The whole of the forested coastal area is therefore covered
by the Okhotsk taiga, a special type of coniferous wood consisting mostly of pines, firs, and birches. They grow here in dense
forests on the slopes descending towards the sea. The characteristic trees are the Ayan pine, the stone birch, and the white-barked
fir, which have already been mentioned above. In addition to being found along the coast of the sea bearing the same name, the
Okhotsk taiga is also found in the region of the mouth of the
Amur, and is prevalent as well on that part of the northern Sikhota-Alin which slopes down towards the coast. It is excellently
suited to the raw coastal climate, but the violence of the winds
from the sea does not permit an unbroken expanse of taiga. It
therefore covers mainly the slopes and valleys, where it develops
an extraordinary dense and almost impenetrable growth. Higher
up towards the mountain ridges it changes very quickly into the
usual vegetation of stunted dwarf trees, followed by formations of
moss and lichen covering the greater part of the wind-swept
ridges which serve the reindeer-breeders as excellent summer pas-
ture. In the Dzhugdzhur Mountains most of the passes leading
from the coast into the interior lie above the tree-line, which
makes their use, particularly during the winter, very difficult.

The vegetation of Kamchatka corresponds in general to the
Okhotsk type, although slightly modified by the relief and milder
climate. Here the characteristic tree is the stone birch (*Betula
ermani*), which is predominant on all slopes descending towards
the Okhotsk and Bering seas, thus creating the general impression

of a deciduous forest. Only in the interior, where continental climatic features prevail under the protection of the two mountain ranges, does the East Siberian taiga survive with its characteristic Dauric larches. Above the tree-line, the mountains are again covered with stunted dwarf vegetation which is particularly dense on Kamchatka and often makes large areas almost impenetrable. Along the west coast a tundra-like mossy steppe has developed, extending over the northern part of the peninsula from west to east. In contrast to the north, where conditions are more unfavourable, towards the south vegetation becomes more abundant as well as more varied. Special mention must be given to the appearance of the Japanese birch (*Betula Japonica*) and numerous specimens of high grass like *Heracleum tanatum* and *H. dulce*, as well as to the frequent occurrence of the bear berry (*Angelica ursina*), which grows up to a height of 10 feet. The appearance of extensive forest pastures in the south has made it possible to introduce cattle-breeding in this area.

The regions of the extreme north-east can be described generally as tundra or forest-tundra.

*Fauna*

The fauna shows the same close proximity of different types which is typical of the natural vegetation, with Eastern and Inner Asian types mingling with the Siberian ones. In much of this country which was once famous for its wealth of game, incredible exploitation has either destroyed all the useful game or driven it into remote areas. However, there are still very large areas hardly touched by human beings where numerous animals have been able to survive in full freedom.

A great number of rodents especially characteristic of the steppes are to be found on the prairies and steppes of Transbaikalia, e.g. the 'Ssusslik' or ground squirrel (*Citellus eversmanni* and *C. dauricus*), the 'Tarbagan', which is a type of marmot (*Arctomys bobak*), the earth- or spring-hare (*Alactaga saltator mongolica*), and others. But the larger animals of the steppe have either been driven out or exterminated. The still untouched forest-lands of Transbaikalia, as well as those of the other regions, are much richer in animal life. Two typically Nordic animals—the reindeer and the elk—are found as far south as the northern Sikhota-Alin. The native Tungus keep the reindeer as a domestic animal, and in addition there are numerous wild reindeer which still exist in the north. The elk (*Alces machlis*) prefers the boggy deciduous forests, and in its widespread wanderings penetrates as far south as the 46th parallel. In contrast to its Nordic relation, the Ussuri elk has rounded rather than flattened antlers, but it is just as big and as primeval in appearance as the other. The animal most favoured by hunters is the stag, in particular the large 'Isyubr' (*Cervus canadensis Luhdorfi*) and the smaller spotted stag (*C. Dybowski*). The latter, which is one of the Sika stags, is easily tamed, and is therefore found in most European zoological gardens. Its horns (the not yet hardened antlers) are particularly valuable as an export to China, where they are used as an expensive popular remedy, and as a result it has been driven by ruthless hunting into the remotest regions. Today there is domestic breeding of both these types of stag. Roes are numerous, and so are wild sheep in the mountain areas where a number of different species are found, namely, *Ovis ammon mongolica* in Transbaikalia, *O. jubata* and *Middendorffi* along the Amur and the Ud, *O. storcki* and *alleni* at the Sea of Okhotsk, and *O. nivicola* on Kamchatka. In the taiga carnivorous animals are fairly numerous. The characteristic animal is the bear, which plays an important part in the mythology of the natives and is respectfully called 'the master'. In addition to the ordinary brown bear there also exists a small black type, as well as the white-breasted collar bear of Tibet (*Ursus tibetanus*), which is considered to be particularly savage. Other carnivors which must be mentioned are the wolf (the common wolf, the red wolf (*Cuon appinus*), and the glutton (*Gulo luscus*)), the lynx, the wild cat (*Felis euptilura*), and several different types of fox. The red wolf is a jackal-like wild dog, usually found where there are wild sheep.

The valuable fur-bearing animals (such as the sable (*Martes Zibellina*), the marten (*M. flavigula borealis*), the ermine (*Mustella erminis*), the otter (*Lutra vulgaris*), the squirrel (*Scurius vulgaris*), and the more rare flying squirrel (*Sciuropterus volans*)) have been almost exterminated in some regions by excessive hunting. Most of these animals have retired into the remote forest regions.

In the Ussuri region and in the Sikhota-Alin other noteworthy inhabitants of the forest are found in addition to those mentioned above, due to the more southern location of these regions. Here the characteristic animals are the Amur tiger (*Felis tigris longipilis*), the wild boar (*Sus leucomystax continentalis*), and the strange marten dog 'Enot' (*Nyctereutes procynoides*). The wild boars live in large numbers, generally in herds, in the vicinity of the boggy deciduous and mixed forests, where they are provided with excellent food by the oak woods. Next in importance is the Amur tiger, which is bigger and has a more valuable fur than the Bengal 'King tiger', but is very rare, and only to be found in the remote corners of the mountains. The marten dogs are hunters of the roes, and are also dangerous robbers which not infrequently even force their way into people's houses.

The feathered world is richly represented. Birds of the tundra, such as the partridge (*Lagopus mutus*), build their nests on the mountains towering above the tree-line, while numerous southern species are also found in the Ussuri region, such as pelicans, white herons, and cormorants. In the woods there are mountain-hens, heath-hens, and numerous woodcocks, and in the less overgrown areas there are partridges, quails, and also pheasants. The latter often migrate in large numbers from Manchuria into the Amur–Ussuri region. Lake Khanka is a veritable bird paradise, and swans, wild geese, ducks, and diverse moorhens are to be found in very large numbers on all the lakes and marshes.

Amphibians and reptiles are to be found everywhere, but are particularly numerous in the warmer Ussuri region. Noteworthy among the snakes is the viper *Coluber Schrenkii*, which grows to a length of 5 feet and a diameter of $2\frac{1}{2}$ inches, as well as the *Ancistrodon Blomhoffi*, which is especially venomous.

The insect world should not be left unmentioned. In the summer huge swarms of gnats develop, making life most unpleasant for human beings as well as for animals. The stings of the small mosquitoes which are generally called 'Gnus' (meaning vermin) by the Russians, are particularly painful.

The wealth of fish in all parts of the sea near the coast is of the greatest economic importance. In the south large shoals of herrings appear every year, coming from the Sea of Japan. The mouth of the Amur is marked by the regular appearance of large shoals of salmon heading up the river to spawn. Two types of salmon are most numerous: the Keta salmon (*Oncorhynchus Keta* Walb.), and the hump-backed salmon (*O. gorbusha* Walb.), known as Gorbusha by the Russians. In addition, the Sea of Okhotsk contains herrings, cod, tunny, and mackerels. The coastal areas of Kamchatka possess the world's richest source of crabs. On the eastern side of the peninsula it is mainly the Pacific species of salmon which are caught, namely the red salmon (*Oncorhynchus nerka* Walb.), the silver salmon (*O. Kisuch* Walb.), and the king salmon (*O. chavycha* Walb.). In the Bering Sea the unusually great wealth of marine animals which originally existed there, particularly whales and seals, has been greatly reduced by man's intervention.

# CHAPTER 2

# The Population

*

### Pre-History and Settlement

Several finds of Neolithic Stone-Age tools prove that the Amur and Ussuri regions were already inhabited by human beings during the transition from the Diluvial to the Alluvial period. Among the tools found there are simple hatchets, chisels, spear points, scrapers, and knives, all chipped out of stone. In addition there were already some ground tools similar to those known from the Neolithic age of North Germany. Further finds from the more advanced Stone Age include coiled pottery similar to that from Europe's corresponding cultural epoch.

We get the first historical information about these same regions from old Chinese literature which goes back to the year 800 BC According to this source the eastern part of the Amur and Ussuri regions was inhabited by the Suches, the centre of Manchuria by the Hueis (also called the Hueimai), and the west by the Tonghus. All three peoples (who were subdivided into numerous smaller tribes) are mentioned again later as living in the same areas up to the second century BC.

The most recent research on the subject indicates that the Suches and Hueis were the ancient Tungus, and that the Tonghus were the pre-Mongolians. Traces of a Neolithic culture of the latter tribe are distributed over the whole of eastern Mongolia. The Suches and Hueis lived mainly in the forest regions, while the Tonghus preferred the wide open spaces, so that even in the most ancient times the division between the Tungus forest-people and the Mongolian steppe-people was already clearly marked. The Tungus have spread out from northern Manchuria and the Ussuri region (which we must regard as their original native country) over the larger part of East and Central Siberia. In doing so, they pushed the Palaeo-Asiatic people—who lived to the north of them and with whom they partly mixed—more and more to the north and north-east. The Tungus showed great ability in adjusting

themselves to numerous different types of country and to a great
variety of different ways of life, making the best of their surroundings and trying to build up their own culture. In the course of
time various branches developed along different lines, and today
they are generally divided culturally into horse-, reindeer-, and
dog-Tungus. Most of the Tungus now live in the region of the
two eastern tributaries of the Yenissei—the Upper and Lower Tunguska—which were named after the Tungus. They are also scattered all over the Far Eastern territories, with the sole exception
of the extreme north-east, which was used by the Palaeo-Asians
as their place of retreat. The advance of the Tungus towards the
north had some advantages for the retreating peoples, since it
enabled them to adopt many of the Tungus cultural achievements.
For instance, it can be assumed that the various Palaeo-Asiatic
tribes only learned about raising reindeer from the Tungus.

Of the Palaeo-Asiatic peoples, the only ones which have survived in their original settlements are the Gilyaks, protected by
the marshes of the lower Amur and the Ud, and also the Ainos on
Sakhalin. Most of the Palaeo-Asiatic people found refuge in the
extreme north-east.

When the Tungus spread out over the whole of East Siberia,
many tribes dissolved into separate groups and clans, since there
was ample room for all. Closer contact was best maintained in their
original homeland, and there was also fairly intensive settlement
in the area to the left of the Amur, particularly by the Dauric
tribes. Here in the plains of the Seya and Bureya the Russians,
according to their first reports, found a densely populated area, inhabited by people who raised cattle and tilled the soil. The Russian invaders robbed the inhabitants and later pushed back by
force any Tungus settlers who had not already retreated to the
more peaceful right-hand side of the Amur, with the result that
even today there are no Tungus to be found in the Amur region
proper. As far as Khabarovsk the Amur separates the Russians on
the left side from the Tungus and the Chinese (who later immigrated here in large numbers) on the other.

In Transbaikalia traces have been found proving human in-
habitation of this country as early as the Palaeolithic Age, but the
exact significance of these traces is still obscure. The finds of the
Neolithic Age provide a much clearer picture of the life and activities of the people there. The inhabitants of that time were fishermen and hunters who also did a moderate amount of cattle-raising,
and who lived in settlements situated mainly near rivers and lakes.

Their food was gathered from edible plants, roots and fungi, berries and 'cedar-nuts' (the fruit of the cembra pine), and their clothes were made out of the hemp nettle.

Chinese historical sources tell us that in the third and second centuries BC this country was inhabited by the Huns, who are described as half-nomadic huntsmen who also raised cattle and tilled the soil. They became known through their trade with the Chinese. About 100 BC the country came under Chinese domination, the limits of which are somewhat nebulous. The Chinese were followed by other foreign rulers from the south, and the country remained under foreign domination until about AD 900. During this period several different tribes came and left again, including the Vigurians, who receive special mention. Later, during the age of Genghis Khan in the twelfth and thirteenth centuries, the Merkites, Kereites, Oirotes, and others—who are all known collectively as the 'Forest people'—lived in this area. They fought against the people of Ghengis Khan and lost, but although they had to submit to his rule, it was hardly noticeable here, since no special attention was paid to these rough forest areas on the fringe of his gigantic empire. It was during this time that the Buryatic tribes were formed, partly from different groups of people seeking protection and partly from the native population. In the face of pressure from the southern steppes, some of the Buryats moved to the west side of Lake Baikal, pushing out the Turkish Yakutes and the Tungus towards the north. The Yakutes moved into the semi-steppe regions of the middle and lower Lena, pushing their habitations northwards to where the Palaeo-Asiatic people lived, thus driving a broad wedge into the area over which the Tungus had spread.

In the fourteenth century the dwellings of the Buryats spread eastwards from the River Oka, a left-hand tributary of the Angara, to the steppes of the Onon and Argun river-basins. At that time the Buryats already knew how to extract salt and how to produce iron, and they are known to have acted as intermediaries in the trade between the Tungus huntsmen and the Chinese. They traded food (particularly millet) with the Tungus in exchange for precious furs (mainly sable), which they exchanged again with Chinese traders for silver and goods from China. Under the leadership of the 'Noyones' the separate tribes had by now established a firm and almost state-like social organization, which was firm enough to put up an initially successful resistance to the Cossack invaders of the seventeenth century. The Cossacks had been attracted to

Transbaikalia by the news they had received of a rich country, full
of precious furs and silver.

They met strong resistance as far west as Irkutsk, where the
Buryats beat back or destroyed several small detachments. In the
course of successive encounters over a number of years, however,
the Cossacks established footholds in Transbaikalia in the form of
a series of individual bases which they enlarged to form small for-
tresses. Verkhne Angarsk was founded in 1646 at the entry of the
upper Angara into Lake Baikal, and this was followed by the
founding of Barguzin in 1648, Nerchinsk in 1654, Selenginsk in
1665, and Verkhne Udinsk (Ulan-Ude) in 1666. However, Cossack
power did not extend very far beyond their bases, and the Buryats
did not readily submit. Twice there were serious revolts, which
subjected the bases to severe siege and kept them for months without outside communication; smaller outposts were conquered, the
garrisons massacred, and the buildings destroyed. In the end the
better organization of the Russians and their use of firearms
finally broke the resistance of the Buryats, many of whom moved
into Mongolia. New counter-invasions were launched from there,
and it was only after the Treaty of Nerchinsk in 1689 that peace
returned to the country and the Russians started to settle there.

### The Old Indigenous Tribes

The descendants of the original tribes at present still inhabiting
Transbaikalia and the Far Eastern territories can be divided into
three groups: the Mongols, the Tungus, and the Palaeo-Asiatics.
The Buryats (the only representatives of the Mongols) are confined to Baikalia, while the Tungus and Palaeo-Asiatic peoples are
spread over the whole of the Far Eastern territories.

The *Buryats* inhabit areas both west and east of Lake Baikal.
They numbered about 280,000 in 1939, and can be divided into
two main groups—the Buryats of Irkutsk and those of Transbaikalia. The former number about 100,000 and live in the area of
Irkutsk, where they enjoy cultural autonomy in the National District of Ust-Orda. The Buryats of Transbaikalia form a minority
group in the Buryato-Mongolian ASSR, where they form only
43·8 per cent (1941) of the total population, with the Russians
forming the majority. A fairly large number of Buryats also live in
the region of Chita, particularly on the Steppe of Aginsk south of
Chita, where they have their own administration in a National
District. The Buryats are regarded as a branch of the Mongols,

comparable to the Khalkha Mongols of Outer Mongolia. History
reveals that some of the Buryats had become settlers quite early,
especially west of the Lake of Baikal, but the majority have remained a typical nomadic people on the steppes of Transbaikalia
until very recently. Gmelin, who travelled across this country in
the eighteenth century, tells us that a great number of Buryats had
flocks of thousands of sheep and hundreds of cows and horses.
Georgi, who stayed in Transbaikalia during that same century,
writes that some of the Dauric Buryats possessed as many as 1,000
camels, 4,000 horses, 2,000–3,000 cows, 8,000 sheep, and hundreds
of goats. Even if these numbers are exaggerated, they undoubtedly
prove that cattle-raising was the basis of the economic life of the
Buryats. After the invasion of the Russians they managed exceptionally well in adapting themselves to the changed conditions of
life, and a great number became cultivators of the land. Often they
had no other choice, since the Russian settlers took their best pastures and converted them into arable land. Pushed into less
favourable regions, the Buryats started with admirable energy
(and without any European guidance) to create anew their own
agricultural land with the help of artificial irrigation, especially in
the vicinity of the Selenga River and in the Barguzin valley. On
the southern steppes of Transbaikalia they stuck to their original
occupation of cattle-raising, and proved to be eminently successful. The Buryato Republic is today one of the most important
regions producing a surplus of cattle within the Soviet Union.
Many interesting features of the Buryat folklore have been lost
with the introduction of the *kolkhoz* economy and modern
methods of cattle-raising. The traditional 'Yurtes'[1] made of felt
have often disappeared and have been replaced by more practical
small wooden houses. However, there are still regions in Transbaikalia where the Buryats go on with their nomadic life unhindered and unrestrained, although Russian influence is everywhere
becoming more pronounced. The Buryats of Irkutsk and Transbaikalia, who have changed over to agriculture and are settling together with the Russians, show this influence most strongly. However, their intelligence and their pride (qualities for which they are
particularly famous) have helped them to maintain a special position for themselves, which is expressed in the Buryats' Autonomous Soviet Republic and in their two National Districts.

The *Tungus* (or Evenki, as they are called in current Soviet
literature) are to be found throughout the whole of East Siberia,

[1] This is a Turkish word meaning movable little houses. (Tr. N.)

their total number being estimated at about 75,000. The Tungus proper number about 60,000 people and live in a very large National District on the right-hand side of the Yenissei, west of the ASSR of the Yakutes. Most of the other Tungus (who are divided into many small, often tiny, groups) live in the Far Eastern territories. They include the Lamutes, Goldes, Olches, Orokes, Oroches, Orochones, and other smaller tribes. The Lamutes (whose name derives from the Tungus word 'lamu'—the sea) live widely scattered over the whole of the coastal area of Okhotsk and the upper basin of the Anadyr, and are also to be found on Kamchatka. Their total number is probably not higher than 3,000. Only a small proportion raise reindeer, the majority being settled by the sea with permanent dwellings at the mouths of the rivers, where they fish and hunt and raise dogs. (Thus the Lamutes could also be called the sea- or coastal-Tungus.) In contemporary Soviet literature they are called Eveni. Very little is known about their folklore. In 1930 the Okhotsko-Evenski National District was founded, but after only four years it was dissolved again because the scattered Eveni were unable to build up their own organization. More intensive Russian colonization along the coast of the Sea of Okhotsk has now made the Eveni a minority in this area. Shortly before the foundation of the Eveni National District they formed 80 per cent of the population in this special area, but in 1934 they were only 40 per cent. At present the Eveni, together with the Russian immigrants, work mainly in the fishing industry.

The *Goldes* are much better known. They inhabit the region near the confluence of the Amur and the Ussuri, and are also scattered along the Ussuri valley and throughout the Sikhota-Alin. They have settled most densely in the valley of the Amur below Khabarovsk. The characteristics of the Mongolian race are particularly marked in the Goldes, with their protruding jaws and cheekbones, straight black hair, and wide flat noses. In former times they made their clothing partly from fish-skin, and for this reason were known by the Chinese as '*Jupi-tadsy*', meaning barbarians in fish-clothes. In modern times this national costume of the Goldes has been completely replaced by clothing of Chinese or Russian origin. The Goldes are exclusively fishermen, hunters, dog-breeders, and trappers. Fish dried in the open is stored for the winter and serves as food for man and dog. Otherwise the fish is usually boiled, but in the summer it is eaten raw as well. Raw bone-marrow and the liver of the Isyubr stag are considered as special delicacies. For hunting big game, self-releasing spring-guns and traps are set along the tracks of the animals. The wheeled vehicle as a means of transport is unknown to the Goldes; in the summer they use boats made from birch-bark or from planks, and in the winter they use the dog-sledge. The position of the women is difficult; polygamy is permitted, and the custom of buying a bride has long survived. The Goldes live in little settlements of two to twenty houses, built of clay after the model of the Chinese '*Fanses*', and sometimes half sunk into the ground. During the summer, however, the Golde prefers to leave his solid house in order to move into his dome-shaped tent covered with birch-bark or raffia mats. In recent years many Goldes have taken to growing vegetables, raising pigs, and breeding fowl.

The *Samagires*, who are related to the Goldes, should also be mentioned. They live along the Gorin, a left-hand tributary of the lower Amur. Their culture corresponds to that of the Goldes, but from many expressions in their language it can be inferred as probable that originally they were reindeer-breeders, who changed later to become fishers and hunters. Farther down the Amur live the Olches, who are also to be found along the coast of the Gulf of Tartary, as well as on Sakhalin, where they call themselves Orokes. The Olches also are hunters, fishermen, and dog-breeders, but, in contrast to the half-nomadic Goldes, they are settled, and they all till the land to a limited extent. There are several signs to indicate that they, too, were originally reindeer-breeders, just as their kinsmen the Orokes still are on Sakhalin today.

The number of Goldes (or Nanais, as they are called today) may amount to 5,000 or 6,000; the Olches and Orokes are a much smaller group of probably not more than 1,000. In 1931 the Nanai National District was founded for the Goldes, as well as the Evenko-Nanai National District for the Samagires and Goldes, and the Olchi National District for the Olches, but in all these areas Russian immigration grew to such an extent that the natives soon became a hopeless minority. In the middle of the Nanai District the town of Komsomolsk developed rapidly and acted like a magnet on the native population, who often left their original homes to find work in industry or to enter one of the numerous fishing organizations, the *kolkhoz* and the *sovkhoz*. Today most of them live and work here together with the Russians, and their complete assimilation with the latter is only a matter of time.

The *Orochi*, who are often called the Udege, after the river of the same name, are neighbours of the Goldes. In 1926 they numbered

1,347 people, and today there are not more than 1,500. Split up into numerous small groups, they inhabit central and southern Sikhota-Alin, living in the valleys running towards the sea as well as towards the Ussuri. Many of them have adapted themselves largely to the Chinese way of life, especially in the south, where they speak Chinese and live according to Chinese customs. However, in the interior of the Sikhota-Alin they have survived as 'real forest-people' (as Arsenyev calls them), having remained almost unmixed with other peoples, and showing pronounced Tungus features. The average height is $5\frac{1}{4}$ feet for the men and $4\frac{3}{4}$ feet for the women, and their hands and feet are strikingly small. The custom of wearing ear- and nose-rings still exists with the Orochi-Udege (as it once did with the Goldes), although now only with the women. They still live in pointed tents, in contrast to the rounded tents of the Goldes, who bend their tent-poles into a domed shape bearing a certain similarity to the Mongolian *yurtes*. On long treks the Orochi finds this tent too cumbersome to take with him, so instead he builds a simple one from branches, for protection wherever he stays. The pure Orochi is wholly hunter and fisherman. The social order of these people is strange, with a council of the elders and most experienced to manage the affairs of the settlement. Everyone is free to do the work he prefers, but must fit in with the general life of the community. All profits and booty from hunting are shared not only by the family but also by the whole settlement. In this way provision is made for the family whose head goes on long hunting expeditions and often stays away for many weeks. Marriage customs still retain some elements of the group-marriage. Belief and superstition are particularly strongly developed; people believe in several different gods, such as the forest-god and the sea-god, and they all think of nature as full of spirits. The religion practised by these people is known as Shamanism, and their totem is a bear. On a certain festive occasion every year the head of a bear is ceremoniously eaten in common. A strange habit of these people is to leave an ill person as soon as the first signs of death are visible, and to return only when he is dead. The graves of the dead (who are interred) are also avoided, so that their surroundings remain undisturbed. The Udege and their culture are well known through the works of V. K. Arsenyev, whose book *The Udege Forest People* (Russ. Vladivostok, 1926) contained the results of his research. But the Udege really became famous in the Soviet Union through the story *The Last of the Mohicans*. Under the Soviet regime efforts have been made to get the Udeges out of their lonely quiet woods and settled in villages where they could be looked after more easily. This closer contact with Russian culture has resulted in the younger generation becoming so fully conversant with the Russian language that they speak it without a trace of any accent (*Isvestia*, 12.4.52), and further development in the process of assimilation can easily be foreseen.

Of other Tungus peoples, a few Manchurians, Daurics, and Solones, who immigrated from Manchuria, still live in the region of the Amur. In Transbaikalia the Orochi have still to be mentioned, living in the taiga zone of the District of Chita; they are mainly hunters, and reindeer-breeding is of only minor importance for them.

Of the Palaeo-Asiatic peoples, there remain in the Amur region only the Gilyaks, and on Sakhalin the Ainos. In addition to these, there is the far larger group inhabiting the extreme north-east, including the Chukches, Koryaks, and Kamchadals, as well as a further group including the Eskimos and the Aleuts.

The *Gilyaks* live along the lower Amur, and spread north and south from the mouth of the river along the coast. They also live on the islands of the Bay of Ud and in northern Sakhalin. Their total numbers are estimated at 4,000, of whom those on Sakhalin account for about 1,700. In appearance they closely resemble the Tungus–Manchurian people; however, their language differs greatly from that of the latter, as well as from that of the other Palaeo-Asiatic people, and reminds one of the idiom of several Indian tribes in north-west America. Their clothing is made up mainly from dog- and seal-skins, and also from fish-skin. Their main occupation is fishing and the catching of marine animals, as well as the hunting of bears and sables during the winter. They always build their dwellings along the river-banks or near the coast, and have different dwellings for winter and summer, often built closely together. As recently as the last century they were still using 'subterranean yurtes' (as Schrenck called them), resembling the caves in use until a few decades ago by the Koryaks and Kamchadals. It can be concluded, therefore, that caves must have been the original winter dwellings of the Palaeo-Asiatic people, and even today there are Gilyaks still living in such caves on the north coast of Sakhalin. The Gilyaks along the Amur live at present in primitive Chinese mud huts. Their summer dwellings consist of tents which are erected on piles as a protection against floods and to secure better ventilation. Buildings of this type are not to be found with any Tungus people. The Gilyaks' only domestic animal is the dog. The dog-sledge of the Gilyaks, the '*narte*', is a very light construction of birchwood, to which the dogs are harnessed singly rather than in pairs, and pull with their necks instead of their chests. The staple food of the Gilyaks is fish dried in the open air, which they call '*ma*'—the same word they now use for bread—and they also like eating the meat of bears and dogs. The only means of hunting until a few decades ago were the bow and arrow, and the spear. The Gilyak still wears on his right forefinger (though now only as an ornament) a metal ring which served originally as protection for this finger when pulling the bow. Group marriage was still customary with the Gilyaks as recently as 1905. Worship of the bear plays a big part in their culture, a characteristic which is common to all the Palaeo-Asiatic peoples. The same belief is still practised by the Tungus, although not to the same extent, and it has even had a certain influence on the Russian inhabitants of the taiga. Three National Districts were founded for the Gilyaks (who are now known as the Nivkhi), one at the mouth of the Amur and two on Sakhalin, but nothing is known of their subsequent development.

About 1,500 *Ainos* came under Soviet rule through the Russian acquisition of South Sakhalin, together with a few hundred more on the Kuriles. Only a few Ainos lived in North Sakhalin. The Soviet administration showed great interest in this ancient people, and a branch of the Academy of Science was set up in South Sakhalin with the task, among others, of furthering the cultural well-being and improving the general standard of living of the Ainos (*Soviet Monitor*, 8.4.47).

The Palaeo-Asiatic people of the north-east are divided up (as already mentioned) into two different groups. The western group consists of the closely interrelated Chukches, Koryaks, and Kamchadals, while the eastern group includes the Asiatic Eskimoes and the Aleuts. In 1640, when the Russians first met these Palaeo-Asiatic people in the extreme north, their culture was still partly on the Stone Age level. They then used stone hatchets, stone knives and bone-pointed arms, and even today they show many archaic features.

The *Chukches* (or Luorvetlanes) live on the peninsula named after them. Some are settled by the sea and live as fishermen and hunters of marine animals, while some wander across the tundra-covered peninsula as nomadic reindeer-herders. Both groups live in large circular pointed tents, made of poles covered with rein-

deer and walrus skins, and weighted down with stones on the outside. The coastal Chukches, about 3,000 in number, live a life
completely identical to that of the Eskimoes in its material aspects.
They use the same leather boat—the *kayak*—and the same metal
harpoon with a float of inflated seal-skin, as well as other objects
which are also the same. In contrast to those on the coast, the reindeer Chukches are complete nomads. They have proved themselves excellent reindeer-breeders, and although they number only
9,000, they possess herds containing a good half-million reindeer.
However, reindeer-breeding does not seem to have been their
original occupation, because many of their expressions and words
relating to their dwellings indicate that they, too, once lived at the
coast, and that reindeer-breeding was probably taken over at some
later date from the neighbouring Tungus. For instance, Bogoras
(37) tells us that the reindeer Chukches refer to the hangings of
their sleeping chambers as 'the coats of the white bear', although
today both the reindeer and the coastal Chukches use reindeer
skins rather than bear skins for their partitions and bedding. The
Chukches have a very strange belief that only those men who die a
violent death acquire the right to a life hereafter, and it is not long
ago that, from a kind of pity, they killed their own old and decre-
pit people, as has been reported, too, from the Eskimoes of North
America. The Chukches, Koryaks, and Kamchadals show a great
number of features in common with the Indians of north-west
America. For this reason, Bogoras gives the whole group of
Palaeo-Asiatic peoples, including the aforementioned Gilyaks, the
collective name of 'Amerikanoides'. Their myths and legends
correspond in content as well as in form, often up to the last
minute detail, to those of the north-west American Indians. The
hypothesis that at one time the Chukches, Koryaks, and Kamchadals were close neighbours, and that the Eskimoes pushed in
between only at a later time, cannot therefore be rejected completely.

The *Koryaks* (now also called the Nymlans) inhabit the northern
half of Kamchatka, and the adjoining mainland. It has been estimated that they number roughly 10,000 people. Like the Chukches, they are divided into two groups: the coastal Koryaks and
the reindeer Koryaks. The former are permanently settled and are
mainly fishermen, who also hunt sea-animals such as walrus and
seals and occasionally whales, their way of life being very similar
to that of the Eskimoes. Today they have already become very
much influenced by Russian culture. They live together in villages

I

in primitive wooden huts, and their traditional leather boats are becoming more and more uncommon, although they are still used by some for hunting and fishing. The reindeer Koryaks are excellent breeders of reindeer and possess large herds. They are nomads who spend the winter in the valleys where they are protected from the wind, and move to the mountain tundra in the summer where they are free from midges. They, too, have become very much alienated from their original culture. The Russian house has served as a model for their square winter huts, built from wood and half sunk into the ground, reminding us of the old European pits which were once used as habitations. It is only in the summer that they use their round portable tents, which in their original form consisted of a scaffolding of poles covered with reindeer skins. However, their movements are confined mainly to such a limited area in present times that they often live all the year in primitive huts made of boards. As a rule the winter huts are built near the rivers and are built to last. The older people are left behind in them during the summer, so that the Koryaks should really be called semi-nomadic. Physically the Koryaks are of small to medium height, with straight black hair, and with faces which are brown-bronze in complexion and practically hairless. They make their clothing from the skins of reindeer, wolves, and dogs, also using seal skins for lighter summer clothes. They show an artistic sense, which is expressed in a liking for gay colours and in their custom of decorating their clothes with different-coloured strips of fur or leather.

The *Kamchadals* (or Itelmes) inhabit the southern part of the Kamchatka peninsula, mainly along the south-west coast and in the Kamchatka valley. In former times they must have numbered many more because older reports talk about 'tens of thousands', but today it is hardly possible to determine their number because the majority of them are completely assimilated with the Russians, and many have almost forgotten their own language. (It is interesting to note that many Russians in the first wave of settlers were completely absorbed by the Kamchadals, retaining no differences in habits or ways of living.) In some of the west-coast villages, between Sedanka and Sopochnoye, there are still some pure Kamchadals to be found, numbering about 800 (1930). This group is often known exclusively as the Itelmes, as distinct from the other Kamchadals. They have given up their original hovels in the ground, which are still to be found in the interior as bases for the hunters, and now live in squat little wooden houses built in the Russian style, which stand in scattered disorderly groups along the rivers. Fishing is their main occupation, but in the winter they go up into the mountains to hunt for furs. The arrival of the shoals of salmon brings days of joy, and also of work, for everybody. As a rule the fish are caught by erecting across the river a barricade which obstructs the salmon's passage upstream. The fish mass in large numbers in front of these weirs, and are scooped out with simple fishing-nets. The communal drying ground is never empty, because it is important to preserve as many fish as possible for the whole year. Occasionally, though not often, an older method is employed, in which the fish are buried in the ground and left to ferment there as a kind of fish-silo, from which fish are taken out as necessary during the winter. During the fishing season an intense smell of fish penetrates the whole settlement and there seems to be no end to eating. It is no exaggeration to say that the Kamchadals live only on fish and tea. The dogs, which are the most important domestic and draught animals used by the settlers of North-east Siberia, also live on fish. The number of dogs is taken as the measure of wealth, and there are families who own 200–300 dogs. They are housed in narrow enclosures near the houses, and fill the whole neighbourhood with their hoarse barking. It is not advisable for the stranger to come too near to these half-wild animals. Nowadays the horse is becoming more and more popular, and is beginning to take the place of the dog as the animal for transport.

Many of the customs described above are slowly disappearing. Today a new order has been created, and most of the Kamchadals are members of the State fishing organization, while many others have turned to agriculture and cattle-breeding in the *kolkhozes* and *sovkhozes*. Complete assimilation into the Russian way of life can be foreseen in the near future.

The situation is quite different with the Chukches and Koryaks. It was easy for the Soviet Russian economic system to get hold of those who lived on fishing, since it helped them considerably through the provision of modern boats and tackle. But even today the majority of both these peoples live as nomadic reindeer-breeders, and are therefore difficult to fit into the Soviet economic system. During the first period of Soviet rule the number of reindeer greatly increased, but an experiment in collective reindeer-raising led to a sharp reduction in numbers. The experience of the Koryak National District will serve as an example. According to Sergeyev (1936, pp. 409 f.) the number of reindeer in this district declined from 264,000 in 1926 to 173,000 in 1932 and 127,000 in 1934. As a result there was a very liberal new statute of collectivization for the reindeer-breeders, which left the members a large number of reindeer in private ownership, and even encouraged them to increase the number privately owned. According to different accounts, the number of animals left to each private owner generally varies between 80 and 130, and in some individual cases rises to 200. During the Second World War the system was further relaxed, but since 1947 there seems to be renewed interest in settling and collectivizing the reindeer-breeders (*Pravda*, 6.5.52). The problem of reindeer-breeding is still unsolved. The reason for mentioning it already in this section is that the question is partly psychological as well as economic, affecting not only the material life of these people, but also their whole culture.

The *Asiatic Eskimoes* live on the shores of the Bering Sea, where they inhabit seventeen villages with a total population of about 1,600. In former times there must have been many more, as shown by the numerous places with names derived from the Eskimo language which are now inhabited by the coastal Chukches. The latter must often have taken possession by force, since their folklore is full of reports of hard fighting with the Eskimoes. These disputes ended long before the arrival of the Russians, and nowadays both peoples live peacefully together even within the same villages. The Asiatic Eskimoes differ in language from their kinsfolk in Alaska, although otherwise they form a cultural unity with them. They are absolutely dependent on the sea, and travel by dog-sledge on their rare excursions into the interior.

On the Kommandorski Islands there live about 500 *Aleuts*, whose language indicates that they are related to the Eskimoes. They, too, live entirely by catching sea-animals, since the islands offer them nothing but birds.

The *Buryato-Mongols*, as mentioned above, have their own autonomous Soviet Republic, which is named after them, and in which they have their own cultural organizations. Elementary schools have been instituted all over the country and high schools have sprung into existence in the towns, so that according to Soviet information illiteracy has almost completely disappeared. Using the Russian alphabet they have created their own literature. Newspapers are published in the Buryatic language, and even a Buryato-Mongolian theatre has been founded in Ulan-Ude. The numerous cultural organizations also take care of political enlightenment. The Buryato-Mongolian ASSR, like all the other autonomous districts of the USSR, has (as it is called in Soviet writings) a culture which is *national* with respect to its form and *socialist* with respect to its contents.

The treatment of the smaller groups of indigenous peoples in the Soviet Union has been subject to many changes during the course of time. In the first stage (from 1921 to 1929) it was mainly the recommendations of Professor Bogoras that were followed (*Shisn Nazionalnostei*, January 1922). The life and cultural standards of the native people were to be protected from every alien influence. Russians, apart from scientists, doctors, &c., should not be allowed to enter the settlements of these tribes, nor to exploit them for profit. Bogoras warned particularly against economic experiments, which he feared would not improve the welfare of these people, and were likely to endanger their very existence. A philanthropic point of view was thus generally taken. From 1924 onwards, councils and local administrations were formed within the individual tribes, according to the form most suitable to them. The characteristic feature of these councils was that no tendencies of class conflict were evident. Up to 1929 the communistic members of these councils had tried in vain to introduce their ideas, but in that year they got their way. In 1930 the tribal administrations were dissolved and replaced by regular administrative organs within the framework of the National Districts which were now created for the individual tribes. By this act Soviet influence began to penetrate all spheres of their economic and cultural life, based on the principle of raising the standards of cultural and economic life of these primitive people. This tendency is still evident today in the desire to settle the nomadic reindeer Chukches (*Pravda*, 6.5.52). The size of the areas and the fact that the population is so widely scattered make arrangements for the regular educating and influencing of the people impossible, and cultural bases have therefore been founded for the native population, to which they can make occasional visits. Nikolas Mikhailov (*Land of the Soviets*, New York, 1939, p. 187) describes how to imagine the life at such a cultural centre.

'When a hunter or reindeer-breeder arrives at a cultural base, he is provided with food and a bed. He is taken to a museum where the natural conditions and economy of his district are demonstrated. He is shown the workshops where, if necessary, his rifle, sledge, and clothing will be repaired. He learns how to breed animals, how to skin them and prepare the fur, how to preserve fish and how to nurse a sick reindeer. A doctor in the clinic examines the hunter and treats him if necessary. The new-comer takes a bath, listens to the wireless, and goes to the cinema.'

Apart from the Buryats who proudly took their fate into their own hands, and the Chukches and Koryaks who (as the leading reindeer-breeders) are able to lead their own lives aloof from the rest of the world, all the other small groups and remnants of groups (however interesting their ethnological stock may be) are of no significance for the development of the country. Their life in the vast lonely spaces which they inhabit is limited to a most primitive level of self-sufficiency or to bartering their produce for the other goods they need. It was left to the Russians not only to open up the country but also to bring it closer to the world at large and to integrate it into the general economy.

### The Russians

The basis of Russian colonization was formed by the original Cossack settlements. After the treaties of Aigun and Peking, the Transbaikalian Cossack army stationed on the Argun was supple-mented by Cossack formations on the Amur and the Ussuri. Be-tween 1858 and 1862, twenty-three such Cossack settlements con-taining 5,000 people were founded on the Ussuri, and seventy-five on the Amur. These Cossack 'stanits' consisted of loosely laid-out villages, as well as more unified settlements organized on a mili-tary basis for the protection of the frontier, but otherwise self-sufficient. A large section of land stretching along the rivers Argun, Amur, Ussuri, and Suifun (along the Chinese frontier) was allotted to them for this purpose. Later settlers attached them-selves to this strip of settlements, increasing its population density and its width. Thus on the one hand there grew up along the fron-tier rivers a strange attenuated line of settlements, which spread into the hinterland only where conditions were favourable for the acquisition of new ground without too much work. On the other hand, there developed a special kind of settlement pattern among the settlers, the typical characteristics of which are still in evidence today. Along the rivers near the frontier, the earlier settlers have become well established as the owners of the larger estates on the best soil. They are mainly the descendants of the Cossacks, who, through continuous fighting and deprivations, and through their successes as well, developed into enterprising cultural pioneers who did not mind taking risks. They represent a hardened, forceful, and proud type of people. The newer settlers, who arrived later, are living mainly on ground of low value in the more remote interior, where they have preserved all the typical qualities of the East European Russian with all his strong points and his weaknesses.

Colonization made only very small progress during the first few decades, in spite of various laws to secure preferential treatment for Russian emigrants (the first such law was enacted in 1861), as well as the many facilities and the encouragement provided. The propaganda campaigns had only limited success. Many people were discouraged by the long and difficult overland route across Siberia, or by the long sea journey, and it was only with the construction of the Trans-Siberian railway that immigration began on a larger scale. However, by 1911 the population east of Lake Baikal was already 1,622,000, including 1,225,000 Russians and about 20,000 other Europeans. Of the remaining 379,000 the largest group were the Buryats with 205,000 people, the rest being Chinese, Koreans, and other small groups of native people. Following the First World War the difficulties arising as a result of the revolution brought many Russians to the Far East. New measures by the Soviet Government for planned colonization also helped to increase the population east of Lake Baikal, so that by 1926 it had risen to about 2,300,000, and by the date of the last census (January 17th, 1939) had reached 4,040,000, the newcomers being mainly Russians. In the Buryato-Mongolian ASSR the Russians had an absolute majority amounting to 52·7 per cent in 1939 (out of a total population of 542,000), which rose to 57·2 per cent in 1941. In the District of Chita, out of a total population of 1,159,500 there are not more than 50,000 Buryats and other native peoples, and in the District of Khabarovsk and the coastal region the proportion of native peoples in a total of 2,338,100 inhabitants is not higher than 3 per cent.

The majority of the Russians work on the land or are cattle-breeders. Fishing and hunting serve as additional occupations, and the Russian professional hunter—the *Promyshlennik*—who is a proper 'wild man of the woods', has not yet died out. The proportion working in industry has been increasing rapidly in recent years.

The Russian peasant continues to lead the sort of life he was used to in his home country, and struggles as hard here as he did there. The type of settlement often indicates, even after several decades, the origins of the settlers. The White Russians,[1] especially those who have come from the more northern areas, prefer to live by the rivers and in the forest areas, building their houses in the same log-cabin style as their traditional '*isba*'. Hunting and fishing are popular pursuits. The White Russians, too, prefer the wooded country, while the Ukrainians are to be found in great numbers in the vicinity of Lake Khanka and around Bochkarevo, where there is comparatively less forest. The latter are mainly descendants of the Cossacks who were brought from the Don region, and are the better farmers, being particularly successful as cattle-breeders. Their houses have the same whitewashed mud walls and thatched roofs as their '*khata*' in the Ukraine, although here there is really no lack of timber. They generally dig wells for their water, even though their houses stand close by the rivers, because water from the wells is said to be cooler and of better flavour. The woods in the neighbourhood of Ukrainian settlements are soon ravaged, the Ukrainians using both axe and fire to destroy them.

The towns are of typically Russian character. Pompous buildings, mostly of poor taste and dating from the time of the Tsars, stand next to narrow tenement houses in the centres of the larger towns, while in the outskirts rows of one-storey log cabins with four or more windows stretch for miles along unpaved streets flanked by wooden footpaths. Some completely new districts have been added to the big towns under Soviet rule. These have paved streets with rows of trees on both sides, and there are airy individual blocks of flats rising to four floors or more which look like skyscrapers among the other very low houses of the town. As a rule these new estates are topped by the tall chimneys and large concrete buildings of the factories which create such a striking impression today. The chief contrast in these towns is the difference between the old and primitive village-like suburbs and the modern industrial plants. The fact that this is part of the Far East is hardly noticeable anywhere. Even in the Chinese quarters of Vladivostok there are the same whitewashed tenement houses, and it is only the Chinese signs and the Chinese junks filling the nearby harbour which remind one that this is an East Asian port.

State control of the economy, with its tight central organization in the towns, and the collectivization in the country, have brought many new features into the life and work of the people, and destroyed much of the old and traditional. People have moved about

---

[1] Russians of Mongolian and Turkish origin. (Tr. N.)

and have mixed together with other newcomers, and the national life of the Russians in the Far East is consequently in a state of upheaval and transition.

### Chinese, Koreans, and others

In Transbaikalia there are very few Chinese. There used to be a fairly large number of them living as merchants in Maimachen (now called Altin-Bulag), on the Mongolian frontier opposite Kyakhta, but after the First World War they were driven away during the rebellion of the Mongols.

In the Amur–Ussuri region the first *Chinese* came searching for Ginseng[1] and hunting leopards, and were followed by merchants, and later by settlers as well. As cultural pioneers they were of great value everywhere in the wilds, where they could work on the land in their own industrious and successful way. However, their capacity to make capital out of everything soon led them to exploit the natives in the most unscrupulous manner. They were therefore regarded as most unwelcome guests by the Russian administration, especially since they took all their plentiful earnings out of the country, and conspired together to suppress all competition in commerce, as well as dealing in smuggled gold. The result was the disaster in the year 1900, when the Russian authorities drove all Chinese across the frontier, nearly 5,000 of them losing their lives near Blagoveshchensk by being driven into the Amur. However, the construction of towns and the attendant industrialization drew them back again and again into the country, where many have remained as settlers or as modest workmen and artisans. They had a strong cultural influence on the natives. For instance, the Udege in the southern Sikhota-Alin not only adopted their material standards of living but even gave up their own language in favour of Chinese. The use of Chinese houses and clothes has spread even as far as the Gilyaks on the lower Amur, and is in competition everywhere with the Russian influence, which is slowly increasing in importance.

The Chinese house—the '*fanse*'—has mud walls and a thatched gable roof. Nearly the whole front is taken up by large latticed windows, covered in with oiled paper, which can be pushed up and taken out. There are no windows at the sides or at the back. In the interior there are small stoves with iron drums on both sides of the entrance, and pipes to carry the smoke from the

[1] The plant *Panax ginseng*. (Tr. N.)

two stoves underneath the sleeping places which are built along the walls and occupy nearly half the room. These bunks—called '*kang*'—are made of stone and mud, and stand about $1\frac{1}{2}$ feet high. The pipes lead on from the bunks to the chimney, also built from stone and mud, which stands by itself away from the house, to reduce the danger of fire. It is quite common for the '*kang*' to have a separate heating system. The outhouses are usually joined to the dwelling-house at right angles, and the enclosure of the square courtyard is completed by a wall or fence. The Chinese like to enclose a square area in front of the house, or to surround the whole place with a thick wall; but the natives are usually quite content with just the house, although this is often only a miserable and dirty mud hovel.

About half of the 87,999 Chinese living in Siberia in 1939 inhabited the southern part of the Ussuri countryside, the others being mainly scattered throughout the towns. The proportion of women among the Chinese is very small, amounting to only 6 per cent, and there is therefore a lot of intermarriage between the Chinese and the Udege. The half-breeds are called the 'Tase'.

The *Korean* part of the population presents a completely different picture. Some old villages have existed in the Posyet region from time immemorial, but the main immigration of Koreans started only after the Treaty of Peking, with the southern region of the Ussuri as their most favoured destination. The Koreans always came with their wives and families, and form a very valuable part of the population. They work mainly on the land, and show special skill in growing Manchurian plants like millet, beans, and rice. Cultivation of the last-named has been successfully carried northwards as far as the area around Khabarovsk. Pigs and cows are kept, the latter being used as draught animals. Of the 170,000 Koreans in the Soviet Union (1939), 100,000 live in the Ussuri region. Some of the remaining 70,000 have been resettled in Turkestan, in the Syr-Darya and Ili, where they work as peasants cultivating rice.

There were several thousand *Japanese* living in the coastal towns up to the First World War, but the number has decreased continually since then, and there are now not more than a few hundred left.

*The Jews* are worth mentioning as a special group, since they have their own autonomous district west of Khabarovsk, on both sides of the rivers Bira and Bidzhan, which are right-hand tributaries of the Amur. About half of the district's total population (which numbered 108,400 in 1939) are Jews, who work in all trades and professions. They have come not only from the Soviet Union, but have also immigrated from other countries.

In addition to the above, there are numbers of Poles, Lithuanians, Latts, Moldavians, Tartars, and others, including Germans, scattered over the whole region east of Lake Baikal. Their total number is estimated to be between 20,000 and 30,000, representing as a group the same mixture of people as is found in the rest of the Soviet Union.

### Population Distribution, Growth, and Structure

In view of the tremendous extent of the areas and the very unequal distribution of the population, general density figures are of little use. Most of the population, representing about 90 per cent, is contained in the large and elongated zone of settlement which starts at Lake Baikal and stretches along the Amur and the Ussuri as far as Vladivostok. The zone is generally narrow, with occasional extensions in width in some areas.

In Transbaikalia the more densely populated areas are along the Selenga and Amur rivers, while in the Yablonovy ridge area the settlements are somewhat more widely distributed. The valley of the Selenga is occupied mainly by Buryats, with the population density reaching forty to fifty persons per square mile in some districts. East of the Yablonovy ridge there is a second concentration of people in the area roughly between the Chita and the Argun. In this agricultural area based on *chernozem* soil the density is up to fifty persons per square mile. There are hardly any inhabitants in the larger northern part of Transbaikalia, and practically none at all in the wilderness of the forested Vitim plateau. In these areas scattered settlements have come into being only at some isolated points, through the development of gold-mining.

In the Amur region the river and the railway were the guiding lines for settlement, but the narrow area between them is not inhabited everywhere to the same extent. In the Seya–Bureya plain the cultivated area widens and becomes an extensive and concentrated region of settlements. The former Cossacks have their estates along the Amur; next to these comes the broad line of fields of the earlier settlers. The more recent arrivals spread out mainly over the peripheral areas. Eighty per cent of the total arable land in the Amur region is located in the Seya–Bureya plain, and here, too, in some parts the population density is as much as fifty persons per square mile. East of the Bureya there is a strip of settlement along the railway line, while a second strip follows the Amur, and merges with the first near Khabarovsk. From here a more densely settled strip winds its way along the Ussuri towards the south. The settled area spreads out where the Iman flows into the Ussuri, becoming an area 150 miles across which extends as far as Vladivostok. Seventy-five per cent of the arable land of the whole coastal region is found in this area between the Iman and Vladivostok.

Settlement along the lower Amur is no longer widely dispersed, the population being concentrated in the two towns of Komsomolsk and Nikolayevsk and in a few sporadic villages by the river. It is generally the case that, outside the zone of settlement described above, the village settlements are to be found only along the rivers. In 1952 there were no more than thirty *kolkhozes* in the lower Amur region. Comparatively few settlements have been founded on the coast of the Ussuri region. The southern part of the coast is more populated than the north, because the coast here is more accessible and its wealth of minerals created employment possibilities for a larger population. Olga Bay and its hinterland should be noted as being more densely populated than the rest.

The interior of the Sikhota-Alin and the whole of the extensive northern area of the Far Eastern territories as far as the Chukchen peninsula are very sparsely populated, the density being as low as 0·25 person per square mile, or even less. Here are mainly the indigenous people who roam the vast open spaces as reindeer-breeders or hunters. The sea as a source of food lured many people to the coast, where numerous settlements of native fishermen, often including Russians as well, were founded at varying distances from each other. In more recent years, planned fishing *kolkhozes* have been founded at all favourable spots and occupied by Russians. The most important places are those which are also starting points for routes into the interior, e.g. Ayan, Okhotsk, Magadan, and Gizhiga on the Okhotsk coast.

In Kamchatka the population has risen considerably during recent years, as a result of the rapid increase in the catch of fish and mammals from the sea. In 1950 the total population was 130,000, which was a five-fold increase over the 1926 figure. Here, too, the newcomers favoured the coast, settling particularly in Petropavlovsk, Ust-Kamchatsk, and Bolsheretsk. In spite of this marked increase in the total population, the population density of Kamchatka is hardly 2·5 persons per square mile.

Sakhalin, like Kamchatka, has had a large population increase through immigration, and again it is concentrated near the coast, based mainly on the development of the petroleum, coal, and fishing industries. The population has therefore crowded into these areas, leaving the barren interior largely deserted. Only in the valley of the central depression are agricultural settlements to be found. South Sakhalin, which was part of Japan until 1945, showed much the same picture in the distribution of its population. It had a larger population than North Sakhalin, but here, too, the people were crowded together in the coastal area, while the interior was inhabited chiefly by small groups of the original native people, like the Olches, Oroks, Gilyaks, and Ainos. The last-named were the largest group among the indigenous peoples, and numbered 1,500 in 1940, as compared with a total of 500 for all the other groups together. The evacuation of the Japanese has presented the Soviet Union with the task of filling the country with their own people, which, according to all the available information, they have succeeded in doing.

The newcomers have moved into the former Japanese settlements, leaving the distribution of population within the area unchanged. (The actual changes in population figures will be discussed later.)

We have at our disposal the census data for 1926 and 1939 when considering the general development of the population. According to these sources, the number of inhabitants east of Lake Baikal

*Population growth*

|  | 1926 | 1939 | Increase (per cent) | Immigration (per cent) |
|---|---|---|---|---|
| Buryato-Mongolian ASSR . | 390,000 | 542,200 | 39 | 23·1 |
| Chita District . . . | 670,000 | 1,159,500 | 73 | 57·1 |
| Khabarovsk District . . | 606,000 | 1,430,900 | 136 | 120·1 |
| Coastal Region . . . | 638,000 | 907,200 | 42 | 26·1 |
| Total . . . | 2,304,000 | 4,039,800 | 57·5 | 59·1 |

has increased from 2·3 millions to 4,039,800, an increase of 75 per cent. Compared with the increase of 15·9 per cent for the whole of the Soviet Union, which can be regarded as the rate of natural increase, this means that 59·1 per cent of the population growth in the Eastern territories has been the result of immigration. The variation between the individual parts of the Far East is considerable. The population increase in the Buryato-Mongolian ASSR was only 39 per cent, whereas it was 73 per cent in the Chita District and as much as 136 per cent in the District of Khabarovsk. Since the redistribution of population within the Soviet Union is directed by the State, these figures show the preferential treatment of those areas farthest away from the European parts of the country. The Coastal Region seems to be an exception to this general picture, having a population increase during the same period of only 42 per cent.

During the same period, from 1926 to 1939, an important change in the structure of the population took place, namely an extraordinarily large rise in the proportion of town-dwellers, from 24 per cent in 1926 to nearly 50 per cent in 1939. Since in the statistics of the Soviet Union the concept of *urban* population is equated with that of *non-agricultural* population, the general occupational structure in the various areas can be deduced from a comparison of these figures. The Buryato-Mongolian ASSR has remained largely agricultural, the urban population amounting to only 30 per cent, which is even lower than the average of 32·8 per cent for the Soviet Union as a whole. This proportion is higher in the other three districts, amounting to 44 per cent in the District of Chita, 45 per cent in the District of Khabarovsk, and 51 per cent in the Coastal Region. This growth in urban population proves that the directed immigration, which was formerly to the advantage of agricultural colonization, is now essentially for the benefit of industrialization. The increase in the urban population is well illustrated by the constant growth of the larger towns. In 1939 there were altogether seven towns with more than 50,000 inhabitants, the populations of these having grown (with the exception of Blagoveshchensk) as follows:

| | 1926 | 1939 | Increase or Decrease (per cent) |
|---|---|---|---|
| Ulan-Ude . . . . | 29,918 | 129,417 | +347·5 |
| Chita . . . . | 61,526 | 102,555 | + 56·7 |
| Blagoveshchensk . . | 61,205 | 58,761 | − 4·0 |
| Komsomolsk . . . | — | 70,764 | — |
| Khabarovsk . . . | 52,045 | 199,364 | +283·1 |
| Voroshilov . . . | 35,344 | 70,628 | + 99·8 |
| Vladivostok . . . | 107,980 | 206,432 | + 91·2 |

In the Buryato-Mongolian ASSR nearly a quarter (22 per cent) of the total population lives in Ulan-Ude. In the District of Chita, on the other hand, only 9 per cent of the total population lives in the town of Chita, the urban–industrial population being distributed among numerous different places. In the District of Khabarovsk the aggregate population of the three large towns—Blagoveshchensk, Khabarovsk, and Komsomolsk—amounts to only 23 per cent of the total population, and accounts for little more than half the district's urban population. The town of Komsomolsk is new, and did not yet exist in 1926. In the Coastal Region conditions are similar to those in the Buryato Republic. Here 23 per cent of the total population is concentrated in Vladivostok alone, plus a further 8 per cent in Voroshilov. Thus the general picture in the Far East (with Chita the only exception) is that there are large concentrations of population in the towns mentioned above, contrasting with an extensive and sparsely populated countryside.

*Urban and rural populations—1939 census*

|  | Urban Population | Rural Population | Total |
|---|---|---|---|
| Buryato-Mongolian ASSR    . | 163,425 | 378,745 | 542,170 |
| District of Chita    .    .    . | 510,900 | 648,578 | 1,159,478 |
| District of Khabarovsk    .    . | 647,653 | 783,222 | 1,430,875 |
| Coastal Region    .    .    . | 464,509 | 442,711 | 907,220 |

## Population Growth from 1939 to 1950

It is difficult to follow up exactly the growth of population after 1939, since no subsequent census has been taken and no official information has been published. However, occasional information about individual regions or places makes it possible to recognize certain general trends, even though there is not enough information to be clear about the detailed figures. The best opportunity is offered by the election statistics of 1950. By a critical examination of these figures, it is possible to estimate the total population, although the results are only approximately correct and quite possibly contain unavoidable mistakes. In spite of the very general indication of population growth provided by these election statistics, they must be used, since there is no other factual knowledge available as an alternative.

On this basis, the total population increased from 4,039,800 (the census figure) in 1939 to roughly 6·3 millions (including South Sakhalin and the Kuriles) in 1950, an increase of about 2·3 millions. Thus there was an increase of only 35·6 per cent in the eleven years from 1939 to 1950, compared with an increase of 75

per cent in the thirteen years from 1926 to 1939. If one applies the
rate of natural increase for the earlier period (15·9 per cent over
thirteen years, or 1·22 per cent a year) without taking into account
the effects of the Second World War, to the period 1939–50, it follows that the total population increase of 35·6 per cent in this later
period consisted of a natural increase of 13·42 per cent plus an immigration of 22·18 per cent. On the basis of these assumptions,
one derives the following general picture of the recent growth of
population in the Soviet Far East:

| | |
|---|---:|
| Population, 1939 . . . . . . | 4,039,800 |
| Natural increase, 1939–50 . . . | 538,140 |
| Immigration . . . . . . | 1,722,060 |
| Total population, 1950 . . . | 6,300,000 |

Even though the immigration between 1939 and 1950 was less
than during the period 1926–39, the overall yearly average of
156,500 is still very large. Since all immigration must presumably
have been stopped during the six years of the war (1940–5), the
majority of the immigrants must have moved into the Far Eastern
territories during the five post-war years. This corresponds to an
average yearly movement of nearly 350,000 people.

For the individual districts it is also possible to give only a
general indication of population growth, especially since there is
an added difficulty due to the change of administrative boundaries
after the Second World War which has made some comparisons of
little value. Only the Buryato-Mongolian ASSR and the Coastal
Region have retained the same administrative boundaries, so that
the other districts must be treated for statistical purposes as one
group.

*Population growth according to districts*

| | 1939 | 1950 | Absolute Increase | Percentage Increase |
|---|---:|---:|---:|---:|
| Buryato-Mongolian ASSR . | 542,200 | 600,000 | 57,800 | 10·7 |
| District of Chita . . | } 2,590,400 | 4,500,000 | 1,909,600 | 73·3 |
| District of Khabarovsk . | | | | |
| Coastal Region . . . | 907,200 | 1,200,000 | 292,800 | 32·3 |
| Total . . . . | 4,039,800 | 6,300,000 | 2,260,200 | 35·6 |

This table shows that the Districts of Chita and Khabarovsk had
the largest share of the population increase, while the increase in
the other two districts was below the average for the whole region.
In the Buryato-Mongolian ASSR there must even have been some

emigration. If an allowance is made for natural increase at the rate of 13·42 per cent mentioned above, the result would be a population increase of 72,863, so that there must have been an emigration of approximately 15,000 people from the Buryato-Mongolian ASSR during the period 1939–50. This is quite plausible, considering the mainly agricultural character of the area (the rural population was 70 per cent of the total in 1939) and the growing intensity of mechanization and technical improvement in agriculture.

In the Coastal Region the absolute increase in the population from 1939 to 1950 was 292,800, of which 121,750 was due to natural increase, and 171,050 to immigration. Vladivostok has grown by roughly 100,000 people, Voroshilov by 70,000, and Artem by 50,000. This growth of the larger towns, together with special reports about the great increase in industrial production, indicates that most of the new population in the area—both immigrants and others—has moved into the industrial sector of the economy.

For the remaining areas comparison with the 1939 figures is not possible, because of the change in administrative boundaries. However, a rough comparison can be made by using the population figures calculated from the 1947 electoral data for the Republics, together with some other information of 1.1.49 used by Shabad in his *Geography of the USSR*. This makes it possible at least to recognize the general trends in the spatial and economic distribution of the population increase, always bearing in mind the fact that none of these comparative figures are based on exact information.

Compared with the other districts, the new district of Chita has had the smallest increase in population, amounting to only 150,000, of which the industries of the town of Chita alone have absorbed about 50,000. Information about increases in the production of coal and non-ferrous metals, &c., indicates increased employment in these industries too. It can be assumed with certainty, therefore, especially in view of the difficulties of extending the arable land in the district, that the largest part of the population increase has been absorbed by industry.

Conditions seem to be different in the Amur Oblast, which was formed in 1948 and includes the important agricultural areas of the Seya–Bureya plain. Here the available information, though not readily analysed, indicates that the relatively large increase of population has gone mainly into agriculture. Reports of agricultural

K

successes are most numerous from this district, and it seems quite likely that the area of arable land has been extended. There is little mention of new industrial installations, and although part of the population increase may have gone into the lignite fields of Raychikhinsk and Kivdinsk and the new coal-mines at the Magdagacha River, the Amur Oblast on the whole has retained its mainly agricultural character. An indication of this is found in the situation at Blagoveshchensk, the district capital, where the population actually decreased, from 61,205 in 1926 to 58,761 in 1939.

The District of Khabarovsk, which has also experienced a relatively large population increase, presents yet another picture. The increase in the towns alone shows that the population increase has gone mainly into industry. For instance, Khabarovsk has grown by 100,000, Komsomolsk by 80,000, and Sovietskaya Gavan by more than 20,000, while Magadan has grown into a town of more than 50,000. If one accepts this total increase of 250,000 in the urban population as correct (I personally think it is higher), it can even be shown that an internal migration from the country into the towns has taken place. There are reports about an extension of arable land in the vicinity of Khabarovsk, but at the same time the reports refer repeatedly to the greater use of machinery in agriculture, so that it is quite possible that still more workers can be released from the land. The greatest population increase has occurred on the island of Sakhalin, where, by comparing Shabad's estimate of 1947 with the electoral figures for 1950, it appears that the population has increased three-fold—from 300,000 to 900,000. It is difficult to find an explanation for this fact, even if the first figure is regarded as too low and the second as too high. In the Russian part of Sakhalin the population before the war was estimated to be 100,000. During the war new oil-fields were opened up, and great progress was made in the production of lignite and coal; a new port, open throughout the year, was built at Okha, and there were many other developments as well. After the war new economic efforts were made, and during this time the population in the Russian part must have greatly increased, possibly to 200,000 or more. In the Japanese part of Sakhalin the population in 1940 numbered 412,000, and the demands of the war economy probably caused the Japanese to send many more people there, building new houses for them and enlarging the industrial works. After the evacuation of the larger part of the Japanese population, the Soviets were faced with the task of occupying the country and bringing the economy back into full production. In these circumstances a simple replacement of man for man was not possible, and the Russians had to resort to bringing in more workers than would actually be required. The difference in economic organization must also be taken into account in this connexion. For the Japanese, with their economic use of labour, every single worker mattered; for the Russians (especially in view of the current political tensions) it was most important to get production going again, and the number of people taking part in this process was only a minor consideration. It must also be noticed that among the Japanese people the proportion of men to women was 130 to 100 —more characteristic of a colonizing people. It is certain, on the other hand (according to information which is confirmed by various news items), that the Soviets are settling whole families in South Sakhalin, resulting in a very different population structure. For all these reasons it is certainly comprehensible that the population of South Sakhalin should be larger at present than it was before the war. Finally, the political and military implications of the situation should also be mentioned, a well-populated country being a greater asset in terms of defence than an empty one.

In addition to the inhabitants of Transbaikalia and the Far Eastern territories proper, whose numbers are generally known, there exists a 'shadow population' which is not included in official documents or in any other Soviet reports. These are the people living in labour camps which, because of their mobility and the ample labour which they can supply, play a not unimportant part in the economy. It is difficult to give exact information about how and where they are actually used. It is known that there are labour camps in Transbaikalia, as well as in the region of the lower Amur, and that they represent the main labour force for the construction of the Baikal–Amur railway as well as for gold-mining and other mining in the area of the upper Kolyma and elsewhere. The existence of these labour camps makes it difficult to ascertain the potential labour force in the individual districts, but in no circumstances should they be overlooked.

The population of the individual districts in 1950 was as follows:

| | |
|---|---:|
| 1. Buryato-Mongolian ASSR | 600,000 |
| 2. Chita District | 1,200,000 |
| 3. Amur District | 900,000 |
| 4. Khabarovsk District | 1,500,000 |
| 5. Coastal Region | 1,200,000 |
| 6. Sakhalin | 900,000 |
| Total | 6,300,000 |

It is also possible to work out roughly the state of the population in 1955, using different publications which followed the last elections (*Izvestia*, 25.12.54, &c.), and making the same reservations mentioned above. The District (*oblast*) of Magadan was created from the former Rayon of Magadan-Kolyma on December 3rd, 1953, and was thus taken out of the District (*Kray*) of Khabarovsk. The new *oblast* has come under the authority of the National District of the Chukches. This action indicates that both the District of Magadan and the National District of the Chukches have gained in importance. It is regrettable that no detailed comparison of the following population figures for 1955 with those for 1950 is possible, but the information available permits only a general survey without any analysis.

*State of the population in 1955*

| | | |
|---|---:|---:|
| Buryato-Mongolian ASSR | | 620,000 |
| Chita District | | 1,380,000 |
| Amur District | | 900,000 |
| Khabarovsk District | | 1,350,000 |
| Including: Jewish Autonomous District | 150,000 | |
| Lower Amur region | 150,000 | |
| Kamchatka[1] | 300,000 | |
| Magadan District | | 300,000 |
| Coastal Region | | 1,650,000 |
| Sakhalin | | 900,000 |
| Total | | 7,100,000 |

[1] Since January 1956 an independent district.

Compared with the overall increase that of the larger towns has been slow. Their growth has been much overestimated. Statistics published in Moscow in 1956 (Narodny Khotsyaystvo SSSR, Moscow) give the following figures for the position as at January 1, 1956. These may be taken as official.

*Development of the bigger towns*

| | 1939 | 1956 |
|---|---:|---:|
| Vladivostok | 206,432 | 265,000 |
| Khabarovsk | 199,364 | 280,000 |
| Komsomolsk | 70,764 | 169,000 |
| Voroshilov | 70,628 | 101,000 |
| Ulan-Ude | 129,417 | 158,000 |
| Chita | 120,555 | 162,000 |
| Blagoveshchensk | 58,761 | 60,000 |
| Artem | — | more than 50,000 |
| Magadan | — | ,,   ,,   50,000 |

# CHAPTER 3

# The Economy

*

## Agriculture

In 1938 agriculture took first place among the different branches of the economy, occupying 55·8 per cent of the total population. The division between rural and urban population in the individual districts was as follows:

|  | Rural (per cent) | Urban (per cent) |
|---|---|---|
| Buryato-Mongolian ASSR . . . | 70 | 30 |
| District of Chita . . . . | 56 | 44 |
| District of Khabarovsk . . . | 55 | 45 |
| Coastal District . . . . | 49 | 51 |

Since 1938 there has been a fundamental change in conditions. The increase in the total population of 35·6 per cent by 1950 has benefited mainly the industrial sector, so that by now the urban (i.e. industrial) population accounts for more than half of the total population in the Soviet Far East. Among the individual districts the Buryato-Mongolian ASSR has kept its predominantly rural character, as has the Amur District (newly formed in 1948), although in the latter case there are no figures available to prove it.

In the southern parts of the Far Eastern territories the natural conditions for agriculture are definitely favourable. The whole of Transbaikalia is included within the 5° C. (41° F.) May isotherm, and most of the Amur District is included within the 10° C. (50° F.) May isotherm. The rapid transition from winter to summer lengthens the growing period, which is usually of adequate length in these areas. Summer cultivation predominates, since the severity of the weather limits cultivation in the winter. Particular difficulties are caused by the fact that in Transbaikalia the precipitation is inadequate, while in the Amur–Ussuri district it is excessive. In the latter area the large amount of moisture prevents the ripening of the crops in the fields, and favours vermin. Water often remains standing on the flat fields and causes the plants to rot. The Russians were therefore forced to abandon the European flat or level cultivation in favour of furrow cultivation, the grain being sown into ridges separated by furrows in which the water can soak or drain away. This is a method which the Chinese have applied successfully everywhere in the Far East. These agricultural methods of course demand much more work, and the Russians, in their customary manner, have struggled hard to cut down on the additional labour required. Special seed drills constructed to suit the particular conditions prevalent in the area have been introduced on the *kolkhozes* since the beginning of collectivization.

North of the Amur district the natural conditions for agriculture become less favourable, not so much because the winter is colder, but mainly because the growing season becomes shorter. It is therefore essential to sow varieties of grain which ripen quickly, and in this respect the Russians have been remarkably successful. By breeding special quick-ripening species, and by developing special methods of seed preparation (known as Yarovization), they have succeeded in pushing the limit of grain cultivation much farther towards the north.

In Transbaikalia the soils in the predominantly wooded areas belong mainly to the podzol type. Several varieties have been formed, which resemble either loamy soils or sandy soils, according to their clay content. Semi-swamp or boggy ground is common in the river valleys. The podzols contain only small amounts of humus (2–3 per cent), but the boggy soils have a very high humus content ranging from 15 to 30 per cent. A soil comparatively rich in humus is also found on the forest-steppes and the ordinary treeless steppes of Transbaikalia. Even typical chernozem soils have developed east of the Yablonovy ridge as far as the Argum River. It is interesting to note that different slopes of the same ridge often show changes in soil profile corresponding to changes in their vegetation. The northern and north-western slopes are covered by taiga with typical podzols underneath; the eastern and south-eastern slopes are occupied by light birch-woods under which there are hardly any podzol-type soils, and where external characteristics indicate the beginning of a change to the dark soils of the chernozem type. In the Amur–Ussuri region most of the country is taken up by the podzol and bog soils, and the various gradations of these types. In the Seya–Bureya plain and the Ussuri–Khanka depression the soil consists mainly of recent fertile

alluvial deposits, making these areas the principal agricultural
areas of the country. The upper horizon of this soil is very rich in
humus, giving it the black colour which led people to describe it
incorrectly as a chernozem or black soil, but in fact these are half-
boggy meadow-lands with massive horizons of humus. In dry
places their physical characteristics and structure do indeed suggest black soil, but in low-lying humid places their half-boggy
origins are clearly recognizable.

On the whole in these areas it is the podzols that predominate.
Their fertility is almost equal to that of the corresponding soils of
northern Germany and middle Russia, and they are very suitable
for agriculture. General estimates of the cultivable land in the
various regions are as follows: 77,200 square miles in Transbaikalia, over 42,460 square miles in the Amur region, giving a total of
178,960 square miles. In comparison, the land now used for agriculture (4,131,380 acres in 1938) represents only a small proportion of this potential. However, it should be noted that the cultivated area has increased by 60 per cent since 1913 (when it was
only 2,577,300 acres), which is a great accomplishment for these
areas so remote from central Russia.

As the following tables will show, the extension of the arable
land followed a different course in the different individual districts. In the Buryato-Mongolian ASSR and the District of Chita
the amount of arable land has been doubled since 1913 and has

### The development of arable land
(in thousands of acres)

|  | Buryato-Mongolian ASSR | District of Chita | District of Khabarovsk | Coastal Region | Total |
|---|---|---|---|---|---|
| 1913 | 421·52 | 631·84 | 1,037·05 | 442·86 | 2,577·30 |
| 1928 | 458·14 | 896·94 | 1,628·66 | 908·60 | 3,872·14 |
| 1938 | 850·74 | 1,322·62 | 1,277·76 | 700·26 | 4,131·38 |

been consistently extended under the Soviet regime. The natural
conditions here are similar to those of the South Russian steppe
and do not require the Russian peasant to adopt great changes in
method. In the District of Khabarovsk and the Coastal Region, on
the other hand, conditions are very different (as already indicated
above). Cultivation in these newer areas has not progressed to the
same extent as in Transbaikalia, and shows a greater variation
from one period to the next. In Khabarovsk the drop in the

cultivated area from 1,628,000 acres in 1928 to the present 1,276,000 acres is attributable to the institution of the five-year plans, since the establishment of a planned agriculture resulted in the elimination of the less productive land. Nevertheless it is remarkable that the official Soviet statistics should show a steady drop year after year, from 1932 to 1938, in the amount of arable land in the Coastal Region. (The figures in thousands of acres for these years are as follows: 1,015·96, 989·12, 949·52, 923·78, 816·20, 708·4, 708·4, 700·26.) The above information, as well as what follows, is taken from the Soviet publication *Possevny'e Ploshchadi SSSR* (11).

In all four regions the cultivation of grain is the predominant use. In 1938, 90 per cent of all arable land in the Buryato-Mongolian ASSR was used for the cultivation of grain, and in the District of Chita the proportion was as high as 92 per cent, so that these two districts must be considered as being almost exclusively grain-growing areas. In the District of Khabarovsk the proportion of grain-growing land was 75 per cent and in the Coastal Region it was 69 per cent. In accordance with the climatic conditions, the cultivation of summer grain predominates, winter-sown crops accounting for only 6,050 acres, or 1·5 per cent of the cultivated land in all four districts together.

*The cultivation of grain in 1938*
(in thousands of acres)

| | All Grains | Winter Crops | Summer Crops | | |
|---|---|---|---|---|---|
| | | | Wheat | Oats | Barley |
| Buryato-Mongolian ASSR . | 767·36 | 23·76 | 293·04 | 186·78 | 32·34 |
| District of Chita      . | 1,194·60 | 14·08 | 385·88 | 367·62 | 69·96 |
| District of Khabarovsk  . | 981·20 | 1·76 | 533·28 | 390·72 | 5·50 |
| Coastal Region      . | 475·20 | 20·90 | 194·26 | 181·72 | 13·20 |

In the Buryato-Mongolian ASSR the cultivation of low-value summer rye predominated up to 1914, but since then wheat has displaced the rye to an increasing extent. By 1938 wheat had taken first place, occupying 40 per cent of the arable land and leaving only 27 per cent for summer rye. In the early days the cultivation of potatoes, vegetables, and fodder was completely missing, but now these are very much favoured and had already taken up 6·2 per cent of the arable land by 1938. In the District of Chita the cultivation of wheat has also greatly increased, having trebled since 1913. It now occupies 46 per cent of the arable land and accounts for just half of the total area devoted to grain. The proportion of arable land devoted to summer rye was only 6·9 per cent in 1938, although this had once been the predominant crop in this area too. The cultivation of buckwheat now takes up a comparatively large area, occupying 3·4 per cent of the total arable land, and is associated with the developing bee-keeping industry.

In comparison with this rather monotonous and one-sided emphasis on the cultivation of grain in Transbaikalia, the agricultural scene becomes much livelier and more varied as one moves into the Amur–Ussuri region. Nevertheless the cultivation of grain is predominant here too, occupying 75 per cent of the arable land in the District of Khabarovsk and 69 per cent in the Coastal Region. There is widespread cultivation of the sunflower, in spite of the humid climate, in the Seya–Bureya plain, where it forms a reminder of the Russian's European homeland. In the Ussuri area maize also appears, but the sunflower does not seem to thrive here. In addition there is a fairly even distribution throughout both districts of two important East Asian oil-bearing plants: the soyabean and the perilla. In 1938 the soyabean occupied more than 176,000 acres. It contains from 13 to 21 per cent fat and from 35 to 38 per cent albumen, and constitutes an extremely valuable product for industrial use, as well as food for both men and animals. The soyabean is of further special importance because of its nitrogen-fixing properties, which enrich the soil and increase the yield of succeeding crops. The perilla (*Perilla arguta*, belonging to the same family as sesame) provides an excellent machine oil. It occupied about 9,900 acres of the cultivated area in 1938, and its cultivation is being systematically extended. Several different kinds of millet are grown by the Chinese colonists in the southern part of the Ussuri district, while the cultivation of rice is carried out by the Koreans and has extended as far as the vicinity of Khabarovsk. Cash crops are represented in the Ussuri district by flax, hemp, and tobacco. The cultivation of sugar-beet, which was introduced after 1920, is of special importance and has become fairly widespread in the vicinity of Lake Khanka. The beets are processed in factories at Voroshilov (Nikolsk-Ussurisk), and the output already supplies much of the sugar required in the Far Eastern territories.

In the wide open spaces of the north, agriculture has been developed only sporadically, primarily to serve the local population. With the exception of the Chukchen peninsula, there are very often small gardens near the settlements where beets, radishes, potatoes, &c., are grown, and (more rarely) oats and barley. Only Kamchatka has any appreciably large areas under cultivation, amounting to about 6,160 acres in 1938.

Of the four administrative districts, the Buryato-Mongolian ASSR and the District of Chita are the only ones which grow enough grain to provide a surplus. Both are well on the way towards becoming the country's granaries, but at present they do not yet produce enough to cover the deficits of the other two districts.

*Arable land per head of population in 1938*

| | Total Arable Land (1,000 acres) | Arable Land per Head (acres) | Total Grain-producing Land (1,000 acres) | Grain-producing Land per Head (acres) |
|---|---|---|---|---|
| Soviet Union . . . | 30,124·82 | 1·76 | 22,530·42 | 1·32 |
| Buryato-Mongolian ASSR . | 850·74 | 1·56 | 767·4 | 1·43 |
| District of Chita . . . | 1,322·62 | 1·32 | 1,194·6 | 1·03 |
| District of Khabarovsk . . | 1,277·76 | 0·90 | 981·2 | 0·68 |
| Coastal Region . . . | 700·26 | 0·77 | 475·2 | 0·53 |
| Transbaikalia and the Far East . | 4,131·38 | 1·03 | 3,418·6 | 0·86 |

There are no equivalent statistics at our disposal for judging the development of agriculture from 1938 up to the present, because none have been published since that time. As a partial substitute there is a great deal of information available from the Soviet Press, but it contains mainly separate reports of a general character, or special reports from widely differing areas and places. It is difficult to gain a clear picture from all these reports, but they provide the only possible means of getting an impression of recent developments. Many reports tell of an immigration benefiting both the industrial and the agrarian sectors of the economy. The rise in production and the extension of the area of cultivated land often form the substance of these reports, and the results of the last five-year plan (up to 1950) are particularly stressed. Irrigation has been introduced in the steppe area of the District of Chita. A beginning was made in 1948 by the construction of a system of numerous canals supplying water to irrigate 28,270 acres. In the vicinity of the big towns, particular attention is paid to the development of produce for urban markets, and there is a great deal of market-gardening. Within the framework of the 1948 plan for laying out the surroundings of Vladivostok there was provision for 3,432

acres of gardens. Similarly, in the vicinity of Khabarovsk large
areas of virgin land are being brought under cultivation in order
to secure more food for the growing town. The first of eight stations in this district for land-betterment machines was erected
here in 1950.

On the island of Kamchatka the development of agriculture is
of vital importance. According to Soviet data, the arable land here
before the First World War amounted to only 8·8 acres, but had
increased to 5,611·6 acres by 1938, and has increased still further
since then. In 1950 there were more than ten *kolkhozes* in existence. In 1952 a scientific expedition was sent from Khabarovsk to
Kamchatka to explore the possibilities of opening up and preparing more land for agriculture. Two stations for land-betterment
machines were set up in the same year. These machines were to
make available for agriculture during the next three years approximately 88,000 acres of bog and taiga.

From Sakhalin, too, there is news about successes in making
new land available, including a special note that the native population have also turned successfully to agriculture, as in the case of
the Gilyaks in the *kolkhoz* 'Chir Unvd' (meaning 'new life'). Two
reports tell us of the speed with which the agricultural development of South Sakhalin has been organized. In 1949 there were
thirty-three *kolkhozes* and three *sovkhozes*, whereas by 1950 there
were already sixty-nine of these collective farms.

The progress of mechanization and agricultural techniques takes
an important place in the more recent reports, which show that
the number of machine-tractor stations (MTS) has increased considerably in all districts. In the Buryato-Mongolian ASSR their
number rose from twenty-five in 1937 to thirty-six in 1948, and in
the District of Khabarovsk there were seventy-six such stations in
1947—nearly double the number available in 1938. Twenty-five
stations for mowing machines were organized in the Buryato-Mongolian ASSR in 1948, in order to secure winter hay for the cattle
*kolkhozes* from 110,000 acres of meadow-land, since there was not
sufficient manual labour available. The first agrarian town of the
Soviet Far East was erected in 1950 in the Buryato-Mongolian
ASSR, containing 400 two-storey houses and thirty single-family
houses. There is remarkable news, too, about special combine har-
vesters being used for gathering the rice and soyabean crops.

Soyabeans and rice take first place among the crops which have
been especially encouraged. The soyabean harvest was bigger
by 16,000 tons in 1949 than it was in 1948. In comparison the

cultivation of rice seems to be making only slow progress. There were 80,080 acres of rice under cultivation in the Far East in 1937, and according to the last five-year plan this area was to be extended to 81,400 acres by 1950, which seems a rather modest extension if one considers that in 1913 there were 125,400 acres of rice-fields. Great attention is being paid to the cultivation of sugar-beet, and there has been a further extension of the area devoted to its cultivation in the vicinity of Lake Khanka, as already mentioned above. Tea is to be a new product of the Soviet Far East, and an expedition was sent out by the Botanic Institute of Leningrad in 1950 to explore experimentally the practical possibilities for planting tea-shrubs in this area.

All the foregoing information should be regarded as only isolated pictures from a continuous film-strip of agricultural progress in the Soviet Far East. They testify to the tremendous effort which the Soviet Union is making to speed the advance of agriculture as far as possible in these districts. It should be noted, however, that the increase of grain crops in the Far Eastern territories by 150 per cent (comparing 1947 with 1913), and the increase of the potato crop by 200 per cent (*Trud*, 25.10.47), must be compared with an increase of population in the same period of about 300 per cent. The fact that increased production has thus been offset by an even bigger increase of population means that the problems of providing food for the population are still much the same as those discussed above, although the two growth curves may have come somewhat closer since 1947. The Far Eastern territories proper (excluding the Buryato-Mongolian ASSR and the District of Chita) are thus still food-importing areas. However, the cultivation of potatoes and soyabeans has reduced dependence on outside supplies, and since Manchuria with her agricultural surplus has become part of the Soviet sphere of influence the import of food no longer presents a problem.

### Stock-raising

Transbaikalia is one of the leading cattle-breeding areas of the Soviet Union. In the Buryato-Mongolian ASSR there are 1,367 horned cattle for every 1,000 people as compared with an average of only 233 per 1,000 in the USSR as a whole, and there are 1,786 sheep and goats per 1,000 people in this area as compared with only 602 per 1,000 for the country as a whole. The most important districts for cattle-raising are situated to the left of the Selenga

River and to the right of the Uda. Methodical cross-breeding of the Mongolian cow with the Simmenthal, and of the native sheep with the Rambouillet-Merino, has been carried out in order to improve the quality of the stock. The steppes to the left of the Selenga are used for rearing the more highly-bred animals, which are kept here in warm sheds during the winter, and fed with specially prepared cattle food. Horses and pigs account for only a minor share (11·7 and 6·7 per cent respectively) of the total number of domestic animals. The cattle-raising industry is said to be equally prosperous in the District of Chita, where the most important horned cattle are the herds of dairy cows. The breeding of horses is served by a number of studs on the steppes of the Onon and the Argun. Camels are also raised in the same area, and there are said to be 7,000 of them. On the whole, Transbaikalia can be said to be a surplus-producing area for both grain and cattle.

The following table shows the outstanding position of the Buryato-Mongolian ASSR and the District of Chita in relation to the stock-raising economy of the Soviet Union as a whole.

*Average number of animals per collective farm in 1938*

|  | Soviet Union | Buryato-Mongolian ASSR | District of Chita |
|---|---|---|---|
| Horses . . . . | 0·7 | 2·0 | 2·5 |
| Cattle . . . . | 2·2 | 6·0 | 6·5 |
| Sheep and goats . . . | 2·9 | 19·0 | 11·9 |

In the Amur–Ussuri region the position is very different. The breeding of cattle is insufficient to meet the demand, and even horses have to be imported. Cattle are kept for milk and as draught animals in the south of the Ussuri District, but otherwise the only dairy-farming worth mentioning is located in the vicinity of the towns. There are generally no pasturing facilities for keeping cattle on any large scale, but single animals are to be found everywhere, even in the far north. On Kamchatka they number several thousands. Pigs are relatively more numerous in the Amur–Ussuri region than in Transbaikalia because they are also raised by the Koreans and the Chinese, but the animals are generally of poor quality.

The general position in the Far Eastern territories is thus that they must import meat as well as grain in order to meet their requirements.

One further point which must be mentioned in this connexion is the breeding of reindeer in the extreme north-east of the district, where excellent grazing land is offered by the moss tundra stretching from the Chukchen peninsula into the interior of Kamchatka. Apart from the European north, these districts take first place among the reindeer-breeding areas of the Soviet Union. The Soviet authorities have contributed to the continual development of activity in this field by the establishment of several reindeer *sovkhozes*. The total number of animals is estimated to be 750,000. The reindeer not only provide meat for current local requirements, but also a surplus which is preserved in a factory especially built for this purpose at Anadyr. The skin of the young reindeer is processed to form the chamois leather which is exported, and for which there is such a great demand.

## Hunting

The valuable fur-bearing animals, which were formerly so numerous, have almost completely disappeared from the inhabited areas and have retreated into the largely inaccessible wilderness. Nevertheless, the Far Eastern territories with their extensive wild forests form even today a most gratifying area for the hunter. About one-third of all the fur of the Soviet Union comes from the Far East, with only a minor share of this coming from Transbaikalia. Squirrels and foxes are the main providers of fur, especially since the sable has been exterminated over large areas and is now only very rarely found. On the tundra the arctic fox is the most important game. The amount of larger game has considerably decreased because of ruthless hunting in former times. For instance, the spotted stag (which is very much sought after for its '*panten*') was formerly found in great numbers in the Amur–Ussuri region, but is very rare in the open hunting grounds today. It is now kept only in the National Parks of the Sikhota Alin, where there are known to be seven national parks containing several thousand stags. There are large areas of the Sikhota-Alin, Kamchatka, and Lake Baikal, which have been declared nature preserves for the protection of the flora and fauna.

The hunting of fur-bearing animals is organized by the State, and is undertaken from numerous bases where the huntsmen obtain their outfits and provisions. They set out together in cadres, and must abide by certain regulations (differing from place to place) laid down in order to preserve the supply of game. When the hunting season is over, the furs are delivered to these bases and the huntsmen are paid off according to their results.

## Fishing, and Hunting of Marine Animals

Fishing in Transbaikalia is of only minor importance because of this territory's inland position. Apart from some small lakes abounding in fish, commercial fishing is concentrated on Lake Baikal. The most important fish is the omul (*Coregonus omul pall*), a variety of salmon the spawn of which is cultivated artificially and then planted in the lake to build up the stock. There are a few factories in various places along the shore which preserve the fish not consumed locally. Also of some importance is the catching of seals (*Phoca sibirica*), which are still very numerous in Lake Baikal.

In the other parts of the Far Eastern territories fishing is of much greater importance. For the native household, fish often forms the only (or at least the main) source of food, and the Russian settler does not like to omit fish from his menu either. Therefore, throughout the whole of the Far East the inhabitants are busy supplementing their food by fishing, wherever there is even the smallest lake or stream. In this connexion the historic development of the area plays a certain part, since fishing represented one of the main sources of food for the first Russian settlers. Moreover nature has blessed the whole area with lakes and rivers abounding in fish, as well as the important ocean fishing grounds skirting the whole of the Far Eastern coast, which are exceedingly rich in fish and belong to the most important fishing areas of the earth. Year after year tremendous numbers of salmon (of innumerable different varieties) come up the rivers from the sea to spawn, often coming far inland. There the inhabitants wait for them, intent on providing food not only for themselves but also for their animals, and not only for a short period but for the whole year.

On the northern coast, fishing generally constitutes the only source of livelihood for the people, and the fact that the coastal strip is inhabited even far into the north is due mainly to the wealth of fish and marine animals provided by the sea.

The abundance of fish and marine animals of all kinds in the coastal seas has not only provided a local food supply, but has also led to the development of a coastal and deep-sea fishing industry which forms an essential part of the economy of the Far Eastern territories. By creating a State-owned fishing fleet, and by fitting it out with modern motor-boats, trawlers, whalers, and special crab-fishing boats, the Far Eastern territories have gained first place among the fish-producing areas of the Soviet Union (according to the figures for catches up to 1938). The share of the Far East in the total quantity of fish caught and preserved amounts to more than a quarter of the total for the Soviet Union as a whole.

*Result of catches in the Far Eastern territories*

| | | | | |
|---|---|---|---|---|
| 1913 | . | . | . | 107,330 tons |
| 1928 | . | . | . | 161,820 „ |
| 1932 | . | . | . | 346,800 „ |
| 1937 | . | . | . | 404,800 „ |

In 1938 the total produce from the deep-sea fisheries of the USSR came to 1,490,000 tons, with fisheries in the Far East accounting for 25·2 per cent and those of the Volga–Caspian Sea area accounting for 23 per cent of the total. A target for total catches of 2·2 million tons was set for 1950. In general only 96 per cent of the target figure was achieved, but the quota of the Far Eastern territories was surpassed by 50 per cent, indicating that the share of the Far East in the total catch for the whole country is now even higher than given above. More accurate information about the individual districts has not yet been published. A total catch of 3,476,000 tons for the whole of the Soviet Union was set as the target for 1955.

In assessing the value of the individual fishing areas, it must be remembered that the catches in the Far East consist mainly of particularly valuable varieties of salmon. It must also be remembered that because of the small number of inhabitants local demand is limited, making the Far Eastern territories one of the most important surplus-producing areas. The lively fishing industry grew up as a consequence of this situation. All the larger places along the coast have cold-storage buildings, and the number of fish canneries has greatly increased, from two in 1913 to forty-two in 1938. During the same period plants were also built for producing locally the tins required. In addition there are ships specially designed for the processing of their own catches while still on board. The crab-fishing boats also resemble floating factories. They work along the west coast of Kamchatka and have secured first place for the Far Eastern territories among the major crab-producing areas of the world.

The coastal strip adjoining the Sea of Japan, from the Korean frontier to the Straits of Tartary, forms the southernmost fishing area. Here herring and sardine fishing are predominant, and the fishing is done mainly in the bays—the largest catches coming from the Bay of Peter the Great. Vladivostok is the centre and heart of the modern fish-canning industry. Up to 1938 the yield of the herring fisheries went partly inland and partly to Japan.

The second major fishing area is formed by the region of the lower Amur. Two species of Pacific salmon use this large river as their favourite spawning ground: first, the Keta salmon (*Oncorhynchus Keta* Walb.), called the dog-salmon by the Americans, which provides the very popular red caviar; and second, the somewhat smaller Gorbusha or humpback salmon (*Oncorhynchus gorbusha* Walb.). The occurrence of these species, especially of the Gorbusha, shows certain peculiarities, on which some detailed research has been done by Peter Schmidt (*Eastern Europe*, 1928, II). Mr Schmidt draws attention to the fact that these species of salmon do not multiply at the rate of the European species, because they spawn only once in their lives, thus producing only one-tenth of the quantity produced by the Rhine salmon, for example. It is also of special interest that the shoals of Gorbusha appear only at intervals of two years. L. S. Berg (27/390) gives the following information about the annual catch of Gorbusha (in millions of fish):

| | | | | | | | | |
|---|---|---|---|---|---|---|---|---|
| 1914 | . | . | . | 14·5 | 1922 | . | . | . | 9·0 |
| 1915 | . | . | . | 1·0 | 1923 | . | . | . | 0·2 |
| 1916 | . | . | . | 9·2 | 1924 | . | . | . | 12·2 |
| 1917 | . | . | . | 0·5 | 1925 | . | . | . | 0·0 |
| 1918 | . | . | . | 14·9 | 1926 | . | . | . | 14·1 |
| 1919 | . | . | . | 0·4 | 1927 | . | . | . | 0·0 |
| 1920 | . | . | . | 12·0 | 1928 | . | . | . | 16·4 |
| 1921 | . | . | . | 0·2 | | | | | |

According to Berg it is only since 1908 that this bi-annual periodicity has developed in the Amur district, and it is not found along the coasts of Kamchatka. The Keta salmon, on the other hand, arrive regularly every year in both areas. The two-year interval between the appearances of the Gorbusha results in a corresponding variation in the total catch of salmon in the Far Eastern territories. Over-intensive fishing in the lower Amur is counteracted by the artificial cultivation of the salmon spawn. The centre of the lower Amur fishing area is Nikolayevsk, where 75 per cent of the population is engaged in the fishing industry.

The third major fishing area of any importance is the eastern side of the island of Sakhalin, where (apart from the different species of salmon) it is chiefly herring, cod, tunny fish, and mackerel that are caught. However, in comparison with the other fishing areas, the island of Sakhalin is of only minor importance.

The fishing area of the Far East which has developed most in recent years is the peninsula of Kamchatka. Here again first place is taken by the various species of valuable Pacific salmon: the red, silver, and king salmon (*Oncorhynchus nerka*, *O. kisutch*, and *O. chavycha* Walb.). All the rivers of the peninsula and of the adjoining mainland are visited every year by large shoals of salmon. Processing of the salmon is distributed among numerous places along the coast, which will be discussed in more detail later in the special section on Kamchatka. The Sea of Okhotsk, off the west coast of Kamchatka, seems to be particularly suitable for the development of crabs, and the crab-fishing fleet is therefore stationed here. The crabs arrive regularly at the beaches in the spring, coming from the depth of the sea where they spend the winter. In addition to the above, the seas around Kamchatka, including the Bering Straits in particular, abound in sea-mammals such as seals, walrus, and whales, although the latter are gradually dying out. The hunting of these marine animals is concentrated around Petropavlovsk, which is the administrative centre of the peninsula. The extent to which the rising catches of fish and marine animals have influenced the development of Kamchatka is best shown by its growth of population. This was estimated to be less than 20,000 people in 1914, rising to 30,000 by 1926, and surpassing 120,000 in 1948. The surplus catch is either used by other parts of the Soviet Union or sent for export, Western Europe being the principal foreign customer.

A very special (and typically East Asian) kind of fishing has been developed along the south coast of the Ussuri region. Its main objects are the sea cucumber or 'Trepang' (*Holothuria edulis*), and the sea cabbage (*Laminaria saccharina*), which is a variety of sea-weed or fucus. The edible 'Trepang' is brought up from depths of 13–33 feet, either by special drags or by divers, while the sea cabbage is pulled off the bottom of the sea with special hooks. The latter is sold in a dehydrated form, and both these products of the sea go to China, where they are very popular foods. All the Soviet Far Eastern sea fisheries are grouped together in the organization called the 'Dalrybtrest' (Far East Fish Trust), which has its head-quarters in Vladivostok. The fishing concessions along the Russian coast which were once given to the Japanese (and secured by a treaty) have been annulled by the war, and the Soviet sea fisheries in the Far East therefore still have enormous possibilities for further development.

## Natural Resources and Industry
### COAL DEPOSITS

*Transbaikalia*

Generally speaking, Transbaikalia is not poor in coal, but the coal deposits occur at numerous different places, many of which are badly served by communications even today. The coal varies considerably in quality and size of deposit. It is nearly all of Jurassic age, and according to its quality must be classed as brown coal. No real hard coal is found in Transbaikalia. The most important coal deposits are the following:

1. *Tarbagatay*, situated on the right-hand side of the Khilok river valley, between the stations of Tarbagatay and Tolboga on the Transbaikalian railway. Here Jurassic lignite with a heating value of 1,867 calories per pound lies in two seams, 26 feet and 13 feet thick respectively, separated by a layer of 'seat earth' 30 feet thick. The total reserves are said to be 50 million tons. Mining started as early as 1890, and at present work is going on from several different shafts. Infiltrating water makes work very difficult, but 200,000–250,000 tons of coal are extracted each year.

2. *Khalyarta*. Here coal is found lying in a terrace in the valley of the Tolboga River, which is a tributary of the Khilok. The pits are situated 7 miles from the station of Tolboga and 10 miles from the pits of Tarbagatay. The coal is the same quality as from the latter, but the seams are not so thick, being only 15 feet and 16 feet respectively. Total reserves are 1,335,000 tons. A branch-line connects the pits with the Transbaikalian railway.

3. *Chernovskoye*. This coal-field lies 11–12 miles west-south-west of Chita, and near the station of the same name, where a town of more than 10,000 inhabitants has sprung up. The coal lies in the valley of Ingoda, on the left-hand side of the river between the two tributaries Chernovka and Kadala, and probably continues from there as far as the town of Chita. This brown-coal deposit is of greater value than the others, since it has a heating value of 1,875–2,050 calories. Three of the five seams, with thicknesses of 3 feet, 8 feet, and 17 feet, have been worked since 1914. The original surface mining was subsequently replaced by underground working, for climatic reasons. Total reserves have not been thoroughly investigated, and estimates vary between 19 and 33 million tons. Yearly production before the war reached 450,000 tons, and this

field now shares with the Bukachacha field the position of top coal-producer in the District of Chita.

4. *Kharamangutsk.* These coal deposits lie near the town of Kharamangutsk, about 2 miles from the station of Darassu on the Transbaikalian railway. The Jurassic brown coal lies in two workable seams, the upper of which is 6 feet thick, and is worked from two pits.

5. *Kholbonsk*, situated 12–15 miles west-south-west of Nerchinsk, on the left-hand bank of the Shilka, has deposits 3 miles wide and more than 5 miles long running alongside the river. Jurassic brown coal with a heating value of 1,805–1,961 calories is extracted from the first and fifth seams at several pits, from both surface and underground workings. These two seams, which are the only ones being worked, have thicknesses of 8 feet and 46 feet.

6. *Bukachacha* is the most important coal-bearing area in the District of Chita, and extends over an area of 10 square miles. It is situated in the valley of the Bukachacha River to the north of the Transbaikalian railway, and is connected to the latter by a branch-line 25 miles long, which was built in 1929. Altogether nine seams have been found, the largest having a thickness of 20 feet. However, these seams do not appear throughout the whole of the coal-field, and there is a considerable variation in position and quality. Tectonic processes have changed part of the Jurassic brown coal into a kind of hard coal which seems to be suitable for coke production. Before the war there were four pits being worked at deep levels, and after the war these were very much enlarged by new installations. Today Bukachacha heads the production list in the District of Chita. The total reserves are stated to be 80–100 million tons.

7. *Kharanor*, situated south-east of Borsya about 1¼ miles from the station of Kharanor. Here the Jurassic brown coal lies in a dry valley 5–6 miles wide, below post-Tertiary beds less than 60 feet thick. Altogether ten seams have been discovered here, but only two of these (with thicknesses of 15 and 50–55 feet) are workable. The reserves are estimated to be 11 million tons. The heating value (2,205 calories) is above that of the ordinary brown coal, and the high proportion (60 per cent) of volatile components makes this coal a particularly suitable raw material for the chemical industry. Mining was once begun here, but was later stopped, and there is no information available about the present position.

8. *Duroy.* These deposits lie in the extreme south-east of Transbaikalia, running along the Argun between the towns of Duroy

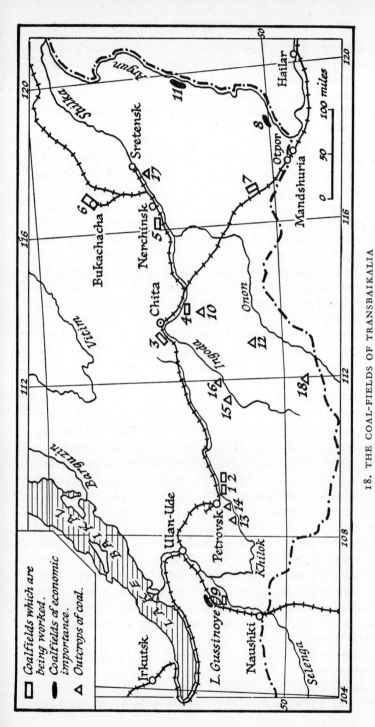

18. THE COAL-FIELDS OF TRANSBAIKALIA

1. Tarbagatay. 2. Khalyarta. 3. Chernovskoye. 4. Kkaramangutsk. 5. Kholbonskoye. 6. Bukachacha. 7. Khabanor. 8. Duroy. 9. Lake Gussinoye. 10. Tyrgetty. 11. Chalbucha. 12. Ureya River. 13. Katayeva. 14. Kuli. 15. Klyuchevaya. 16. Gorekinskoye. 17. Matsiyevskoye. 18. Byrtse River.

and Kaylastay. Three seams between $1\frac{1}{2}$ and 5 feet thick extend over an area of 8–10 square miles and total reserves are estimated to be 30 million tons. This is good quality brown coal with a heating value of 1,970 calories. Further brown coal deposits have been found along the Argun, but nothing is known about their quantity or quality.

9. *Lake Gussinoye.* The size and importance of the deposits at the well-known 'Goose Lake', in the Buryato-Mongolian ASSR, have only been realized since the Second World War. They extend over large areas to the north-west and south-east of the lake, and altogether seven seams (from $2\frac{1}{2}$ to 30 feet thick) have been found. The total thickness of workable seams is said to be 75 feet, and the total reserves are estimated to be 200–250 million tons. The quality of the coal is reduced by its high ash content, and it is extracted mainly to serve the railway from Ulan-Ude to Ulan-Bator, as well as the chemical industry which is being set up at Lake Gussinoye. There is also a power-station based on this coal which is already working near Tomcha.

Apart from these important coal deposits described above, other beds are also known to exist, but they have not been adequately explored and no information is available.

### The Region of the Amur

In contrast to Transbaikalia, the Amur region is provided with coal deposits which possess the character and quality of hard coal, although they are also of Jurassic origin. The various reasons for this improvement in quality, as compared with the Transbaikalian deposits, is not wholly ascertainable. At present one is forced to accept whatever information can be obtained by following up a number of different sources. In general, the Jurassic coal deposits in the Amur region have been strongly affected by the process of folding: elevations, depressions, and fractures, followed by the erosion of the anticlines, have split the beds up into a large number of small deposits. Unbroken coal-fields, either large or small, appear only rarely. However, in order to present a clearer picture, the small deposits resulting from this splitting-up process will be grouped together and treated comprehensively as a series of large individual basins.

### Hard-coal Deposits

1. *Biro-Bidzhan.* The anthracite fields here represent the continuation of the Hegan coal-fields in the Small Khingan, extending

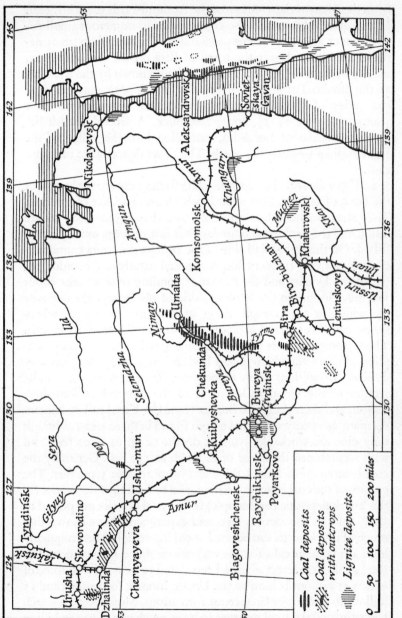

19. THE COAL-FIELDS OF THE AMUR REGION

from the Manchurian side across the Amur towards the north-east. In the Biro-Bidzhan field the coal appears in numerous small deposits over an area of 100 square miles. The most important deposits are situated near the town of Bira on the Amur railway, mainly in the valley of the Turuk, and are known by the Russians as the Birsko-Turukskoye deposits. This deposit emerges near the station of Bira as a 'coal mountain', and is worked in three seams which are $2\frac{1}{2}$, $2\frac{1}{4}$, and 7 feet thick. A second deposit lies near the station of Londoko, extending into the valley of the Kamenushka towards the north. The other deposits are insignificant.

2. *Upper Bureya.* The coal deposits found here are the largest of the Soviet Far East, with regard to both area and size of reserves. They stretch over a total area of more than 1,500–2,000 square miles, and the geological boundary has not yet been exactly established. On the right-hand side of the Bureya the strata containing coal are not very frequent and are limited mainly to the region between the Umalta and the Niman, extending over an area about 110 miles long. On the left-hand side of the Bureya the deposits are wider, as for example along its tributary the Urgal, where seams have been found extending up to 40 miles from its mouth. The tectonic structure of the coal deposits gives them a very complicated character which makes both research and utilization very difficult. Conditions seem to be most favourable in the middle section of the Urgal valley, next to the Yoreksko-Olonzhinsk Rayon, and then along the Bureya from Ust-Urgal to Ust-Niman. As many as twenty seams have been found in these areas, although only nine are workable, lying at depths of up to 2,000 feet, and with a combined thickness of as much as 130 feet. Generally the coal-bearing strata have a thickness of more than 3,300 feet. The quality of the coal is not consistent, and its heating value varies (in the Yorek deposits, for example) from 2,266 calories per pound to 3,006 calories. Numerous tests and experiments have shown that much of the deposits can be used as coking coal, but the frequently high ash content calls for the utilization of special methods. The total geological reserves have been stated to be 60 billion tons, of which 45 billions belong to the Upper Jurassic formations and 15 billions to the Lower Cretaceous formations. More recent research has estimated the total reserves to be as much as 120 to 130 billion tons (8/I/80).

3. *Tyrma Basin.* This coal-field is a continuation of the deposits along the upper Bureya, and has only been separated from it by

tectonic processes and subsequent erosion. The main deposit is along the middle course of the Tyrma, 70 miles from where it flows into the Bureya. The coal-bearing stratum is about 1,200 feet thick, and has (apart from several seams of little value) two seams varying in thickness from 5 to 15 feet, according to position. The quality of the coal is supposed to be inferior to that of the upper Bureya coal-field, but it is nevertheless of industrial importance because of its proximity to the Amur railway.

West of the Bureya, hard coal is to be found only in small deposits, as for example the deposit along the River Dep, 28 miles from where it flows into the Seya. Here there is a reserve of only 490,000 tons, which is used for providing coal for river transport on the Seya. It is only recently that a further more extensive deposit has come into prominence along the upper Amur. It runs along the river, with outcrops in the valley floors of the tributaries Urusha, Kerak, Burinda, and Magdagacha. The quality is generally inferior, with an average heating value of 1,896 calories, but some of the seams are of anthracite or semi-anthracite character. Mining started at Magdagacha in 1947.

*Brown-coal Deposits*

1. *Lower Bureya*. These brown-coal deposits, the largest in the Amur region, lie between the Amur River and the Amur railway, stretching from the lower Bureya in the east to the Savitaya in the west. They are of Tertiary age (Miocene and Pliocene), and generally form only one seam, ranging in thickness from 7 to 23 feet, with an average thickness of 20 feet. There is some surface mining. The most important pits lie at Kivdinsk and Raychikhinsk, the joint production of which reached about 700,000 tons before the war. Since the war new installations have been built capable of producing 250,000 tons a year. A disadvantage of this brown coal is that it was deposited under very humid conditions and it is therefore liable to crumble away into fine particles when exposed to the air. The total reserves are stated to amount to 510 million tons, of which 245 million tons are grade A.1.

2. *Mukhen Deposits*, situated in the river-basin of the same name, 80 miles north-east of Khabarovsk. Here two seams $5\frac{1}{4}$ and $10\frac{1}{2}$ feet thick have been discovered, lying only 23–33 feet under the surface. This coal is of a rather poor quality, closely resembling lignite.

3. *Khungari Deposits*, situated near the middle reaches of the Khungari River, which flows into the Amur below the Mukhen.

This Tertiary field was discovered only in the 1930's. It has two seams each 6 feet thick, which have average heating values of 1,506 calories and 1,944 calories.

4. *Naloyevskoye Deposit*, also discovered only recently. The coal lies along the coast of the Straits of Tartary, about 12 miles south of the mouth of the Amur.

## Coastal Region

On the whole the Coastal Region has been better explored than the other regions of the Soviet Far East, and more can therefore be said about the coal deposits in this area. Up to the present, sixty-nine hard-coal and thirty-eight brown-coal deposits have been established, containing coal of all qualities from anthracite to brown coal. A particular characteristic of coal in this region is the variety of ways it is found deposited. Some fields stretch over large areas, while others have been broken up into small individual deposits by tectonic movements. Most deposits lie in synclines with predominantly north-east strike-lines. According to their geological age, these deposits can be divided into three groups. The oldest belong to the Upper Trias (Mongugay series) and include the anthracites and semi-anthracites. The second group, of much greater importance, belongs to the Upper Jurassic (Nikansker series) and the Lower Cretaceous periods, and provides mainly hard coal. The third group contains the Tertiary brown coal. The quality of the coal does not always correspond to its age, since much of it has changed in value as the result of tectonic processes. The Tertiary brown coal from Tavrichanka, for instance, closely resembles hard coal in quality.

Within the coal-bearing Mongugay series of the Upper Trias, three independent coal-fields are discernible: the Maikhe–Pochikhe deposit, the Mongugay deposit, and the Rasdolnaya deposit.

1. *The Maikhe–Pochikhe deposit.* This deposit lies between the River Maikhe, which flows southwards into Ussuri Bay, and the Pochikhe, which is a left-hand tributary of the Suifun, and is situated to the north of the railway line which leads from Ugolnaya on the Ussuri railway to Suchan. The eastern part, between Surazheyevka and Radchikhinsk, is the best known. Here the coal-bearing strata lie in an asymmetrical syncline extending over an area of 12 square miles and containing estimated reserves of 300 million tons. Only a small part has been explored, but five workable seams with a total thickness of 16–20 feet have been established. The heating value of the coal itself lies between 3,231 and

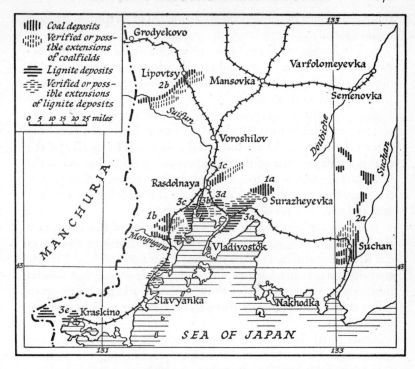

**20. THE COAL-FIELDS OF THE VLADIVOSTOK REGION**

*The coal-fields according to their geological age*

TRIASSIC: 1a. *Maiche-Pochikhe deposits.* 1b. *Mongugaya deposits.* 1c. *Rasdolnaya deposits.* UPPER JURASSIC—LOWER CRETACEOUS: 2a. *Suchan deposits.* 2b. *Suifun deposits.* TERTIARY: 3a. *Artem-Ugolnaya.* 3b. *Tavrichanka.* 3c. *Fedorovski.* 3d. *Ippolitovka.* 3e. *Kraskino.*

3,284 calories, but the quality of the deposit is reduced by the high ash content and the intrusion of barren lodes of waste matter. The western branch of this deposit lies immediately to the north of the Tertiary brown-coal deposits of Artem, and stretches from the small River Batalyanso as far as the Pochikhe. Here, too, the coal-bearing strata lie in a syncline, but in this case they have been very much disturbed. Prospecting here has resulted in the finding of three productive seams between 3 and 11 feet thick. The heating value of 2,867 calories is slightly less than that in the eastern section of the deposit, but on the other hand the proportion of ash is not so high. Extraction is made difficult by the complicated tectonic structure, and mining has not yet begun, although it is planned to start during the next few years. The total reserves in this western part of the deposit are estimated to be from 300 to 400 million tons.

2. *The Mongugaya Deposit* lies in the south-west of the area between the Amur Bay coast and the Manchurian frontier, roughly opposite Vladivostok. It is scattered over this area in several localized deposits corresponding roughly to the river-basins of the Mongugaya, the Amba, and the Bira, and containing a total reserve of 200–250 million tons. Of the eight seams discovered here only three ($1\frac{1}{2}$–6 feet thick) are industrially usable. The quality of the coal is similar to that of the Surazheyevka deposit, but it has the disadvantage that here, too, it is only in the narrow central part of the seam that pure coal is found. There is no mining here at present and none has yet been planned.

3. *The Rasdolnaya Deposit* begins at the station of Rasdolnaya on the Ussuri railway, and stretches towards the north-east as far as the River Suputnika. It is the smallest in area of the three Triassic coal deposits. It has been explored very little as yet, but natural outcrops in numerous places show several workable seams up to 3 feet thick. Unfortunately these show a strong tendency to run perpendicularly.

Apart from the three major coal deposits of the Upper Trias mentioned above, there are numerous places along the western foot of the Sikhota-Alin where deposits of the same age have been found, especially along the right-hand tributaries of the Ussuri. At the beginning of the Triassic period a narrow arm of the Boreal Sea penetrated from the north to the extreme south of the present Ussuri–Khanka depression, and then retreated again slowly towards the north at the end of this period (3/7). During this process the sedimentary marine deposits changed to deposits of a lagoon type and then to the continental coal-bearing Mongugay series, to which the three large coal deposits mentioned above belong. Upper Triassic deposits run in a wide strip along the west side of the Sikhota-Alin, from which it can be presumed that additional deposits of the same age will be found farther to the north. The existence of such deposits is also indicated by the findings of coal near the right-hand tributaries of the Ussuri (already mentioned above), although these finds were only made by chance during surveys for new communication routes.

The Triassic deposits described above are surpassed in importance by the coal deposits of the Upper Jurassic and Lower Cretaceous periods, which generally provide an excellent rich gas and coking coal. The most important and most valuable deposits are concentrated in two large basins, the Suchan and the Suifun.

4. *The Suchan Deposit* lies in a syncline with a north-easterly strike-line, and stretches mainly along the River Suchan up to 25 miles from its mouth. The deposit has a maximum length of 35 miles and an average width of 15 miles, extending over an area of 110 square miles. Total reserves amount to more than a billion tons, contained in three coal-bearing series with thicknesses of 1,000 feet, 500–800 feet, and 1,300–1,600 feet. These series lie under an unproductive layer consisting of sandstone and conglomerates, which reaches depths up to 5,000 feet along the axis of the syncline. The top coal-bearing series has six seams between $1\frac{1}{4}$ and 20 feet thick. Even in the individual seams the thickness varies considerably, e.g. the 'Velikan' seam (second from the top) varies between $2\frac{1}{4}$ and 20 feet. In the second series there are more than eight seams, all of which have an average thickness of more than 3 feet. In the third series four more workable seams are to be found, but their thickness and their quality decrease rapidly the deeper they lie. The Suchan deposits were discovered as early as 1888, and mining had already started at the end of the last century, mainly to provide coal for the Russian Navy. In 1933 nine shafts were working, and by now there are several additional ones, producing in recent years a total output of more than 500,000 tons. The present mines are situated in the south-east sector of the coal-bearing syncline, together with Suchan—the centre of the industry. The latter is connected by a branch-line 110 miles long with Ugolnaya on the Ussuri railway. A second rail line runs southwards from Suchan towards the coast, where it terminates at Nakhodka on the bay of the same name. The excellent quality of the Suchan coal guarantees good prospects for the future development of this area, and an increase in production would make exports possible, especially to Japan and China, which are not well provided with good coking coal.

5. *The Suifun Deposit* is, in area, the largest deposit of hard coal in the Ussuri region. It covers more than 1,200 square miles in the shape of a large rectangle between the Manchurian frontier and the Ussuri railway, with the middle course of the Suifun flowing diagonally across it. The northern boundary of the coal-field is formed by an elongated Palaeozoic granite batholith lying below hilly ground, which extends from Faddeyevka at the Manchurian frontier by way of Vladimirovka and Lipovtsy towards the east. Here, in the shape of a deep bay, the basin extends beyond the

Ussuri railway and on beyond Voroshilov, ending at the Rakovka River, a left-hand tributary of the Suifun. The River Yandsogou can be regarded as the natural southern boundary of the basin, since to the south of the river the coal-bearing strata are covered by an unbroken layer of basalt, and no further outcrops of coal can be found. The whole of this deposit within the Ussuri region forms only the eastern end of a very large coal-field lying principally in Manchuria and extending as far as Kirin and the Sungari River. On Soviet Russian territory the coal-basin is divided by the diagonal course of the Suifun into two parts—north-east and south-west. These differ considerably from each other, both in the character of the relief and in the degree of economic and cultural development. *The South-west part* had an original surface layer of basalt which has been divided up by powerful erosion into numerous table-like elevations. The coal-bearing strata are found only between these elevations, especially in the eroded valleys. The remoteness of the area and its general lack of communications have resulted in it being only very thinly populated. *The North-east part*, on the left-hand side of the river, has a totally different appearance. It is completely free of any basalt top cover and has a gently undulating relief. The fertile ground is devoted mainly to commercial cultivation, and the area is thickly populated. Moreover, the Manchurian railway runs across this region, as well as the Ussuri railway in the east, with the two railway lines meeting in Voroshilov. In addition, there are large quantities of excellent clay and limestone to be found over large areas, making conditions particularly favourable for industrial development.

Structurally the Suifun coal-basin is a wide shallow syncline running from west to east, dipping fairly steeply in the north but more gradually in the south. The basin contains two different series of the Lower Cretaceous period, of which only the lower one is coal-bearing. The exact stratification is known only for some parts where extraction is already in progress. For instance, at Konstantinovka on the Manchurian border (where coal has been extracted since 1888) there is one seam between 3 and 8 feet thick, in addition to others of no significance.

There is a corresponding seam of coal at Ilyichevka, Vladimirovka, and Lipovtsy (all of which lie along the northern rim of the basin), where its thickness is as much as 10 feet or more. Along the eastern rim of the basin at Nadyezhdinsk (2–2½ miles east of Voroshilov), coal is extracted from two seams, each 11½ feet thick, which in some places merge into one seam. The total reserves of the Suifun deposits are said to amount to 4 billion tons. However, up to the present all shafts and workings have penetrated only into the upper part of the coal-bearing stratum. This stratum corresponds geologically to the coal-bearing series of Suchan, and it is therefore assumed that at lower levels even larger deposits may exist. If this assumption should be confirmed, the total reserves may be doubled or trebled. The quality of the Suifun coal is described as particularly suitable for distillation, and its purity is specially emphasized. Konstantinovka is the foremost producer in this mining area. The total output from the Suifun deposits is of little significance as yet, and amounts to only 200,000–300,000 tons yearly.

*Tertiary brown coal* is found in numerous basins, the most important of which is of considerable breadth and stretches along the railway line to Suchan from the branch station of Ugolnaya, about 11 miles to the east. It extends over a very wide area (70 square miles) and contains several seams with a total thickness of 40 feet. By 1938 production at Artem, which is situated in the centre of this brown-coal area, was already more than three times as great as that at Suchan. West of Artem the same deposit is worked at Ugolnaya and Uglovaya. Total reserves of the deposit are stated to be 1·5 billion tons.

The second brown-coal deposit which must be mentioned is at Tavrichanka, situated on the Rechnoy peninsula in the northern part of Amur Bay, where the quality is very close to that of hard coal. At Tavrichanka, which has a 7-mile connexion by rail with the Ussuri railway, annual production is 150,000 tons. Immediately to the west of Tavrichanka comes another brown-coal deposit centred on Federovsky, with six workable seams of a total thickness of 27 feet. In addition to these deposits the brown coal of Ossinovka is of considerable importance. This deposit lies 7 miles south of the station of Ippolitovka and 85 miles from Vladivostok. It contains reserves of more than 20 million tons, and consists mainly of a single bed of brown coal 63 feet thick, a large part of which can be extracted by surface mining without any difficulty. Also worth mentioning are the brown-coal deposits in the vicinity of Posyet Bay in the extreme south-west, where mining takes place at Kraskino.

## Sakhalin

On the whole the coal deposits of Sakhalin are still very little explored, but what has been found so far seems to justify great expectations. The deposits are in three large adjoining coal-fields. The best known of these is the so-called Western coal-field, which apparently forms the principal deposit, judging by the results of research up to the present. It runs along the west coast, mainly between the coast and the western mountain range. The coal is of Tertiary age, but has been changed by tectonic processes so that in quality it closely resembles hard coal and, according to some reports, is said to be as valuable in parts as the best European hard coal. It is for this reason that the coal deposits of the Lower Miocene and the Upper Oligocene (of which these western coal-fields consist) are called hard coal in the Russian literature on the subject, and described as gas and coking coal with regard to quality. The coal-fields start about 22 miles north of Aleksandrovsk, and are divided up into ten separate fields, which in most cases lie along the edge of a syncline filled with Tertiary deposits. There are differences in the values of the individual deposits, and variations in both the number and thickness of the seams. For example, in the coal deposit of Machinskoye (the most northerly of the ten) only seven seams with an aggregate thickness of 16 feet have been established, while in the deposit of Ust-Agnevo there are eight workable seams with a total thickness of 65–80 feet. The geological reserves of the western coal-fields are said to amount to at least 2·5 billion tons. At some of the deposits—for instance at Mgachi, Starovladimirskoye, Arkosa, Makaryevskoye, Oktyaberskoye, Medvezhinskoye, and other places—partial extraction had already started before 1931, and as early as 1933 the total Soviet production from the western coal-fields reached more than 250,000 tons a year. Since the Japanese had concessions at that time for the exploitation of some of the deposits, an estimate of 500,000 tons for the present output does not seem too high. The centre of the western coal-mining area is Aleksandrovsk.

The second Sakhalin coal-field which must be mentioned is the so-called Central field, lying in the depression between the two mountain ranges, in the Tym and Poronay river-basin. The coal here is also of Tertiary origin, but nothing has been made known about the area or reserves of this coal-field since its recent discovery. A third coal-field, elongated and very much disrupted, runs almost parallel to the coast in the western mountains, where the coal-bearing strata belong to the Gilyak series of the Upper Cretaceous formation. Only a few parts of this coal-field are known or explored, but from the numerous widely scattered outcrops in the mountains it may be inferred that there are large reserves. Nine workable seams with a total thickness of 33–40 feet have been ascertained in the basin of the River Nai-Nai. In quality the coal is described as rich hard coal, but with a high ash content.

The large extent and considerable development of the island's Tertiary deposits on the one hand, and the limited amount of geological research on the other, both lead to the presumption that further coal deposits will be discovered. It has already been found, for instance, that the Western coal-field continues along the coast towards the north, although the character of the Tertiary coal changes as a result of tectonic influences into a loose kind of brown coal and lignite which is much less valuable.

### Kamchatka and the Northern Regions

Large deposits of brown coal have been discovered in recent times along the west coast of Kamchatka, stretching in a wide sweep over several hundred kilometres from the Sopochnaya River as far as Palana in the north. The coal-bearing strata probably belong to the Lower Oligocene period. The structure of this whole complex of Tertiary strata is made up of a series of folds running from north to south, disrupted by fractures running in the same direction. Productive seams between $5\frac{1}{2}$ and 9 feet thick have been found in the upper part of the coal-bearing series, containing brown coal which is strongly bituminous. Fairly large open seams have been found at Palana, where eleven seams with a total thickness of 75 feet have been established. These seams, like those of Korff Bay, change in quality from lignite in the upper layers to better-quality brown coal lower down. These deposits are not yet mined, but they may become very important in the future for coastal shipping and also for the fishing industry.

Another brown-coal deposit has been discovered on the west coast of the inner Penzhina Bay. This deposit is supposed to correspond in age and quality to the deposit on west Kamchatka.

Two coal deposits along the coast of the Bering Sea, one at Korff Bay and the other at the mouth of the Anadyr, are at present already of essential economic importance. The Korff Bay deposits date from the Lower Miocene period and consist of eleven workable seams with a total thickness of 65 feet. The average heating value amounts to only 1,560 calories, and the reserves are estimated to be 100 million tons. The mining centre for these deposits is Ugolnaya. The brown coal at the mouth of the Anadyr is divided into three deposits, the best-known being the deposit on the small River Ugolnaya, which flows into Anadyr Bay from the left. It has

M

two seams 5 and 19 feet thick, from which is extracted coal of the greatest importance for shipping. Korff Bay and the mouth of the Anadyr are therefore particularly important bases for shipping on the northern sea route.

## Total Production

Total output of coal in the Buryato-Mongolian ASSR and in the District of Chita cannot be accurately stated, and an existing estimate for 1950 of 3 million tons a year seems slightly too high. In the remaining Far Eastern territories extraction has made great progress and, on the basis of all available information, it can be taken for granted that production has reached a total of 13 million tons a year. Nevertheless, output at Korff Bay and in the Anadyr region must have been insufficient to meet the demand, because according to Press reports the whole coastal area of Okhotsk and the extreme north complained of a shortage of coal, and several hundred thousand tons had to be brought in from the southern coal-mining areas. It is not possible to say to what extent the Russians have succeeded in putting the Japanese pits back into production again. Their output before the war amounted to 2 million tons a year, of which 75 per cent was used in the country itself and only 500,000 tons exported to Japan.

### PETROLEUM

The search for petroleum on the mainland has so far been in vain, in spite of the frequent occurrence of Tertiary deposits which at first appear promising. However, these deposits have proved to be mainly continental formations, although there is still hope with regard to the lower Amur region. Petroleum fields and occurrences have been found only in the peripheral areas of the Far East: on Sakhalin and Kamchatka, for example, and farther along the northern fringe where the geological structure of the Anadyr plain and parts of the Chukchen peninsula makes the existence of petroleum possible.

## Sakhalin

The first information about petroleum discoveries on Sakhalin dates back to the year 1880, and exploratory drilling had already started in 1892. The work of F. F. Kleis, a German, must be mentioned in this context. He founded a German–Chinese company, and between 1898 and 1914 made a fundamental contribution to the opening up of the petroleum areas. A Russian and an English company were working at the same time, but their results were generally of little economic importance. In 1920 the island was occupied by the Japanese, who recognized the value of the petroleum deposits and started immediately to exploit them. By 1923 production was already 1,252 tons a year. In 1925, after the Japanese had left, the Soviet Union initiated geological research with regard to petroleum deposits on the island, and started a planned exploitation of the petroleum fields.

Natural outcrops of petroleum are very frequently found in the eastern coastal plain, in a zone running from Okha in the north to Okuni in the south. At many places they form very large accumulations of asphalt, or appear as goudron deposits in the so-called asphalt lakes. Most of the outcrops are associated tectonically with the continuation of the most eastern anticline of the East Sakhalin Mountains. On the western coastal plain natural outcrops are very rare, and are known only in the most northerly part, near Langary.

The east coast has the largest quantity of petroleum. Six deposits have been discovered here, lying in a line along the coast from Okha in the north to a point at about the same latitude as Aleksandrovsk. The oldest and best-known of these is the deposit of *Okha*, which lies on the western shore of the Bay of Urkt and extends southwards as far as the Gilyako-Bunan River. Sixteen oil-bearing horizons have been established here, of which only four are major sources of oil. The top two horizons are already partially eroded and are of no economic importance. The third is also very close to the surface and outcrops at the River Beryakan, where it has created the 'Great Asphalt Lake' with an area of 7 acres and a depth of 2–5 feet of pure asphalt. The surface is normally hard, but melts in the warmth of the summer, when it becomes too soft to walk on. The thickness of the individual horizons and the amount of oil which they contain vary from one part to another. Only the thirteenth horizon has sufficient gas-pressure to produce oil without pumping, which it will do for only limited periods at a rate of 500 tons per boring per day. At Okha natural gas is extracted as well as oil, the quantity varying between 200 and 88,000 cubic feet per boring per day. The producing wells at Okha go down as far as 2,500 feet.

About 6 miles south of Okha is *Ekhabi*, the centre of the next petroleum field which lies between the Gilyako-Bunan and Khutuska rivers. The anticlinal structure of Okha is repeated in this deposit, but in this case the anticline is divided by transverse fractures into three deposits lying on a north–south line. The northern part of the Ekhabi field was opened up in the years immediately preceding the Second World War, and was found to be a much richer and more productive field than the one at Okha, the corresponding horizons producing many times more at the former than at the latter. The increase in production from the Ekhabi field has been remarkable, rising from 62,763 tons in 1937 to 165,900 tons in 1938. It is hoped that the production here will rise still further and will be kept up for many years. In 1938 the borings were between 2,100 and 2,300 feet deep.

Another petroleum area, generally called the *Kydylanya–Chayvo Petroleum Region*, begins south of the Kydylanya River, which flows into Piltunsky Bay. From north to south the most important fields are Paromay, Piltun, Nutovo, Yuzhno Nutovo, Garomay, and Baotassin. The oil-bearing horizons are connected with the same anticline as those in the Okha and Ekhabi regions, although they often lie deeper here as a result of faulting. The tectonic structure becomes more complicated towards the south, and in the southern part two oil-bearing anticlines appear. There are several asphalt lakes near Nutovo, of which the biggest contains 11,000 tons of asphalt.

South of the mouth of the Tym begins the *Nyisko Nabilsky Petroleum Region*, which took its name from the bays along the coast. Here, too, several petroleum fields have been established, among which the Katangli field is the most important. Some trial borings produced such a quantity of petroleum that production was commenced in 1937. Four other fields are of industrial importance. The petroleum deposits here are associated with two anticlines, in which the oil-bearing horizons are the same as those at Okha and Ekhabi.

On the west coast of Sakhalin oil has been found only in the extreme north. Two petroleum fields have been found here, and exploitation was started straight away because of their favourable position in relation to communications. The first, called the *Langary* field, lies 12 miles from the mouth of the Langary River, while the second is located about 9 miles to the north, at Lake *Sladkoye*. Tectonically the two are connected with each other, and they possess the same oil-bearing horizons, which in this case, too, are located in the flanks of the anticlines. Langary is situated at a distance of hardly 60 miles from Nikolayevsk on the Amur, and it is therefore understandable that production in both fields has been strongly encouraged.

In contrast to the north, South Sakhalin (which was in Japanese hands until 1945) does not seem to have any important petroleum deposits. Although the Japanese applied the most modern methods of research, they did not succeed in finding any traces of petroleum in sufficient quantities to make exploitation worth while.

### Kamchatka and the Northern Region

Along the east coast of Kamchatka natural outcrops of petroleum have been known since 1913, yet exploration has led to the discovery of only one petroleum field. It lies north of Kronotski Bay, about 35 miles from the coast, in the valley of the small River Bogachevka, from which the petroleum field takes its name. Unfortunately the Tertiary deposits (Oligocene–Miocene) in the Bogachevka basin are covered with a layer of Quaternary lava between 1,600 and 2,000 feet thick, and the petroleum-bearing strata do not come to the surface until the end of the valley, where they have yielded only small quantities of oil and gas. Trial borings (which have been carried out using the cracks in the lava fields) have proved the existence of extensive deposits, but the thick top layers of lava and tuff make exploitation extremely difficult and in some places impossible.

On the west coast of Kamchatka, petroleum was found in 1936 in an area more than 12 miles wide and 50 miles long which runs along the coast of the Sea of Okhotsk and is centred on Tigil. The petroleum occurrences are associated with shallow anticlines, containing oil-bearing strata of Miocene age with a total thickness of 1,650–5,000 feet. The petroleum is found in sand-beds, which are interrupted by dark grey loams containing embedded brown-coal seams from 1 to 1½ feet thick in some places.

Further occurrences of petroleum are found in the basin of the Penzhina River and in the Korff Bay hinterland.

### Significance and Utilization

The importance of petroleum extraction in the Far Eastern territories of the Soviet Union cannot be over-estimated. It provides the petroleum needs of the industrial areas as far inland as Transbaikalia, as well as the needs of coastal and ocean shipping and the army in the Soviet Far East. Without the petroleum of Sakhalin, the Far Eastern territories would have been dependent on imports from overseas or on supplies from the European part of the Soviet Union, which in the latter case would have meant transport by the Siberian railway over a distance of 4,500–5,000 miles.

The production of petroleum in the Far Eastern territories is concentrated in the independent trust 'Sakhalinneft'. The Okha field is connected by a railway and a pipe-line with the petroleum port of Moskalvo on the west coast of the island; petroleum from the other fields is carried by coastal tankers. Apart from two rather small refineries which are supposed to exist at Okha and at Moskalvo, most of the petroleum is processed on the mainland in the refineries of Vladivostok, Khabarovsk, and Komsomolsk. There is also another refinery at Ulan-Ude. Khabarovsk and Komsomolsk have very recently been equipped with modern cracking installations. The productive capacity of the refineries in these two towns is estimated to be 1·2 million tons and the cracking capacity 600,000–700,000 tons. A much-needed pipe-line which had been planned for a long time is under construction, or perhaps even completed by now. This pipe-line was intended to carry the total output of Sakhalin to Komsomolsk and Khabarovsk, but part of the output will probably be transported across the dam joining Sakhalin and the mainland, which was completed in 1952. Hassmann (80) says with reference to the pipe-line that it is to lead from Okha to Mikolayevsk and then along the Amur via Komsomolsk to Khabarovsk.

The total reserves of petroleum on the traditionally Russian parts of Sakhalin are stated to be about 150 million tons (2/11/14). Total production from the island in 1938, including the Japanese concessions, amounted to 562,000 tons, while according to Fedorov (59) Russian production in the same year amounted to only about 356,000 tons. However, several investigations (59) have indicated that production from the Russian fields could easily have been increased, had it not been limited by the lack of transport. According to Hassmann (80), petroleum production in the years after the war developed as follows:

| | | | | | |
|---|---|---|---|---|---|
| 1946 | . | . | . | . | 882,000 tons |
| 1947 | . | . | . | . | 1,030,000 ,, |
| 1948 | . | . | . | . | 845,000 ,, |
| 1949 | . | . | . | . | 1,000,000 ,, |
| 1950 | . | . | . | . | 1,200,000 ,, |

One of the most recent reports on production says that the output of petroleum on Sakhalin in 1952 surpassed the 1948 production by 65 per cent. On this basis production in 1952 must have amounted to 1,396,200 tons. However, the figures given above for post-war development are thought to be too low, particularly for 1948 and subsequent years, and an estimate of 1·8–2·0 million tons for the total output in 1953 may not be too high.

## PEAT BEDS

The formation of peat is closely connected with swampy conditions, but does not necessarily occur wherever the land is swampy. This is the case to a large extent in Transbaikalia. The irregular flow of water in the rivers causes flooding which thoroughly saturates the adjoining land, with the result that the valley floors of these rivers are often characterized by bog. Nevertheless peat beds of any large extent are rarely found, and Transbaikalia possesses very few altogether. Conditions are different in the other areas. The *Atlas of Energy Sources of the USSR* gives some information about the availability of peat, but it is mainly of a general character about the locations of the beds, and it is especially stressed that the statements are not meant to be taken as exact. The information is included here because it is of additional help in giving a clearer idea of the country and its conditions.

Surveys of various areas have led to the general conclusion that boggy land accounts for roughly 140,000 square miles or 15 per cent of the total mainland area of the Far Eastern territories (excluding Sakhalin and Kamchatka). This extraordinarily high proportion is attributable in the first place to the existence of the perennial ice-floor and in the second place to the extensive tundras in the north-east. Further surveys have revealed that 10 per cent of the boggy areas consist of peat bogs containing beds of peat capable of economic utilization. Various trials in the Soviet Union indicate that the average thickness of the peat beds is 5 feet, of which only two-thirds can be worked. Even so, this means that there are very large stocks of peat in the Far Eastern territories. We shall not go into any further detail, as these are all somewhat theoretical quantities, the realization of which is still very much a question of the future. Of greater immediate importance are the existing peat beds in the areas which have already been opened up, and which are therefore accessible for economic utilization.

Extensive peat beds are known in the Amur–Ussuri region, running mainly along the river valleys. Where they are situated in areas subject to flooding they are economically of small value, because of their high moisture and ash content. Those which are found on the old river terraces, and often also on the watersheds between the tributaries, are very different and are noted for their low water and ash content and their great thickness. The peat beds which have developed in the foothills have the same characteristics. According to Soviet statements these types of peat, when absolutely dry, have a heating value of 10,000–11,000 calories/lb. Depending on morphological conditions, peat 'massifs' of considerable size have developed in some regions, including the plain of the Amur, which is particularly rich in this kind of peat bed near Khabarovsk. An extensive peat-massif lies about 50 miles below the town, between the right-hand tributaries of the Amur—the Nemptu and the Mukhen. Discussions regarding new development plans for this area always mention this peat-massif first among the sources of energy, and for this reason it is described briefly here as an example. It is divided up into five fields of the following sizes:

| Name of Field | Area (acres) | Reserves (millions of cubic feet) | Potential Capacity of Power Plants (kilowatts) |
|---|---|---|---|
| Mukhenskoye    .    .    .    . | 8,090 | 61·8 | 22,500 |
| Nelytinskoye    .    .    .    . | 1,739 | 27·5 | 10,000 |
| Industrialisatsiya .    .    .    . | 1,546 | 17·8 | 6,500 |
| Amkhalginskoye .    .    .    . | 15,000 | 180·0 | 65,000 |
| Yuskovskoye    .    .    .    . | 10,000 | 97·5 | 34,700 |
| | 36,375 | 384·6 | 138,700 |

Soviet planners have calculated that the reserves in these fields would be sufficient to supply the above power plants for twenty-five years at the rate of 5,000 working hours a year. These statements are mentioned here to indicate the economic importance of the large peat beds.

There are further important peat beds in the lower Amur region at Birobidzhan, and also in the area between the Sikhota-Alin and the Ussuri. The peat beds in the other regions have not yet been thoroughly explored and are therefore outside the scope of their development plans.

Although the large peat beds are not utilized at present, they are important for long-term planning, and the time may well come when large power plants may be erected on these peat beds as they are already in the European part of the Soviet Union.

### IRON-ORE DEPOSITS AND THEIR UTILIZATION

Iron-ore resources in Transbaikalia and the Far East are not very large relative to the proportion of the country's total area occupied by these territories. Transbaikalia constitutes 5 per cent of the total area of the USSR, but on January 1st, 1938, it possessed only 2·2 per cent (roughly 265 million tons) of the total known iron-ore reserves of the whole country. The disproportion is still bigger with regard to the Far Eastern territories, which occupy 12·5 per cent of the total area of the USSR but have only 1·6 per cent (187 million tons) of the total iron-ore reserves. Attention must be drawn, of course, to all those areas which have not yet been explored, of which there are still very many in the Far Eastern territories, and which provide many possibilities for the discovery of new iron-ore deposits. In the following paragraphs only the most important of the known deposits will be discussed.

## Transbaikalia

1. The iron-ore deposits of *Balyaginskoye* are probably the most widely known and the most developed. They form the basis of the iron works of Petrovsk-Sabaikalsky, which are situated 14 miles to the south-east and connected with the deposits by a railway. The ore occurs as magnetic iron ore in the shape of rods and nodules, composed of 45·5–47·2 per cent iron, 0·042 per cent phosphorus, and 0·90 per cent sulphur. Open-cast mining was carried on until recently, but now there are also underground workings. The ore is broken up on the spot and enriched by roasting. The reserves of the different grades of ore are stated to be as follows: A, 2,851,000 tons; B, 288,000 tons; C, 308,000 tons. The output of iron ore amounted to 113,000 tons yearly by the end of the second Five-Year Plan. Since then additional installations at the Petrovsk-Sabaikalsky ironworks have enlarged their capacity to 150,000 tons of pig iron, and the present yearly output of iron ore can be assumed to be between 300,000 and 350,000 tons. On the basis of the above figures the early exhaustion of the mines must be anticipated, and mining of other iron-ore deposits will have to be started.

2. The iron-ore deposits of *Balbagarskoye* are situated in the Kurba district, in the valley of the Kurba River, which flows from the north-east into the Uda about 45 miles above Ulan-Ude. The deposits start about 40 miles from Onokhoy, the nearest railway station. They are divided up into numerous separate deposits, and are composed of a haematite-and-quartz conglomerate. Total reserves are stated to be: A plus B, 2·4 million tons; C, 81·7 million tons. Nothing is known about their iron content, but on-the-spot enriching is considered to be necessary.

3. In the Buryato-Mongolian ASSR some deposits of iron pyrites have been found which are estimated to contain a total of

120 million tons. The largest of these, the *Mugdor Gorkhonsk* deposit, has a reserve of 96 million tons. Iron-ore deposits of secondary importance have also been found at *Myssovsk*, near the shores of Lake Baikal.

4. In eastern Transbaikalia the most important iron-ore deposits are concentrated in the area around *Nerchinsky Savod*, where the frequently mentioned *Shelesny Kryazh* ('Iron Mountains') are located. These form an important iron-ore deposit consisting of magnetite which stretches over 5 square miles and is supposed to contain total reserves (grades A–C) of 112 million tons. The ore has an iron content varying between 40 and 60 per cent, and also contains sulphur and arsenic. Close to the Argun, 25 miles from Nerchinsky Savod, are the limonite iron-ore deposits of *Beresovskoye*, containing total reserves (grades A–C) of 75 million tons. Further iron-ore deposits have also been found in this same drainage area of the Argun—for example, at Yakovlevskoye, Bystrinskoye, and Beklemizhevskoye. According to superficial estimates the total reserves of iron ore in East Transbaikalia are assumed to amount altogether to several hundred million tons. However, the remoteness of these deposits, and particularly the lack of suitable coking coal (the nearest coal-mines, which contain coal only partially suitable for coking, are at Bukachacha), seem to make the early utilization of the iron-ore deposits of East Transbaikalia rather unlikely.

## The Amur Region

1. *The Bureya Mountains* contain the largest iron-ore deposits of the Far Eastern territories. They stretch in a continuous band north-eastwards from the Amur for 60 miles, and are situated mainly within the Autonomous District of the Jews. Altogether ten deposits have been established, which can be divided into four groups. The northernmost is the Botomskoye deposit, which reaches as far as Kimkan on the Amur railway. The type of ore varies, some of it closely resembling the haematites. The iron content is highest in the north, where it averages 48 per cent, decreasing towards the Amur, where it varies between 34 and 43 per cent. Total reserves (grades A–C) are stated to be 59 million tons. An earlier statement referring to total reserves of 500 million tons (including category C2) must have been drastically amended, since according to surveys dated 1.1.38 the total reserves in the whole of the Far Eastern territories (including the District of Khabarovsk and the Coastal Region) amount to only 187 million tons.

2. *Limonite Iron-ore Deposits.* Near *Nikolayevsk* on the Amur are limonite iron-ore deposits containing 26–45 per cent iron. Reserves are stated to be 14·2 million tons of categories A and B, and 9·5 million tons of category C, making a total of 23·7 million tons.

The Nikolayevsk deposits are meant to supply the iron-works of the 'Amur Steel' combine in Komsomolsk, where a steel plant and a rolling mill are now in operation. However, since the capacity of the blast-furnaces has been planned for roughly 500,000 tons of pig iron, their supply of ore from Nikolayevsk may eventually prove inadequate, and the Bureya Mountain deposits may have to be called upon in the near future. There is no further news available about the iron-works planned near Kimkan, based on ore from the Bureya Mountains, which was to be supplied with Bureya coal from the Tyrma area. It appears therefore that this project has not yet progressed beyond the planning stage.

### Coastal Region

1. The magnetite ironstone on the coast of *Olga Bay*, on the Sea of Japan, constitutes the largest iron-ore deposit. It appears as a rule in deposits originating by contact metamorphism along the lines of contact between limestone and granite. These deposits are found in a number of separate fields, of which the following three are the most important: Byelaya Gora (1,150,000 tons), Magnitny Myss (143,000 tons), and Mramorny Myss (82,000 tons). The Byelaya Gora ores contain 50·7–56·9 per cent of iron and are made especially valuable by their manganese content of up to 2 per cent. Further deposits are found at Anna Bay. The general reserves (including category C2) of the Olga group of deposits are stated to be 29 million tons.

2. Twenty-seven miles to the east of the Suchan collieries there are the *Sudsukhete* iron-ore deposits in the valley of the Sudsukhete River. The type of ore varies considerably, ranging from magnetite ore to limonite ore of the contact-metamorphism type. The iron content of the ore varies from 34 to 61 per cent, and at some places is combined with nickel. Rough estimates place the reserves at 1,150,000 tons.

3. A further smaller and unimportant deposit is situated on the coast of the Sea of Japan at *Posyet Bay*, 30 miles from Vladivostok. It consists of magnetite sands with an iron content of 31–63 per cent, and total reserves of 1·3 million tons.

4. The *Sergiyevskoye* deposits, situated at a distance of 4½ miles from the railway station of Talovka on the Manchurian branch of

the Ussuri railway, are in just as favourable a position with regard to communications as the Posyet deposits. They consist of magnetite ore containing 34–61 per cent iron and 0·61–1·86 per cent manganese. The reserves of categories A–C amount to only about 280,000 tons.

Numerous occurrences are known in addition to the deposits mentioned above, but it is unlikely that they will be utilized in the near future. Up to 1939 iron ore was mined only at the Olga Bay and Sergiyevskoye deposits. No information is available about the present utilization of the deposits, but to bring the coastal iron ores together with the coking coals of Sakhalin seems only natural.

### NON-FERROUS METALS

There are two areas which are particularly noted for their endowment of non-ferrous metals: South-east Transbaikalia and the Coastal Region. Tin and lead, with their usual associated ores, are the most important in both areas. Transbaikalia surpasses the Coastal Region in its large variety of metals, including tin, wolfram, molybdenum, lithium, and many others, but excluding copper, which is found in only very small quantities.

## Zinc and Lead Distribution

With regard to both the reserves and the production of these two metals, Transbaikalia and the Coastal Region are of considerable importance for the Soviet Union as a whole. According to Balsak, the proportion of the total reserves and total production of the Soviet Union attributable to the District of Chita and the Coastal Region in 1937 was as follows:

|  | Zinc (per cent) | | Lead (per cent) | |
|---|---|---|---|---|
|  | Reserves | Output | Reserves | Output |
| District of Chita . . | 7·00 | — | 10·20 | — |
| Coastal Region . . . | 4·41 | 11·50 | 5·54 | 12·50 |
| Total . . . | 11·41 | 11·50 | 15·74 | 12·50 |

## Transbaikalia

The non-ferrous metals are concentrated in South-east Transbaikalia in the triangle between the Shilka and Argun rivers and the branch of the Transbaikalian railway leading to Manchuria. Zinc and lead deposits are found in this area, occurring in typical mixed ores. On average, the zinc and lead content varies between 10 and 15 per cent, often combined with 1 per cent antimony and 0·1–0·2 per cent tin. Copper appears only rarely and, if at all, only in very small quantities, but there are fairly large amounts of arsenic. There are 550 different occurrences of zinc and lead, of which only thirty-four are of economic importance. These can be grouped according to their geographical distribution into five mining districts (rayons), where old works built during the times of the Tsars have been operating.

### 1. *Rayon Alexandrovsky Savod*

This mining district comprises five deposits, of which Aka-tuyevskoye is the most important. The ore appears here in extensive lodes, containing only negligible amounts of lead (2·85 per cent) and zinc (1·88 per cent), but with an average silver content of $9\frac{1}{2}$ oz. per ton, which has justified their economic exploitation in the past. Total reserves of the district are as follows:

| Category | Ore | Zinc | Lead |
|---|---|---|---|
| A2 . . . . | 71,300 | 1,800 | 1,800 |
| B . . . . | 270,800 | 7,000 | 8,500 |
| C1 . . . . | 258,600 | 6,700 | 7,200 |
| Totals . . . | 600,700 | 15,500 | 17,500 |
| C2 . . . . | 292,500 | 8,000 | 10,500 |

### 2. *Byrkinsky Rayon*

This district, like the one we have just discussed, is also situated in the south, east of Borsya. It comprises five deposits, the most important of which is located at Savinskoye and was worked from a mine of the same name. The ore appears here as a band 2,000 feet wide and 50–65 feet thick. The lead content (4–6 per cent) and zinc content (4–7 per cent) are not very high, but exploitation is favoured by the convenient structure. Total reserves of this mining district are as follows (in thousands of tons):

| Category | Ore | Zinc | Lead |
|---|---|---|---|
| A2 . . . . | 1,600·0 | 42·2 | 27·4 |
| B . . . . | 609·9 | 28·4 | 23·0 |
| C1 . . . . | 3,530·0 | 166·8 | 73·5 |
| Totals . . . | 5,739·9 | 240·4 | 123·9 |
| C2 . . . . | 458·8 | 18·7 | 13·5 |

### 3. Rayon Gasimursky Savod

This district comprises two deposits with relatively insignificant reserves. The ore in the Tayninskoye deposit is associated with lodes usually found in dolomitic limestone. In former times these deposits supplied the Gasimursky metal-works. The total reserves in thousands of tons are:

| Category | Ore | Zinc | Lead |
|---|---|---|---|
| $C_1$ . . . . | 40·0 | 4·0 | 2·0 |
| $C_2$ . . . . | 180·0 | 17·6 | 9·2 |

### 4. Rayon Nerchinsky Savod

Twenty deposits are found in a small area here, located along the Argun both north and south of the metal-works which were famous in former times. The best-known deposits are those partly exploited by the Nerchinsk works, but the most important deposits are those of Mikhaylovskoye and Kadaniskoye. In the first of these two deposits the ore forms a series of lodes deposited between layers of limestone, while in the second the ore appears also in large pockets. Apart from zinc and lead, there is also a deposit of cinnabar ore which is worked at Nerchinsky Savod. The total reserves of this district in thousands of tons are:

| Category | Ore | Zinc | Lead |
|---|---|---|---|
| $A_2$ . . . . | 548·0 | 84·6 | 37·0 |
| B . . . . | 426·5 | 43·8 | 20·8 |
| $C_1$ . . . . | 899·1 | 60·8 | 41·1 |
| Totals . . . | 1,837·6 | 189·2 | 98·9 |
| $C_2$ . . . . | 2,655·2 | 205·0 | 134·8 |

### 5. Ustkariski Rayon

This district includes only the two deposits of Yekaterininskoye and Preobrazhenskoye, from which only oxidized ore is extracted, for use at Shilkinski Savod. The ore is all Category $C_2$, and the reserves in thousands of tons are: ore, 1,050·0; zinc, 34·5; and lead, 23·5.

After the Bolshevist revolution, work was stopped in nearly all these mines because it did not seem to be profitable. However, in recent years a large zinc–lead *kombinat*[1] has been formed at Ner-

---

[1] Author's note: A *kombinat* consists of a group of related plants and other enterprises producing one or a group of related products.

chinsky Savod, based on the supply of ore from thirteen pits which are grouped around three centres. No information is available about the nature and volume of production.

## Coastal Region

The distribution of zinc and lead in this region is limited to a narrow strip which stretches for about 90 miles along the Sea of Japan, from the mouth of the Pkhussun River in the south to the Tetyukhe River area in the north. Altogether more than fifty deposits have been established, but only fourteen are worth exploiting. The most important deposits are concentrated in three groups, of which the most northern is situated near the River Tetyukhe, the middle one between Vladimir Bay and Olga Bay, and the most southern in the Pkhussun river-basin.

The Tetyukhe group is by far the most important of these, since it contains more than 90 per cent of the total reserves of the Coastal Region. The deposits here are due to contact metamorphism between the beds of quartz-porphyry and limestone. Large pockets and nodules were formed, which appear both in the main valley of the Tetyukhe and also in its side valleys. The zinc and lead content of the deposits in the Coastal Region is higher as a rule than in Transbaikalia, and silver is often found here as well. In this latter respect it is also worth mentioning the deposits located on the Great and Little Sinancha Rivers in the Terney district, about 20 miles north of the mouth of the Tetyukhe. Although the total reserves here are not very large, these deposits are remarkable for their great value, since they contain 23·5 per cent zinc, 15·1 per cent lead, and 16 oz. of silver per ton of ore. The silver content of the Tetyukhe deposits does not usually exceed 10 oz. per ton. The total reserves of the Coastal Region in thousands of tons are:

| Category | | | | Ore | Zinc | Lead |
|----------|--|--|--|-----|------|------|
| A2 | . | . | . | 804·4 | 79·1 | 63·1 |
| B | . | . | . | 2,121·6 | 220·5 | 99·7 |
| C1 | . | . | . | 1,436·4 | 115·8 | 47·6 |
| Totals | . | . | . | 4,362·4 | 415·4 | 210·4 |
| C2 | . | . | . | 1,974·9 | 114·8 | 73·2 |

The Tetyukhe deposits were discovered by the Chinese as early as the 1840's. Then between 1911 and 1919 a business magnate from Vladivostok called Briner worked here and created (in 1915) a concentration plant, which was transferred as a concession to the British Tetyukhe Mining Corporation in 1924. In 1928/29 55,000 tons of ore were treated by flotation, yielding 14,000 tons of zinc concentrate and 6,000 tons of lead concentrate. In the first six months of 1930, 74,000 tons of ore were extracted, and 14,000 tons of concentrates were exported. Following the acquisition of this plant by the Soviet Government, two more plants were built in the vicinity of the old one (Sovietsky Rudnik Nos. 1 and 2). The amount of ore treated can be estimated as 85,600 tons in 1937, and 108,100 tons in 1938. There is no information available concerning further developments.

The metal concentrates are transported by a narrow-gauge railway 20 miles long to the docks at the mouth of the Tetyukhe, where they are loaded on to ships for further transport.

### OTHER MINERAL RESOURCES

#### Copper

In the Coastal Region copper is known to occur at eighteen places, but only two of these are worth individual mention. One is in the vicinity of Plastun Bay, and the other is found near the Yaudsukhe River, which flows into Dzhigit Bay. The samples of ore vary in copper content between 5 and 8 per cent in some places, but the average amount is 1·5 per cent, and it therefore does not seem profitable to extract it. On the Chukchen peninsula investigations have raised great hopes of finding a variety of copper ores, and up to now copper has been found at five places. All available information indicates that there is a great wealth of this metal on the peninsula, but nothing has been made known about the nature and size of the reserves.

#### Tin

Until the beginning of the second Five-Year Plan (1933) the District of Chita was the sole producer of tin in the Soviet Union, and even today this district is of decisive importance in the supplying of this valuable metal to the Soviet economy. The most important deposits are situated near the River Onon in South-east Transbaikalia, where four separate deposits extending over a large area have been discovered. The tin content of the ore varies between 0·17 and 3·78 per cent, but the average is only 0·6–1·0 per cent. The ore is extracted by the Khapcheranga and Sherlovo-gorsk mining *kombinats*, and at the Onon mines near the railway

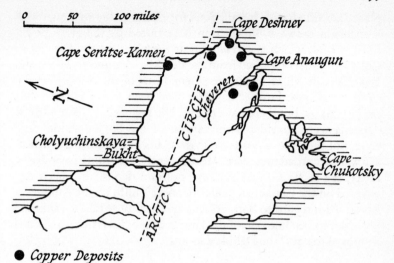

**21. COPPER DEPOSITS ON THE CHUKCHEN PENINSULA**

station of Olovyannaya. A new mine has been constructed at the
foot of the Sokhondo. The Khapcheranga *kombinat* is the foremost producer, and has the advantage of being near some coal deposits from which it draws its fuel. In the Coastal Region tin is
found in the vicinity of the Bolshaya Sinancha, which has already
been mentioned above in connexion with zinc and lead ores. Extraction started here at the end of the 1930's. Since then further deposits have been discovered near Butygychag in the Kolyma district, and these (together with the Ege-Khaya deposits in the
Yakutsk ASSR) were considered the most important in the Soviet
Union until 1942, when two further occurrences of tin were discovered. These deposits, which proved to be of major importance,
are the Mikoyan deposit in the western part of the Bureya Mountains, and (even more important) the Pyrkakay deposit on the
Arctic coast of the Chukchen peninsula. The total reserves of
these deposits are said by Smirnov to surpass those of all other
deposits of the Soviet Union (*Reports of the Academy of Science*,
Geological Publications, 1945, No. 6).

*Wolfram*

This mineral is found together with molybdenum near the
upper Dzhida River, in the Buryato-Mongolian ASSR, where
there exists a large mining *kombinat* centred on Gorodok. The

**N**

plants are fitted with installations for dressing the ore, and with suspension railways. Production is favoured by the close proximity of coal, which is extracted near the plant. In the District of Chita wolfram is supplied from the Belukha, Antonova, Gora, and Bukuka beds, all of which are situated east of the railway station of Olovyannaya. Further deposits have been found in the valley of the Chikoy, but these have not yet been opened up. The Dzhida deposits were considered the largest of the Soviet Union until 1942, but then the deposits of Tyrny-Auts in the northern Caucasus were accorded first place. More recently, according to Smirnov (1945, see section on tin), a new wolfram deposit has been discovered on the Chukchen peninsula, near Yultin on the Amguema River. With regard to both volume and quality of the ore, this bed promises to become one of the largest of the Soviet Union, and is supposed to equal the Dzhida deposit.

## Molybdenum

This mineral is extracted in the Buryato-Mongolian ASSR at Gutay on the Chikoy River. Deposits are also to be found in the Amur region and in the Coastal Region, but so far only one bed on the upper Bureya has proved to be of economic importance. A *kombinat* was established during recent years at the mouth of the Umalta (a right-hand tributary of the Bureya) for the extraction of molybdenum and antimony. Production is greatly facilitated by the Bureya coal found nearby. There are also other smaller deposits containing ore of good quality, of which the Shakhtema and Davenda deposits in Transbaikalia should be mentioned.

## Fluorspar

This is extracted from six mines in South-east Transbaikalia, the largest of which are Kalanguy, near the railway station of Khada-Bulak, and Solonechnoye, in the Argun river-basin. Smaller reserves, though of high quality, are found in the Abagay-tuy deposits. Until 1937 Transbaikalia supplied 85 per cent of the fluorspar produced in the Soviet Union. The reserves are stated to be more than 1·2 million tons.

## Bauxite

An important deposit of bauxite has been discovered south of Lake Baikal, near Okinsk, where extraction started in 1947 and where an aluminium plant was built at about the same time. Another large deposit of bauxite has been established in the East Sayan Mountains at Sagakhani-Eshen.

Among the *other mineral resources* of Transbaikalia should be mentioned the deposits of lithium, which Soviet spokesmen claim to be the largest in the world. There are also several occurrences of natural soda, and asbestos and graphite have also been reported. There is news that uranium has been found, but only in the extreme south-west of Transbaikalia.

Only the most important minerals could be mentioned in this chapter, and even then only those which represent deposits already being utilized or potentially profitable to industry. The lack of transport connexions with the general communications network is striking, especially with regard to the railways. Even those production centres whose economic importance is particularly stressed in the Soviet literature, such as those on the upper Dzhida and the Khapcheranga, and many others, too, are without any connexion by rail with the rest of the country's communication system. As a rule they are connected only by improved tracks, although these are sufficiently good to be used by heavy traffic throughout the whole year. These difficulties of communication adversely affect many mines, which in spite of their large-scale installations and good management cannot develop to their full capacity.

### GOLD

There is no doubt that the Soviet Union can justifiably claim to be one of the most important gold-producing countries of the world. From a variety of published accounts and other sources it can be deduced that the Soviet Union is doing everything in its power, regardless of cost, to enlarge its gold-mining industry. However, for a number of years, the output of gold has been kept a strict State secret. There is also absolute silence about the proportion of total production coming from individual areas, and no exact information can therefore be given in this respect. It is certain, however, that the areas dealt with in this book still belong to the most productive areas of the USSR, in spite of occasional reports in the Soviet Press about the development of new goldfields in other parts of the country. The best example may be the Kolyma district, which was opened up from Magadan on the Sea of Okhotsk and has put the Soviet Far East in the forefront again as a producer of gold.

In the following paragraphs a comprehensive survey will be

given of all the gold-producing areas which were mentioned in publications of the Soviet Union before and during the last war, and how they have been directed and cared for by the public administration during that time. It can hardly be assumed that they have been given up since then. Newer sources of information have been used for some areas.

*The Vitim Plateau* in the Buryato-Mongolian ASSR belonged for a long time to the most productive gold-producing areas of Siberia, and is still a very productive area. Gold is extracted from the alluvial deposits with the help of modern dredgers and hydraulic machines. The centre of this gold-producing area is Zipikan, which is connected with Chita by a regular air service. This indicates the importance of the area, as does the fact that extraction here is directed and controlled from five administrative offices for gold-mining.

In *East Transbaikalia* gold is extracted at numerous but more scattered places. These gold-fields were already known at the end of the eighteenth century, and have generally become unproductive since then, the only parts which are still of importance today being the remote river valleys such as the upper courses of the Tura (a tributary of the Ingoda) and the Ilya (a tributary of the Onon), the valleys of the upper Chita and Uldurga, and to an even lesser extent some tributaries of the Argun. As a substitute, extraction of gold ores has been started from mines discovered in the valleys of the Ingolda, the Shilka, and the Chikoy. Modern gold *kombinats* were founded, the most important being situated at Darassun, about 45 miles north-west from Nerchinsk, and at Baley, in the valley of the Undra, about 25 miles south of Nerchinsk. At both refineries arsenic and other metals are also extracted.

In the third place must be mentioned the gold-fields of the Amur, which cover a very large area and which must therefore be divided up into three parts: the Amur–Seya area, the Selemdzha area, and the Bureya Mountains.

*The Amur–Seya area* comprises all the gold-fields in the area drained by the tributaries of the upper Amur, including the Seya. Some parts of the area have special prominence, such as the district north of the railway station of Mogocha, where extensive deposits of alluvial gold are found in the valleys of the northern tributaries of the Amasar. The alluvial gold deposits of the neighbouring rivers, which flow northwards to the Tungir, belong to the same administrative area. A second area lies to the north of the railway station of Skovorodino, where the workings concentrate particularly on the alluvial gold of the upper Urusha, the Oldoy, and the Urkan (a tributary of the Seya), all to the north of the Amur railway. (The lower courses of the numerous tributaries of the Amur, between the railway line and the river, have become unproductive, since the washing of the auriferous gravels started here in 1867.) The number of administrative offices for gold-mining—there were four before the war—indicates that this district near Skovorodino is quite a productive one. The area of the upper Nyukzha (which flows northwards to the Olekma) also belongs to this district. In addition to the alluvial gold-workings in the above areas, there are also numerous gold-lodes in the Seya mining district. This district comprises the whole of the depression between the Stanovoy Mountains in the north and the Tukuringra Mountains in the south. The main centre of the district lies in the eastern part of the depression on the southern slopes of the Stanovoy Mountains, including the right-hand tributaries of the Seya—the rivers Sugdzharikan, Bomnak, and Tok. The centre of administration is at Mikhaylo-Semenovsky. The western part of the depression, which takes in another group of the right-hand tributaries of the Seya—the rivers Ushuley, Bryanta, Unakha, and the whole course of the Gilyuy—is just as rich in gold. Here there are two administrative centres looking after the organization of the works. In general, only auriferous gravel is worked, but occasionally there is underground mining of gold-bearing sands lying below the surface. Auriferous ores also exist, particularly in the vicinity of the Gilyuy, where a mountain especially rich in gold-veins was named the 'Golden Mountain', but there is no information available which would indicate extensive mining of these ores. For this, the communications of the area are still too little developed.

*The Selemdzha gold-mining district* is not very large, and includes mainly the auriferous gravels of the tributaries flowing into the upper Selemdzha from the Dzhagdy Mountains. These gravels, however, are rich in gold near the head-waters of the rivers, and there are rich primary deposits in the whole of their drainage basins which are exploited to a large extent, though mostly by rather primitive methods. The main administrative centre is at Karaurak, with a second one situated higher up in the valley of the Khargu River (a left-hand tributary of the Selemdzha).

*The gold deposits of the Bureya Mountains* are relatively insignificant, and are situated near the inaccessible head-waters of the

Niman, a tributary of the upper Bureya. This gold district is under one administrative office, which is located in Sofiyski.

Apart from the gold-producing areas mentioned above, all the others in the Amur–Ussuri region and the Coastal Region are of minor importance. The only others worth mentioning are those collectively administered from one centre, such as the gold area in the valley of the Sutar (in the Autonomous Republic of the Jews) with Radostny as its centre, and the three gold-fields west of the lower Amur near the rivers Amgun and Kerbi (north of Lake Orel). On Sakhalin it is only south of the upper Poronay that a similar area is to be found. Throughout all of Kamchatka and the Coastal Region the extraction of gold is negligible.

In contrast to the lessening importance of the areas mentioned above, *the Kolyma* has suddenly leapt into the centre of interest, and today its production probably surpasses that of all the other gold-producing areas of the Far East, as well as of the Soviet Union as a whole. The first news about the occurrence of gold in the upper Kolyma area takes us very far back, and there were even reports from Cherski about them. However, it was not until 1933 that the Soviet Union was induced to start exploiting these gold-fields, as a result of the first expedition of the Central Institute for Scientific Research and Geological Exploration under the guidance of Bilibin, whose report was available in 1932. Early successes and the realization of the wealth available in these areas stimulated their ruthless exploitation, involving the use of labour camps. The latter, together with the harsh climate, have made the Kolyma district into one of the most ill-famed and most dreaded areas of the Soviet Union.

In order to open up this area, the port of Magadan (now estimated to have 50,000 inhabitants) was built on Nagayevo Bay, and connected with the gold-fields by a highway which by 1940 had already reached a length of more than 400 miles and connected all the important mining centres. This highway is kept open for motor traffic all the year round. The whole area gets its supplies by sea, mainly through Magadan and partly from the north via the Kolyma. However, since these routes are blocked by ice for more than six months during the long winter, a highway has been started from the centre of the gold district to provide a permanent overland connexion between the centre of the gold district and Yakutsk on the Lena. It is also of vital importance for the development of the area that hard coal has been found on the Kolyma River near Verkhne-Kolymsk. Several *sovkhozes* have been set up to provide the local population with vegetables, milk, and fresh meat.

The main gold-fields are situated west of the Buyunda (a right-hand tributary of the Kolyma), near the rivers Srednikan and Orotukan. At first only very productive auriferous gravels were worked, but later the mining of auriferous ores was started. The latter occur in abundance, particularly in the mountains along the Srednikan, Utina, and Khatynakh rivers. The most important centres of this gold district are Srednikan, Orotukan, Khatynakh, and Seymchan. The output of gold in the Kolyma district, compared with the total production of the Soviet Union, has developed as follows (in thousands of lb.):

| | 1933 | 1934 | 1935 | 1936 | 1937 |
|---|---|---|---|---|---|
| Soviet Union . . . | 222 | 322 | 399 | 437 | 472 |
| Kolyma District . . | 0·8 | 3·2 | 21·4 | 33·0 | 54·0 |
| Per cent produced in Kolyma District . . | 0·4 | 1·0 | 5·4 | 7·3 | 11·3 |

| | 1938 | 1939 | 1940 | 1941 | |
|---|---|---|---|---|---|
| Soviet Union . . . | 510 | 560 | 600 | 640 | |
| Kolyma District . . | 80·0 | 137·0 | 137·0 | 149·0 | |
| Per cent produced in Kolyma District . . | 15·6 | 24·3 | 22·7 | 23·2 | |

Production in the Kolyma district has thus risen to nearly 25 per cent of the total output of the Soviet Union. There are definite plans for raising the gold production of the Kolyma district to 200,000 lb. Friedensburg, in his recently published article on 'Gold' (63/178), has compiled all the available estimates and calculations of total gold output in the Soviet Union. He points out quite rightly the confusion which prevails about this question and which afflicts even experts in other countries, but in spite of this I do not hesitate to publish the above table, which is based on my own sources.

Present (1952) production may be assumed to be 670,000 lb. for the country as a whole, and there is no doubt that the Kolyma district heads the list of gold-fields in the Soviet Union. The known reserves in this district would guarantee a regular output of 200,000 lb. for fifteen to twenty years.

FORESTS AND TIMBER PRODUCTION

The forests of Transbaikalia and the Soviet Far East cover areas which, in terms of European conditions, are the size of whole countries, extending over a total of about 700,000 square miles. The Far Eastern territories include 17·5 per cent of the total area of the Soviet Union, but contain 21 per cent of the total forested area. The following tables show the distribution and size of the forested areas in the Soviet Far East:

| Region | Wooded Area (millions of acres) | Percentage of the Total Area | Timber Stands (millions of acres) | Percentage of the Total Area |
|---|---|---|---|---|
| Buryato-Mongolian ASSR . | 70·9 | 84 | 46·2 | 57 |
| District of Chita        .        . | 142·2 | 80 | 106·7 | 60 |
| Far Eastern territories        . | 257·4 | 37 | 145·5 | 21 |
|  | 470·5 |  | 298·4 |  |
| USSR    .    .    . | 2,362·1 | 44 | 1,196·0 | 23 |

Although Transbaikalia contains large areas of steppe, it can nevertheless be called a country rich in forests. In the Buryato-Mongolian ASSR the forested area—or the 'wood-fund', as the Russians call it—is said to amount to 70·9 million acres (1936), and therefore covers more than 84 per cent of the total area of the Republic. However, included in this figure of 70·9 million acres are enclosed pastures and meadows amounting to 6 per cent of the total, and a further 13 per cent is accounted for by marshland, the bare tops of the *golzy*, and other areas of sparse vegetation covered by scree. This leaves only 57·6 million acres (81 per cent of the total 'forested' area) which actually carry timber, and of these only 46·2 million acres (65 per cent of the total 'forested' area) are stands of fine old timber. Forest fires and windfalls, &c., account for the large difference between the last two figures. These figures reveal how the statistics on the areas generally designated as forest-land (or 'wood-fund') should be interpreted in terms of the actual situation regarding the individual stands of timber. They also serve as an explanation of the table of wooded areas given above. The proportion of actual stands of timber is highest in the northern forested areas, particularly in the mountains and the area around Lake Baikal, while the proportion is smallest in the south, especially in the area around Kyakhta.

The proportions of different species within the actual stands of timber is as follows:

| | | |
|---|---|---|
| Conifers . . . . . | | |
| Larch . . . . . 47 | | |
| Pine . . . . . 24 | | |
| Cembra pine . . . . 16 | } 93 per cent | |
| Fir . . . . . 6 | | |
| Deciduous trees . . . . | 7 per cent | |
| Mainly birch, aspen, and poplar | | |

About 65 per cent of the forest consists of timber ready for cutting, being more than a hundred years old. All these figures can be taken only as rough estimates, since there has been no exploration nor stocktaking in large parts of the forest areas. The magnitude of the tasks which still have to be undertaken both here and in the other Far Eastern territories is shown by a statement made in 1936 by V. F. Panayev, that only 18·4 per cent of the total forested area of the Buryato-Mongolian ASSR had then been explored (12/II).

Exploitation of the timber resources is conditioned locally by the degree of accessibility, and is limited to the area around the Selenga and its tributaries. These rivers carry most of the felled timber down to Ulan-Ude and Ilinskoye for processing, and also to the shores of Lake Baikal, where wood-processing industries have sprung up at the mouths of the Barguzin and upper Angara rivers. The most important plant in this area is situated at Myssovsk, where there is a large timber *kombinat* with sixteen sawmills. The railways must also be mentioned as a means of timber transport. The more inaccessible forests still remain in their natural condition.

In the District of Chita the situation is similar, but the proportion of the total area covered by forests is slightly larger than in the Buryato-Mongolian ASSR. Exploitation of the timber resources is restricted to those areas near the railway and those near the Amur and its tributaries. The main timber-manufacturing centres are Chita, Khokhotu, and Bada.

In the remaining Far Eastern territories the percentage forest cover seems relatively small, being only 37 per cent (i.e. 21 per cent actual forests). The reason for this is the fact that the north-eastern regions, such as the Chukchen and Koryak peninsulas, the Anadyr region, the Okhotsk coastal area, and Kamchatka, belong to the areas which are completely devoid of forests or have only very little. This also explains the big difference between the general woodland area or 'wood-fund' (257·4 million acres) and the actual area covered with stands of timber (145·5 million acres). According to the *Atlas of Energy Sources of the USSR*, 1·1 per cent of the total woodland or 'wood-fund' is lost to meadows and pastures (covering 2·7 million acres), 24·7 per cent to bog and bare rock and barren slopes covered with scree (covering 63·7 million acres), 17·7 per cent to thicket and to forests damaged by fires and storms (covering 45·4 million acres), leaving only 56·5 per cent (145·5 million acres) as the area covered with standing timber.

Thus most of the actual forests in the Soviet Far East are located in the south, particularly in the Amur–Ussuri and Coastal Regions. This is of great economic importance because it is also in these areas that the woods are more readily accessible. The proportion of forest to total area in these regions is considerably higher than in the country as a whole, amounting to 66 per cent in the District of Khabarovsk, 51 per cent in the Coastal Region, and 37 per cent in the Amur District. The Lower Amur District (with a forest cover of 28 per cent) and the Seya region (with 25 per cent) have the smallest proportion of forest-land. In North Sakhalin the proportion of woodland is 66 per cent, and in South Sakhalin the proportion even reaches 85 per cent (7·2 million acres). The species of timber within the actual forests (excluding South Sakhalin) are apportioned as follows:

|  | Per cent |
|---|---|
| Larch | 36 |
| Fir | 27 |
| Cembra pine | 12 |
| Pine | 8 |
| Tanne | 1 |
| Total conifers | 84 |
| Birch | 9 |
| Oak | 4 |
| Lime | 2 |
| Ash, Aspen | 1 |
| Total deciduous trees | 16 |

The deciduous forests increase generally towards the south, so that the proportion of the valuable deciduous timbers is much higher in the Ussuri region and in the southern Coastal Region than the average shown in the above table. The timber reserves of the Far Eastern forests are also proportionately larger than in Transbaikalia, since here as much as 70–80 per cent of the timber is ready for cutting. Total timber reserves in these forests are estimated to be 220 billion cubic feet, of which 180 billion consists of coniferous wood.

The whole river-system of the Amur, with its numerous tributaries which are suitable for shipping and floating logs, facilitates exploitation of the timber and has made it possible to develop a prosperous timber industry in the Amur–Ussuri region. The industry is centred on Khabarovsk and stretches principally southwards from there along the Ussuri and its tributaries. Here are found the following local centres of the industry (reading from north to south): Khor, Dormidontovska, Bikin, Lessopilyny, Iman, Lessosavodsk, and Vladimirovka. The Vladivostok area is another major centre of the timber industry, including the local centres of Okeanskaya, Shkotovo, Lukyanovka, and Tigrovka. Recently Sovietskaya Gavan, on the coast of the Sea of Japan, has become an important centre of the timber-processing industry. Komsomolsk has acquired a large *kombinat* for the production of cellulose and paper. Aleksandrovsk on Sakhalin, and Petropavlovsk on Kamchatka, have also been provided with plants for the manufacture of timber goods.

Timber-felling has increased considerably compared with the period before the Second World War. Careful estimates indicate that in 1952 the annual rate of felling was 175 million cubic feet in the Buryato-Mongolian ASSR, 210 million cubic feet in the District of Chita, and 1,060 million cubic feet in the remaining Far Eastern territories. Taking all factors into consideration this estimate is more likely to be too low than too high.

By the acquisition of South Sakhalin the Soviet Union added greatly to its timber industry, since the Japanese had developed an excellent timber industry here before the war, which consisted of sixty-eight saw-mills and eleven large cellulose and paper factories. Karafuto exported to Japan more than 43 million cubic feet of timber a year, and many times the value of this timber in the form of cellulose and paper. The great importance of the timber-manufacturing industry for the whole economy can be seen by examining its share of the total value of production in Karafuto. Of the total production, 60 per cent was industrial, and of the latter 90 per cent was accounted for by the output of the cellulose and paper factories, and 92 per cent by the whole of the timber-manufacturing industry. All this is now at the disposal of the Soviet Union.

### ENERGY RESOURCES

The available sources of energy are first of all the common fuels such as coal, petroleum, peat, and wood, and secondly waterpower. In terms of present-day production of energy, coal plays the most important part, with petroleum claiming second place.

Peat and wood are of only modest local importance, while the
utilization of water-power has commenced only in recent years. It is
not possible to give precise information about the utilization of the
individual sources of energy, since no publications are available:
this is also true of the production of electric power, about which
only a general picture can be given in the paragraphs which follow.

Because of its numerous coal beds, which are widely scattered
over the country, Transbaikalia is well provided with regional
supplies of fuel for industry, as well as for the production of electric power. Here a beginning has been made in shifting the production of electric power into the coal district itself and transporting current to the consumer instead of coal. The steam-generating
station of Tomcha should be mentioned first in this connexion. It
is based on the coal of Lake Gussinoye and was built some years
ago near the railway line leading from Ulan-Ude to Naushki. Its
primary task is to provide power for the wolfram deposits, and it
is probable that overland cables supply the area of the upper
Dzhida. An older power-station (about 10,000 kilowatts) is based
on the coal deposits of Kholbonsk and supplies the town of Nerchinsk (more than 15 miles away) as well as the gold *kombinats* of
Darassun and Baley (35 and 30 miles away respectively). Power-
stations have also been built in the coal areas of Bukachacha (generating about 9,000 kW) and Kharamangutsk (about 3,000 kW),
but they supply only the local mining installations. All the big
towns and the larger places along the railway line have their own
power-stations, the coal for which has to be brought from some
distance away. With regard to Ulan-Ude and Chita (which have
the largest power plants), we are faced with the strange fact (due
entirely to their historical development) that these two towns possess several power-stations, with the capacity of the more recently
built generating plant attached to the factories surpassing that of
the older power-stations supplying the towns. In Ulan-Ude, for
instance, the capacity of the power-station at the locomotive factory (producing 27,000 kW) is several times more than the capacity of the plant supplying the town itself. Chita has five power-
stations, with a total capacity of about 50,000 kW, which operate
on coal from Chernovskoye; only the railway repair shops have
built their own power-station in the coal district itself. Petrovsk
Sabaikalsky also possesses its own power-station. All the power-
stations mentioned above use coal for fuel, but plants which are
more remote from the railway lines, e.g. the copper *kombinats*, are
usually dependant on mixed fuel such as local peat and wood. The

development of hydro-electric power has not yet made very much progress beyond the stage of research and planning. The first hydro-electric generating station was built at the waterfall of Kynkorsk in 1948, but this is of limited size and is meant only to supply agricultural needs. There are reports from several areas about such small hydro-electric stations being built as part of the organization of *sovkhozes* and *kolkhozes*.

In the Amur region the situation is much the same, with all the larger places having their own power-stations, since there is no network for the transmission of power. These stations (apart from Raychikhinsk) all depend on external sources of fuel, and since the supply of coal is more difficult than in Transbaikalia (the coal deposits here being fewer and more widely scattered), most of the generating stations use mixed fuels. Here, too, they are commonly found along the railway lines. In addition to coal and wood, the farther one gets towards the east, the more petroleum is used as well, and some places (e.g. Birobidzhan) even possess generating stations based solely on oil. However, the use of coal prevails on the whole, and most of the Amur region depends on supplies of brown coal from Raychikhinsk. Those places situated north of the 'Amur bend' are the most unfavourably placed, since the nearest coal areas which could serve as sources of supply are more than 400 miles away. It is therefore understandable that a more accessible new coal-field has now been opened up at Magdagacha. The power-stations of Svobodny (capacity about 5,000 kW) and Kuybyshevka (3,000 kW) are adapted for the use of mixed fuels, while the Blagoveshchensk plant (25,000 kW) uses coal. The coal district of Raychikhinsk is self-sufficient in power and also supplies power to the fairly important industrial towns of Savitaya and Bureya, although these are both only about 25 miles away from the coal centre. Khabarovsk possesses five power-stations, of which the largest (with a capacity of more than 10,000 kW) supplies the town with electricity, while the others (about 4,000 kW each) are attached to factories. The enlargement of these power-stations is expected to increase the total installed capacity of Khabarovsk to 50,000 kW. The most important plant of the Amur region (45,000 kW) has been built at Komsomolsk, and another is under construction here. Nikolayevsk on the Amur also has a fairly large power-station (24,000 kW) which supplies the industrial plants in the neighbourhood. The utilization of the water-power which exists in such abundance in the Amur region has still hardly begun. It is reported that a large hydro-electric station was built after 1947 between Khabarovsk and Komsomolsk to provide additional power for these two towns, but nothing more is known about the position or output of this generating station. More use is made of water-power when building small rural power-stations in connexion with the *kolkhozes* and *sovkhozes*, either individually or in groups. In 1950, for instance, a fairly large hydro-electric station was built in order to supply a group of four *kolkhozes*. The state of electrification in the Amur region was still regarded as unsatisfactory in 1950, but it seems that greater efforts have been made since then to remedy the situation. By 1952, ten out of thirty *kolkhozes* in the lower Amur region already had their own power-stations, and the remaining twenty had theirs under construction. Similar news is available about what has been achieved in the rest of the Amur region. The output of these agricultural power-stations is usually very small, and generally lies within the range from 26·0 to 55·6 kW which is typical for the whole of the Soviet Union. The fishing *kolkhozes* are also being provided with their own small power-stations, six of which were built on the coast of the Sea of Okhotsk in 1949, three more in 1950, and four in 1951.

Petropavlovsk, the capital of Kamchatka, has a power-station (12,000 kW) based on coal and petroleum. Here, as in other areas, the electrification of agriculture is being carried out by the use of small power-stations, and by 1952 the supply of current from new installations could be guaranteed to ten *kolkhozes*.

A large thermal power-station at Magadan supplies its port and industries, and another at Seymchan supplies the gold-mining district on the upper Kolyma.

In the Coastal Region the southern part around Vladivostok has made the greatest progress with regard to electrification, because the coal deposits are situated so close together. Even the railways are electrified here. The largest power-station (50,000 kW) lies in the brown-coal area of Artem near the railway station of Ugolnaya, and supplies the railway as well as Vladivostok. The latter has two power-stations of its own (12,000 kW and 13,000 kW), and in addition to these the docks have their own installation (about 6,000 kW). The Suchan coal-field is equipped with its own generating plant, which supplies the current for neighbouring industry as well. Since all the plants mentioned above are based on coal, it is somewhat unexpected to find that the power-stations of Voroshilov (two plants with capacities of 6,000 and 5,000 kW) and at Spassk (9,000 kW) are based on oil. All the larger places along the Ussuri railway, which are concerned mainly with the timber industry, have their own power-stations based on mixed fuels, using mainly wood-waste from the timber yards in addition to coal. There are also many rural power-stations in the Coastal Region, but although there were already more than 100 in 1950 the rural electricity supply was still considered to be inadequate.

On the coast of the Sea of Japan there are power-stations at the port of Tetyukhe (about 3,000 kW) and at Olga Bay (6,000 kW). A large new installation (25,000 kW) has been built at Sovietskaya Gavan, to supply the timber and shipping industry there.

On the island of Sakhalin there is a power-station in the petroleum area of Okha (24,000 kW) and a coal-based power-station at Aleksandrovsk (about 10,000 kW). In the formerly Japanese part of the island nearly all the coal-mining areas have their own generating plants, but these are only small ones built to satisfy the local needs.

Surveying the development of power supplies throughout the Far Eastern territories as a whole, one is struck by the scattered distribution of power-stations of all sizes. They were built whereever power was needed, and the question of supplying them with fuel was apparently given only minor consideration. The result is a heavy burden on the transport facilities, and the major step has yet to be taken of converting natural fuels (especially coal) into power at the places where they are found, and then transmitting them in the form of electrical energy. The enormous distances are a great obstacle, but the intermediate steps are not so long that they could not be covered by a network of transformers. It is also strange that so little use is made of large hydro-electric installations, although the Soviet Union is so experienced in carrying out such projects. Sufficient preliminary work has already been done in this direction, as is amply illustrated in the *Atlas of Energy Sources of the USSR* which shows the large energy resources (particularly water-power) which are as yet untouched. The potential energy from water-power in the Buryato-Mongolian ASSR is estimated to be 7 million kilowatts. The District of Chita is less well provided, but the remaining Far Eastern territories compensate for this lack with their estimated potential water-power resources of 31 million kilowatts.

## MANUFACTURING INDUSTRY

Some of the different branches of manufacturing industry have been mentioned earlier when dealing with the corresponding raw materials. This applies mainly to the timber and fishing industries, which greatly surpass all the other branches of industry in terms of the number of works and the size of the labour force employed. The Far Eastern territories are so enormously rich in fish and timber that they are not only self-sufficient in these products but are also contributing more and more surplus produce for supplying other parts of the Soviet Union. Thus timber and timber products, and fish and fish products are the main goods being sent out from the Far Eastern territories. The development of other types of industry was strongly influenced by the Second World War. Various factories which were shifted to the Far East remained there after the war, and others were newly built—or changed their production in order to replace lost production in areas hit by the war, or to guarantee the supply of their own needs. In general the provision of supplies was thus more favourable after the war than before, and has improved further since the war through the building of new plants.

The location of these industrial plants seems to have been determined again and again by the same principle—that they should be spread throughout the regions in such a way that transport over long distances can be avoided. The purpose of this planning is to equip the individual areas with industrial plants which will make them self-sufficient for their principal needs. The town of Magadan, where the harbour is open for barely six months of the year, and which provides supplies for the mining districts on the upper Kolyma, serves as an excellent example. In addition to the repair yards for ships and the repair shops for motor vehicles, factories have been built here for the manufacture of dredging machines, drilling machines, and other mining equipment. There are also factories for the manufacture of glass, pottery and electric bulbs (*Pravda*, 12.11.47) which according to various reports have even exceeded their production targets. The increase of the town's population to more than 50,000 inhabitants (1950) is therefore quite plausible.

On the other hand (in addition to the factories producing mainly for local needs), there are large industrial undertakings to be found, based largely on local raw materials and founded mainly during the second Five-Year Plan, which are responsible for the provision of very large areas and sometimes even for the whole of the Far Eastern territories. This often results in a heavy strain on the communication lines and produces friction here and there with regard to deliveries.

Great efforts have been made during recent years to develop further the *shipbuilding industry*. Vladivostok, with all its docks for merchant vessels and warships, was formerly the leading centre for this industry, but it has now been surpassed by Komsomolsk. Nothing has been reported about the capacity of the dockyards there, but it is possible to get a rough idea of their size from the estimates of the cost of construction which appeared in the second Five-Year Plan. The amount was six times as high as that fixed for the construction of the Marty Docks at Nikolayev in the Ukraine on the shores of the Black Sea. The latter were built at the same time and comprised six docks. The first sea-worthy ship left Komsomolsk in 1939. Since then the dockyards have been enlarged. The Komsomolsk shipyards are the second largest of all the industrial installations built in the Soviet Far East, being surpassed only by the 'Amur-Steel' works, which supply the steel for the ships, and for which the costs of construction were slightly higher than for the Komsomolsk shipyards. The well-known dockyards at Vladivostok and at Nakhodka in the same area have both been enlarged, as have those at Nikolayevsk at the mouth of the Amur, and at Khabarovsk. New dockyards have been built at Sovietskaya Gavan, as well as at Petropavlovsk on Kamchatka, at Aleksandrovsk on Sakhalin, and at Magadan. The two latter places are only repair yards, and no new ships are built there. Warships are built at Vladivostok, Komsomolsk, Khabarovsk, and Nikolayevsk, and it is said that the dockyards at Sovietskaya Gavan have been extended recently as a base for smaller warships. Dockyards for the building of river-craft are found in the different river-basins. Shipping on the Selenga is provided for at Ulan-Ude. In the Amur region there are three dockyards: Kokuy, near Sretensk on the Shilka (the left-hand source of the Amur); Blagoveshchensk, with the famous Lenin Dock, at the mouth of the Seya; and Khabarovsk, at the beginning of the lower Amur.

Among the *machine industries*, the manufacture of the various means of transport is the most important, and is carried out in very large workshops. There are railway repair shops for the repair and maintenance of the railways at Ulan-Ude, Chita, Khabarovsk, and Ruzhino near Vladivostok—all of them very large installations, with the railway-engine and coach-building yard at Ulan-Ude the largest of them all. It takes up a whole district of the town, which now has three times as many inhabitants (according to Soviet Russian reports) as the whole of Ulan-Ude (Verkhne Udinsk) before the First World War. Since Ulan-Ude then had

O

approximately 15,000 inhabitants, there must now be about 45,000 people connected in one way or another with this railway yard. This corresponds with the importance of these works, which are responsible not only for the railways of the Soviet Far East but also for the whole of East Siberia. The capacity of the Ulan-Ude works indicates a potential annual production of 2,000 passenger coaches and up to 12,000 goods wagons, in addition to an unknown number of railway engines. The other railway yards mentioned above are equipped for the repair and complete overhaul of railway engines and also, to a lesser extent, for the building of coaches. The manufacturing centre for motor vehicles is the 'Kaganovich Works' at Khabarovsk, which is the largest of its kind in the Far East. There are aircraft factories at both Khabarovsk and Vladivostok. In contrast to the transport manufacturing industry, the manufacture of agricultural machinery is spread over a great number of places, and only Khabarovsk has a large-scale factory.

*The Building-material Industry.* The growing industrialization of the Soviet Far East produced such a demand for modern building materials that it caused a bottleneck in this industry, and numerous small brickyards and lime-kilns had to be built, scattered over wide areas, in order to serve the local needs, at least for the time being. The building of Komsomolsk, for example, required the erection of a large mechanized brickyard in the town itself. The very large demand for cement had to be satisfied mainly from other parts of the Soviet Union until the beginning of the Second World War, since up to 1937 there were only two cement factories in the Far East. These were located at Spassk north of Vladivostok, and had a production in 1937 of 164,000 tons. However, by 1942 production in the Far East had already risen to 525,000 tons, including production from the newly-built cement-works at Komsomolsk, Khabarovsk, and Londoko in Birobidzhan. The latter were recently extended and now come second to Spassk as the largest works of the Far Eastern territories. Another cement factory has also been erected recently at Temlyuy, 61 miles west of Ulan-Ude, in order to supply Transbaikalia.

*Light Industry.* Under this heading a new textile works at Ulan-Ude is worth special mention. It was removed to this district in 1941 and has since been enlarged to such an extent that it now produces several million feet of cloth every year, and is the most important textile factory in the Far Eastern territories. There is also a large clothing and hosiery factory at Birobidzhan, and further large-scale enterprises of the clothing industry are to be found at Khabarovsk and Vladivostok. The two most important centres of the leather and fur industry are both located in Transbaikalia. One of these is situated at Chita, which has the largest fur and leather *kombinat* of the Far Eastern territories, while the other is at Chikoyski Savod (east of Kyakhta on the river of the same name), which gets some of its raw materials from the Mongolian People's Republic. Chita alone produces enough fur and leather to supply the whole of East Siberia. There are factories for the manufacture of shoes and other leather goods at various other places as well, and the total production of shoes amounts to about 3 million pairs yearly. The supply of glass and glassware, crockery, and china for a large part of the Far Eastern territories comes from only one very large plant situated at Ulan-Ude, which is the biggest glass and glassware factory of Siberia. This plant manufactures special-purpose glass in addition to ordinary window-glass and plate-glass. The factory was planned for a production capacity of 14,000 tons of sheet-glass and 6,000 tons of plate-glass, and it supplies glass for the whole of East Siberia. There is also a glass factory at Magadan (already mentioned above), and there is reported to be a small glass factory in the vicinity of Vladivostok.

Numerous small enterprises of the *food and provisions industry* are to be found in rural areas, and there are large-scale mills at Khabarovsk, Svobodny, and Blagoveshchensk. Of the latter, the first two have a capacity of 200 tons of grain daily, and the third is supposed to be bigger still. The larger farinaceous works which are so typical of Soviet Russian towns are to be met here, too, the largest being located at Khabarovsk. The meat surplus of Transbaikalia is either smoked and cured or tinned in the two meat-packing plants at Ulan-Ude and Chita. The supply of sugar depended entirely until a few years ago on the two sugar refineries at Voroshilov in the Ussuri–Khanka District, the larger of which was able to process up to 1,400 tons of sugar-beet daily. However, since 1943 the cultivation of sugar-beets has been extended to the District of Chita and the Buryato-Mongolian ASSR to provide these areas with their own sugar supply, and a sugar refinery has been built at Bichura in the Buryato-Mongolian ASSR, with another to be built at Chita. For the production of vegetable oils there are numerous small plants connected with agricultural enterprises, as well as two large oil-mills, one at Blagoveshchensk mainly for processing sunflower seeds, and the other at Voroshilov which specializes in the processing of soyabeans and perilla seeds.

# CHAPTER 4

# Communications

\*

### General Significance of the Communications System

A strong desire to get to the sea was the basic reason for the Russians' continuous march towards the Pacific. The unfavourable nature of the Sea of Okhotsk made them turn towards the south, where the outlet of the Amur raised their hopes, and towards which they persevered with tenacious patience for a century and a half until they had reached this goal too. However, they were disappointed in their hopes, since Nikolayevsk, at the mouth of the Amur, proved to be neither a suitable port nor an open door to the Pacific.

Vladivostok was found to be a much better site, with an excellent harbour, but it grew only slowly because the hinterland had not yet been developed, and because the route out of Siberia across Russian territory, via Khabarovsk, was too long. However, even before the Amur Railway was built, the distance to Vladivostok was reduced by the construction of the Chinese Eastern Railway (as the Russians call this railway across northern Manchuria), which was built straight across Manchuria under a treaty with China, thus shortening the route by about 600 miles. The railway through northern Manchuria was completed in 1904, and the Amur Railway in 1916.

The harbour of Vladivostok is ice-bound on an average of 110 days a year, and can be kept open only with some difficulty during this time by the use of ice-breakers. The Russians therefore looked still farther south and fixed their eyes on the harbour of Dalny, the 'Far Distant', whose name was later changed by the Japanese into Dairen. The Russians built a railway to Dalny, starting from Harbin, and for the protection of the harbour erected the naval station of Port Arthur. The route from Harbin to Dalny was 200 miles longer than the route to Vladivostok, but blocking by ice was almost negligible here, and a second outlet to the Pacific had been achieved.

This southern position was lost during the Russo–Japanese

War, and in 1935 the Russians were forced to sell the North Man-churian Railway as well. However, as a result of the Second World War all these positions were regained, and new treaties which re-instated the former conditions indicated the desire of the Soviet Union to follow in the old path of the Tsars. Before long there will be a railway from Ulan-Ude in Transbaikalia, via Ulan-Bator (Urga), to Peking and Tientsin. This railway, on a treaty basis like the one through Manchuria, will provide a further outlet to the Pacific, and will shorten the route to the sea by 300 miles as compared with the route to Vladivostok. Only the central portion of this rail link is still missing. (But see p. 19, f.n.)

This system of communications has resulted in the Soviet Union exerting a strong influence on the adjoining territories. When the North Manchurian Railway was being built (1897–1904), North Manchuria was very thinly populated, and Harbin was no more than a small fishing village, yet by 1938 this former village alone had a population of 470,000. With the increasing settlement of the country, Russian influence spread, carried along the railway routes which formed the nerves of the country's eco-nomic life. This influence was particularly strong in northern Man-churia, where colonization followed the construction of the rail-way, and even the Japanese were unable to eradicate it during the period from 1931 to 1945.

It is reasonable to presume that with the return of the main eco-nomic arteries to Russian hands, their influence will start to spread again, and at present no limits can be foreseen. In this re-spect, the geographical encirclement of Manchuria on the east by Ussuriland (which possesses in Vladivostok the nearest world port for northern Manchuria) is equalled in importance by its en-circlement on the west by the People's Republic of Mongolia. On this side Transbaikalia plays a very important part. Not only does it form a natural continuation of the Mongolian landscape, but the Buryato-Mongols are also the people most closely related to the Khalkha-Mongols. The former have progressed much more, both culturally and economically, under Russian and Soviet dom-inance than have their brothers on the other side of the frontier, and it is only natural, therefore, that they should exercise a strong influence beyond their borders. Buryato-Mongolian conditions within the Soviet Union have served as a model for the develop-ment of the People's Republic of Mongolia and her State organiza-tions, an obvious case of the spread of the influence of the Soviet Union far beyond her political frontiers.

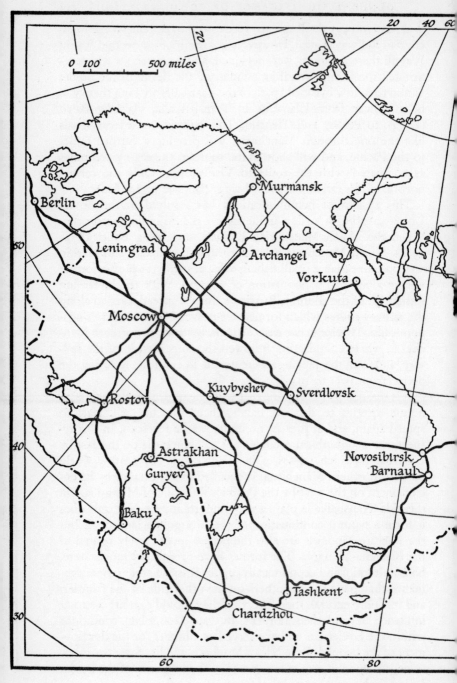

22. THE SOVIET UNIO

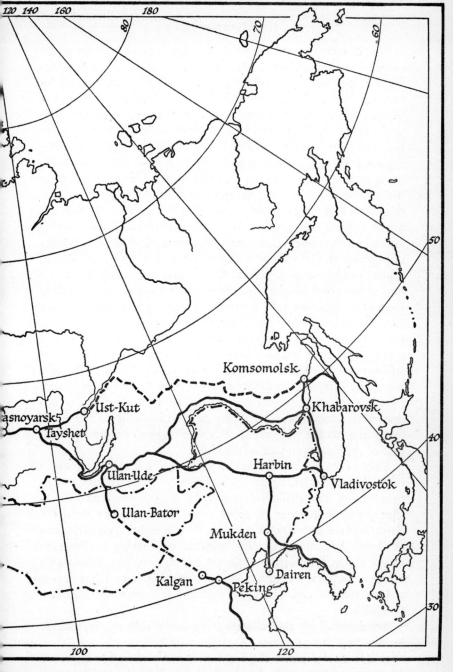

## Land Communications

Communications are of the utmost importance because of the vastness of the territories. However, the course of their development proves that the means of communication were provided not because the economies of the individual areas demanded them, but because of the State's general policy with regard to communications. When the Amur and Ussuri railways were built, they went through areas which were often unpopulated, and it was only during and following the construction of the railway lines that people came in larger numbers, so that the railways became the pacemakers for settlement and the development of the economy. Today this is still the case, and communication lines are the vital factor in gaining new regions for settlement and utilizing the rich natural resources of this widespread country. With the low density of population, methods of transport which require a great deal of capital and labour (e.g. railway lines) often prove to be uneconomic, unless considerations of a more general and long-term nature are taken into account. In any case only the organization of a great state, with all its power and enterprising drive, is able to carry out such tremendous tasks, and this applies equally to the old Russia and to the Soviet Union. These difficulties are the reason for the still very incomplete network of railways. In contrast to the railways, the means of transport whose establishment is less costly have been much better developed. This applies particularly to airlines and water routes, the present development of the latter (according to the judgement of Soviet experts) surpassing even that of the European part of the USSR.

Most of the traffic is carried by the railways. The main artery is formed by the eastern part of the Trans-Siberian Railway, which runs across Transbaikalia from Lake Baikal via Ulan-Ude to Chita, and from there (keeping some distance away from the Amur and the Ussuri) to Vladivostok. At Karymskaya, to the east of Chita, the Manchurian line branches off, leaving Soviet territory at the frontier station of Otpor, and running south-eastwards across Manchuria through Harbin. It enters Soviet territory again at Grodyekovo, and joins the Ussuri line at Voroshilov (Nikolsk-Ussuriisk).

Administratively the railways come under four offices, and are known by different names.

1. *The East Siberian Railway* has its administrative centre at Irkutsk, which controls the area between Taishet and Kizhi (the

latter lying on the administrative border between the Buryato-Mongolian ASSR and the District of Chita). A total length of 810 miles of railway lines, including the branch lines, comes under the jurisdiction of this administrative board.

2. *The Molotov Railway* has its administrative centre at Chita, and is responsible for the railways between Petrovsk (the first station east of Kizhi) and the station of Ksenyevskaya on the upper course of the Black Uryun, a total of 830 miles.

3. *The Amur Railway* has its administrative centre at Svobodny and is responsible for the railways between Ksenyevskaya and the station of Arkhara (situated to the east of Bureya), a total length of 931 miles.

4. *The Far East Railway* is centred at Khabarovsk and administers the railways between Arkhara and Vladivostok, a total length of 1,236 miles.

This purely administrative division is rather impractical from the geographic point of view, which is better served by a division into three parts as follows:

(1) *The Transbaikalian Railway* from Myssovaya, where it leaves Lake Baikal, to Kuenga, where the line emerges from the valley of the Shilka and branches off to the north to follow the course of the Amur;

(2) *The Amur Railway* from Kuenga to Khabarovsk;

(3) *The Ussuri Railway* from Khabarovsk to Vladivostok.

References to the individual railway lines in the following paragraphs will be according to this geographical division.

The main traffic from the Soviet Union to the east moves along the route through Manchuria (via Harbin) to Vladivostok, since this is approximately 600 miles shorter than the roundabout way via Khabarovsk. The Amur and Ussuri railways are therefore of secondary and more local importance, but since they run the whole way on Soviet territory, and are consequently safer, they also serve as substitute lines which can function immediately if the other railway should be rendered unusable. This was the case at the time of the Japanese rule in Manchuria from 1931 to 1945. It was only during this period that the urgent necessity for a second track through the eastern part of Transbaikalia became evident. A second track for the section from Ulan-Ude to Urusha (976 miles) was built in 1933–5, from Urusha to Khabarovsk (817 miles) in 1934–6, and from Khabarovsk to Vladivostok (476 miles) only during the years 1936–9. The North Manchurian Railway was built originally as a

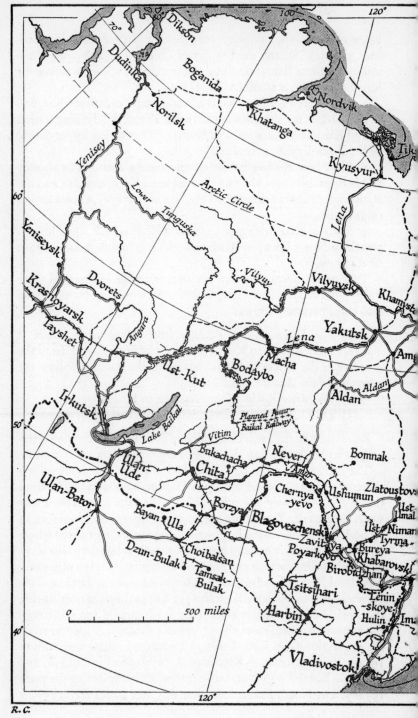

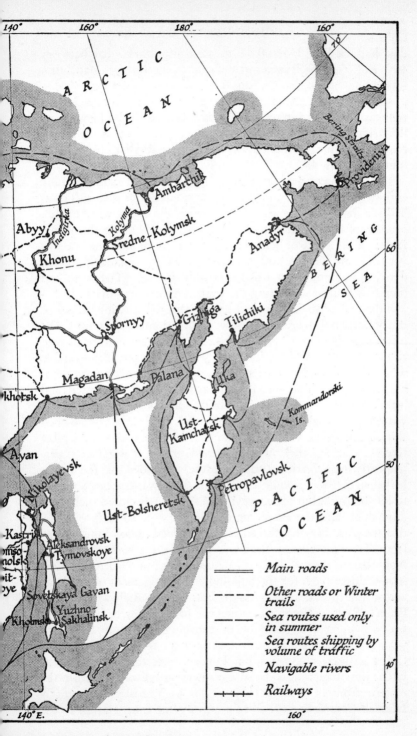

ARCTIC OCEAN

Abyy

Khonu

Ambarchik

Kolyma

Indigirka

Sredne-Kolymsk

Spornyy

Anadyr

Bering Straits

Provideniya

BERING SEA

70°

60°

Gizhiga

Tilichiki

Magadan

Palana

Ukha

khotsk

Ust-Kamchatsk

Kommandorski Is.

Ayan

Nikolayevsk

Ust-Bolsheretsk

Petropavlovsk

PACIFIC

OCEAN

50°

Kastri

Aleksandrovsk

Tymovskoye

nolsk

omso-

iit-

ye

Sovetskaya Gavan

Yuzhno-Sakhalinsk

Kholmsk

40°

140° E.

160°

| | Main roads |
| --- | --- |
| | Other roads or Winter trails |
| | Sea routes used only in summer |
| | Sea routes shipping by volume of traffic |
| | Navigable rivers |
| | Railways |

ND AND WATER COMMUNICATIONS

double-track line. It is of the greatest importance that between 1931 and 1945 the Russian gauge of the line through Manchuria was left unchanged, so that this line was at the Soviet Union's disposal immediately after the end of the war. The South Manchurian Railway (from Harbin to Dairen) was changed by the Japanese to their standard gauge during the years 1905–45, but on the North Manchurian line Russian railway engines and Russian coaches continued to be used.

The construction of the Transbaikalian Railway started in 1895 and was meant to be completed in 1898, but floods such as Transbaikalia had never experienced before did such an immense amount of damage that traffic could be started along the whole length of the route only in 1900. The construction of the line was very difficult. The ground in Transbaikalia is permanently frozen, thawing in summer to a depth of only 3–6 feet. The work had therefore to be done during the warm season, using dynamite below the melted surface, with the result that the thawing masses of the permanently frozen subsoil were turned into a quagmire. The installation of water-pipes proved to be particularly difficult, and to prevent them from freezing they had to be put into heatable wooden galleries. It had been laid down in the regulations governing construction that only Russian materials were to be used, and it therefore became necessary to bring some of them in via Vladivostok and Khabarovsk. To make this possible a State-owned shipping line was established on the Ussuri, Amur, and Shilka rivers up to Sretensk, which opened up these waterways permanently to navigation. Originally it was intended that the Transbaikalian Railway should be continued eastwards from Sretensk to Khabarovsk, but the surveying of this line disclosed such great difficulties, and the economic conditions were so unfavourable, that the plan was dropped and it was decided to build the railway from Transbaikalia to Vladivostok straight across Manchuria. Negotiations with China led to a concession in 1896 to the Russian–Chinese Bank for the building and management of a railway across Manchuria, to be called the East Chinese Railway. The East Chinese Railway Company, which was founded on the basis of this concession, received the rights of managing this railway for eighty years from the date of opening, after which the line was to go to China without compensation. Furthermore, the Company was under the obligation to build a connecting railway line from the eastern frontier of Manchuria as far as Voroshilov (formerly Nikolsk-Ussuriisk), as well as a railway line from Harbin to the

ice-free ports of South Manchuria—Dalny, and Port Arthur. The
main line from Manchuria to Grodyekovo was started under Russian direction in 1897 and finished in 1904, completion having
been delayed because about 590 out of the 839 miles of completed
line were torn up by the rebellious Chinese during the Boxer Rising in 1900. The consequence was that Manchuria was occupied
along the main rail lines by Russian troops, who remained until
1904–5, and thus made it possible for the Russo–Japanese War
to take place on Manchurian soil.

The construction of the last part of the Trans-Siberian Railway,
between Vladivostok and Khabarovsk, was also completed prior
to the construction of the Amur Railway, the southern half having
been started in 1891 and finished in 1894, while the northern half
was completed in the years from 1894 to 1899. The problem of
labour was particularly difficult to solve in these still thinly populated areas, and (as with the Transbaikalian Railway) the answer
was found in the use of military detachments and convicts, as well
as settlers who were forced to move there.

The construction of the Amur Railway was the longest delayed
of all. No accurate knowledge of the country was available, and
many factors—the wide, unpopulated regions, the unfavourable
climate, and the difficult conditions of the ground, as well as the
length of over 900 miles—all had a discouraging effect. However,
the end of the Russo–Japanese War brought the final decision.
Construction started on some sections in 1908, but it was only in
1916 that the whole of the line was open for traffic. Here, too, the
permanently frozen subsoil constituted one of the main difficulties. The railway embankment disintegrated (literally 'melted
away') after being thrown up, and cuttings were filled up again and
again as a result of solifluction. Water had to be pumped out from
layers underneath the ice-floor. Here, too, a strict order had been
issued that only Russian labour was to be employed on the building of the railway, and that no yellow-skinned workers were to be
used. This policy had excellent results, not only because many
millions of rubles were kept in the country, but mainly because it
helped to colonize the area. Many thousands of workmen who had
been hired from Russia got to know the Amur region and settled
there after the railway had been completed.

The Trans-Siberian Railway goes through all the most important places of the Far Eastern territories. The distances between
the largest of these, in railway miles, are: Irkutsk to Ulan-Ude,
304 miles; Ulan-Ude to Chita, 344 miles; Chita to Khabarovsk, 885

miles; Khabarovsk to Vladivostok, 488 miles, with connexions
from Karymskaya to Otpor (frontier station), 227 miles, and from
Karymskaya via Harbin to Vladivostok, 1,231 miles.

A number of branch-lines lead from the main line to places
which are of economic importance, as well as those which are important as centres of communications. The following branch-lines
along the Transbaikalian and Amur railways should be mentioned (reading from west to east):

|  | Miles |
|---|---|
| Ulan-Ude to Naushki (Mongolian frontier) . . | 158 |
| Petrovsk to Balyaginsk (iron ore) . . . . | 12 |
| Tolbaga to Khalyarta (coal) . . . . . | 5 |
| Ingoda to Ildigun (timber, agriculture) . . . | 32 |
| Priiskovaya to Nerchinsk (connexion to town) . . | 6 |
| Kuenga to Sretensk (Shilka port) . . . . | 34 |
| Pashennaya to Bukachacha (coal) . . . . | 45 |
| Skovorodino to Dzhalinda (Amur port) . . . | 37 |
| Ushumun to Chernyayevo (Amur port) . . . | 29 |
| Kuibyshevka to Blagoveshchensk (Amur port) . . | 67 |
| Bureya to Raychikhinsk (coal) . . . . . | 27 |
| Arkhara to Innokentyevskoye (Amur port) . . . | 22 |
| Isvestkovy to Ust Tyrma (coal) . . . . | 118 |

Of all these lines, the railway from Ulan-Ude to Naushki is of
the greatest importance. It was completed as far as the Mongolian
frontier in 1939, and since then it has been extended to Ulan-Bator
(Urga), the capital of the Mongolian People's Republic. During
recent years several additional branch-lines have been built. One
line, for instance, extends for 93 miles from Skovorodino to
Tyndinsk, into the basin of the upper Gilyuy, where it is to con-
nect up with the new Baikal–Amur Railway (BAM). Another
example is the line from Isvestkovy to Ust Tyrma (mentioned last
in the list given above), which has also been extended in recent
years via Chekunda to Ust Niman in the basin of the upper Bureya,
and by now has probably reached the wolfram–molybdenum
*kombinat* at the mouth of the Umalta. Apart from its local task of
opening up the Bureya coal-fields, this railway is also intended to
be a cross-country connexion from the Amur Railway to the
BAM, which, according to the original plan, is to cross the
Bureya at Chekunda. In addition, two other new rail lines have
been built from the Amur Railway to the River Amur, one from
Savitaya to Poyarkovo (providing a new means of transport from
the Raychikhinsk lignite deposits), and the other from Birobidzhan to Leninskoye.

A new railway line serving to open up the lower Amur basin has been completed only recently. It runs some distance away from the Amur on its left-hand side, and at the moment leads from Volochayevka only as far as Komsomolsk—the promising new industrial town. Almost opposite Komsomolsk, at Pivan on the right-hand side of the Amur, starts the timber railway which traverses the Sikhota-Alin and then leads south-east to Sovietskaya Gavan (Soviet port), on the coast of the Sea of Japan. The two rail lines are connected at Komsomolsk by a railway ferry.

Several timber railways push out into the Sikhota-Alin from the Ussuri line, the most important of these being the branch-line from Mansovka to Tury Rog, which opens up the rich agricultural areas on the west side of Lake Khanka. The coal-rich surroundings of Vladivostok are served by several railway lines, the most important of which branches off north of Vladivostok at Ugolnaya, leading to Suchan in the east, and extending two southern branches to reach the sea-coast at Dunay and Nakhodka. In recent years another line has been built branching off north of Vladivostok and running along the west coast of the Bay of Peter the Great, terminating at Kraskino on Posyet Bay.

The Baikal–Amur Railway already mentioned above (known as the BAM for short, meaning Baikal–Amur Magistrale) is the largest railway enterprise of our time. A veil of secrecy surrounds this railway, which is roughly 2,200 miles long. Construction began in 1938, and according to different but not reliable reports it is now supposed to be completed. This line starts at the station of Taishet, situated on the Siberian Railway between Kansk and Nizhne Udinsk, and crosses the Angara to reach the upper Lena, which it follows almost as far as the mouth of the Vitim. It then follows the latter as far as the mouth of the Kalar, passes over the Kalar massif towards the east, crosses the Olekma at the mouth of the Nyukzha, and goes on to the valley of the Gilyuy. It runs alongside this river to its junction with the Seya, follows the latter, southwards as it breaks through the Tukuringra Mountains, and then turns again towards the east. It crosses the Selemdzha at Norsk, at the point where the river starts to be navigable, and then crosses the Bureya at Chekunda—the centre of the largest coal deposit of the Far East which is just beginning to be opened up. The BAM ends at Komsomolsk on the Amur. Several cross-country lines are to link up with the Amur Railway, of which two have already been completed. On its way, the BAM runs across forest areas, rich in timber and still completely untouched, crosses the most important gold-fields in the northern part of the Amur region, and makes important natural resources accessible. To a large extent it traverses areas thinly populated and scarcely known, and it is said that the difficulties of constructing this railway were immense. It is a railway of the future, and it is expected that following its track a belt of settlement will slowly appear. The nuclei of these settlements are already formed by the railway workers who have been settled in permanent accommodation.

There are hardly any properly constructed highways running from west to east, since both the main railway line and the main water-courses run in this direction through the zone of settlement. The old Siberian route, which ran from west to east across all these areas before the construction of the Trans-Siberian Railway, has long since lost its importance as a cross-country route, and is nowadays used only for local purposes. The Ussuri section (between Vladivostok and Khabarovsk) is an exception, since during recent years this part has been made into a motor road with firm foundations, as a supplement to the railway. The quality of the road is indicated by a report which says that a motor car needs about eighteen hours for this journey of approximately 480 miles. Great importance has recently been attached to extending this motor road still farther, the chief continuation being from Khabarovsk to Komsomolsk. This is the most important highway of the Far East. Most of the other roads have more the character of feeder roads, but they are nevertheless of great economic importance, and as a rule are suitable for lorries.

On the steppes of Transbaikalia overland traffic can move without hindrance throughout the year, even without a road system, but in the Amur–Ussuri region road traffic is hampered by the great humidity of the soil and the monsoon rains. The sudden heavy rains wash away the gravel and very often destroy the roads. Where there are no foundations—and this is generally the case—the roads become swamped and ruined so quickly that it becomes difficult to use them any longer. In addition, the swollen rivers often wash away the light bridges, and flooding interrupts connexions between various localities, sometimes for weeks.

However, some of the country roads are of far more than local importance and have the character of highways. These are much better maintained, and are provided with a firm surface and well-built bridges, so that they are open throughout the whole year for the lorries which are the principal means of transport. Of these roads, the most important is the Kyakhta route, which up to now has had to serve as the trade route with Mongolia. A western branch of this road leads into the valley of the Dzhida to Gorodok —the centre of molybdenum extraction in western Transbaikalia. A good road also leads northwards from Chita to Romanovskoye on the upper Vitim, and another leads directly south to the tin-mines of Khapcheranga and the Sokhondo, on the upper reaches of the Onon. A major highway starts from the station of Never, east of Skovorodino, and leads across the gold districts on the upper reaches of the Gilyuy and the Aldan to Yakutsk, the capital of the Republic of the Yakuts.

During the winter the rivers form valuable natural lines of communication, since their ice-cover is strong enough to carry the heaviest vehicles. Goods which have been stored during the summer at places remote from the main lines of communication, are then brought to the centres of the country by sledge caravans or lorries. Long lines of lorries can be seen during this period even on the Amur and the Shilka.

In the northern part of the Amur region all built-up roads come to an end, and there begins the great wide north of the Far Eastern territories, where there are strange conditions with regard to communications which will be dealt with in a special section.

### Water Communications and Hydrographic Conditions

The development of water transport is very much favoured by the fact that the areas which are most important economically all belong to one river-basin—that of the mighty Amur. The western part of Transbaikalia has its own network of water routes, but here, too, the regions which are most important economically are dominated by a single river-system—that of the Selenga.

*The Amur* is the largest river of the Far Eastern territories. It derives from two sources, the Shilka and the Argun, of which the former is also formed from two sources, the Onon and the Ingoda. The Onon is the longer of these, and taking it as the original source of the Amur gives the latter the tremendous length of about 2,690 miles. Even the Amur proper, measured from Pokrovka, where the Shilka and the Argun meet, is still very long, measuring 1,769 miles to its mouth. The total area of the Amur river-basin attains the extraordinary size of 793,000 square miles. Of the whole river-system at the disposal of the Soviet Union, 4,400 miles are regarded as navigable by steamers and another 4,260 miles by rafts.

P

The upper Amur is 560 miles long, and runs from Pokrovka to Blagoveshchensk at the mouth of the Seya; the Amasar, the Oldoy, and the Seya form its left-hand tributaries. The upper part of the river is bordered by high and occasionally rocky hills, covered with coniferous woods. Below Dzhanlinda the hills recede, and on the broad river-terraces appear cultivated stretches of land and numerous settlements. The river-bed becomes wider, and flat sand islands emerge here and there in the slowly meandering river. The middle course of the Amur stretches from Blagoveshchensk to Khabarovsk—that is, from the mouth of the Seya to the mouth of the Ussuri—and is 616 miles long. Large and important tributaries flow into this stretch of the river, including the Bureya from the left and the Sungari and the Ussuri from the right. The left bank is formed chiefly by the flat Seya–Bureya plain, while on the right are the hills of Manchuria. The width of the river reaches ½ mile to 2 miles in this part, narrowing to roughly 1,600 feet where it breaks through the Bureya Mountains. The lower course of the Amur, below Khabarovsk, is 592 miles in length, and expands in width to become an extraordinarily broad lowland river with numerous channels and islands. Here, too, the left bank is mainly flat and marshy, while the right-hand side is hilly and drier. Here and there mountain ranges close on the river from both sides and force its waters into one well-defined channel. The last part of the river is hemmed in by mountains on both sides, but even so it reaches a width of from 3 to 6 miles in some places.

The Amur is navigable along its whole length, and its source-rivers are also suitable for a regular steamer service, as far up as Sretensk on the Shilka and Olochi on the Argun. The velocity of the Amur varies according to the local gradient of the river, which has to overcome three different barriers: the Great Khingan Mountains, the Bureya Mountains, and finally the Sikhota-Alin. The average velocity of the Shilka and the upper Amur is 3·4–3·7 miles per hour, while the middle Amur runs at 2·6 miles per hour, and the lower reaches at 2 miles per hour or less. The volume of water varies considerably, particularly in the upper reaches, due to the almost complete drying up of the source-rivers (especially the Shilka) during the low-water season, which in this region is during the winter. At this time the Shilka carries only 300 cubic feet per second at Sretensk, compared with the normal flow of 5,000 cubic feet per second and the high-water flow of 14,800 cubic feet per second.

The following table shows the volume of water carried by the individual sections of the Amur, and the variations in level at various places along the river.

| Place | Length of Section (miles) | Fall of Section (feet) | Volume of Water | |
|---|---|---|---|---|
| | | | Yearly Average (cu. ft./sec.) | Minimum Flow (cu. ft./sec.) |
| Pokrovka | 148 | 180 | 42,300 | 4,400 |
| Albasin | 118 | 161 | 52,900 | 5,800 |
| Chernyayevo | 132 | 128 | 60,000 | 7,100 |
| Kumara | 140 | 108 | 63,500 | 7,800 |
| Blagoveshchensk | 102 | 56 | 141,200 | 19,400 |
| Poyarkovo | 81 | 56 | 176,400 | 24,700 |
| Innokentyevskoye | 157 | 118 | 194,100 | 30,000 |
| Yek. Nikolskaya | 118 | 46 | 299,900 | 52,900 |
| Mikh. Semenovskaya | 160 | 49 | 352,900 | 63,500 |
| Khabarovsk | 224 | 54 | 391,700 | 70,600 |
| Komsomolsk | 255 | 39 | 412,900 | 74,100 |
| Bogorodskoye | 106 | 15 | 430,500 | 77,600 |
| The mouth of the river | | | | |

Corresponding to the changing volume of water, the water-level also fluctuates more in the upper sections of the river than it does in those lower down. The average yearly variation in the water-level amounts to 31·8 feet at Sretensk, 19·7 feet at Khabarovsk, and only 7·9 at Nikolayevsk. The high-water flow occurs very suddenly as the result of heavy downpours during the summer, and varies a great deal from year to year. Flooding from this vast river occurs so rapidly that it causes considerable devastation. The largest known flood was in 1872, when in a short time the water rose by 33 feet at Blagoveshchensk, and by as much as 50 feet in the narrow valley where the river breaks through the Bureya Mountains. The wild and untamed masses of water washed away numerous settlements near the river, with the people, their cattle, and all their property. The year 1928 was also remarkable for its particularly devastating high water, which again caused great distress and hardship in the town of Blagoveshchensk.

Navigation on the Amur is limited to the summer months, since at other times the river is frozen over. The average duration of the ice-free period is 155 days at Sretensk, 170 days at Blagoveshchensk, 185 days at Khabarovsk, but only 160 days at the mouth. The river is noticeably affected by the more southern location of the middle reaches, and by the inflow at Khabarovsk of the two large streams coming from the south—the Sungari and the Ussuri—which become ice-free at an earlier date and carry warmer water into the Amur. In the mountain areas thick morning fogs hinder visibility during the navigation season, forcing the ships to a slower pace, or even to a standstill. Further obstacles are the rapids and boulders in the upper reaches, and the sandbanks which make navigation dangerous along almost the whole course of the river. These sandbanks consist mainly of soft, muddy masses of sand forming elongated, constantly shifting mounds which often appear as islands at low water. The lower Amur has no obstacles and can be used at any time by ships having a draught up to 10 feet. The last 340 miles can even be navigated by ships with a draught of 20 feet or more, and if it were not for the wide flat sand barrier preventing ships from entering the mouth of the Amur, sea-going vessels could sail up the river for over 60 miles. During the course of the year the volume of water in the remaining sections of the Amur varies to the following extent: from May to August the river is navigable for ships with a draught of 5 feet as far as Blagoveshchensk, while those with a draught of about 3½ feet can proceed without obstruction as far as Sretensk, and thus into the Shilka; in September navigation up to Blagoveshchensk becomes dangerous for ships with a draught of 4 feet, and up to Sretensk for those which draw 3 feet or more. These limitations apply only to through traffic, and it is possible to have unlimited local use of larger ships where there are no shoals obstructing their course.

The Amur (which is the main waterway of the whole country) owes its great importance as a communications route to its numerous large tributaries, which are generally navigable by ships and are suitable to an even greater extent for rafts, thus providing access to large areas of the country.

*The Shilka* is the main source of the waters of the Amur, and drains an area of more than 110,000 square miles. Its source, the Ingoda, is suitable for rafts over a distance of 282 miles, and at high water under certain conditions is also navigable by shipping from Chita onwards. The Ingoda and its right-hand tributaries come from regions rich in forests, and carry mainly timber down to the Amur. The Onon is suitable for rafts for a length of 340 miles, being a steppe river in its upper reaches and running through forests lower down.

*The Argun*, with a total length of 980 miles, drains an area of 100,000 square miles. It has its source in the Great Khingan

Mountains in Manchuria, where it is called the Khailar and where it draws on the numerous right-hand tributaries which keep it from suffering any lack of water. Along its lower course the river is very closely hemmed in by mountains, which cause several large rapids; the bed is stony and often filled with large boulders, which sometimes form a chain across the river, making it difficult for ships to pass. There is regular navigation only along the last 33 miles, although the middle course along the frontier is 700–1,000 feet wide and of adequate depth, being sometimes as much as 26 feet. However, traffic by timber rafts is very lively along the whole of its course.

*The Seya*, 760 miles long and up to 1¼ miles wide, is the most important left-hand tributary of the Amur. There are very large falls in its upper reaches, and it is only below the point where the river breaks through the Tukuringra Mountains that it becomes calmer. The monsoonal air-masses, which are forced upwards by the mountains in the upper reaches of the Seya, produce a particularly heavy precipitation in this area, with a corresponding effect on the volume of water in the river. There is frequent high water as the result of downpours, and the river is continually flooding its banks. During the summer there is a much larger flow of water, and under certain conditions it is navigable by medium-sized ships for a length of 600 miles, and by smaller ones for as much as 700 miles. The terminus for the regular shipping service is Seya Pristan (port). Here the goods are stored in large warehouses during the summer, in order to be carried by sledges in the winter to the tributary, the Gilyuy. The new Baikal–Amur Railway crosses the river at Seya Pristan. The Selemdzha River, a left-hand tributary of the Seya, is 430 miles long, and is navigable as far as Norsk.

*Volume of water in the Seya*

| Place | Yearly Average (cu. ft./sec.) | Minimum Flow (cu. ft./sec.) |
|---|---|---|
| Seya Pristan   .     .     .     . | 38,800 | 780 |
| Tyda mouth  .     .     .     . | 47,600 | 1,590 |
| Selemdzha   .     .     .     . | 74,100 | 3,700 |
| Mouth of the Seya .     .     . | 82,900 | 4,400 |

*The Bureya*, the next large left-hand tributary of the Amur, is 460 miles long, and its lower reaches are up to 2,300 feet wide. The upper and lower reaches flow through mountainous areas and contain numerous obstructions, so that in spite of its great volume of water the river is navigable only in its final section. However, at high water ships can reach Chekunda, 210 miles along the river, and sometimes even get up to the mouth of the Umalta. The upper Bureya is important as a transport route for carrying provisions to the gold-fields. The Seya and the Bureya both carry large quantities of timber down to the Amur.

*Volume of water in the Bureya*

| Place | Yearly Average (cu. ft./sec.) | Minimum Flow (cu. ft./sec.) |
|---|---|---|
| Niman mouth . . . | 13,800 | 280 |
| Ushmun mouth . . . | 20,400 | 410 |
| Talakan mouth . . . | 34,600 | 670 |
| Daldakan mouth . . . | 36,200 | 690 |
| Mouth of the Bureya . . . | 37,700 | 710 |

*The Ussuri River* runs along the frontier to Manchuria. It is more than 560 miles long, including its source the Daubikhe, and its width varies between 300 and 3,300 feet. It is navigable from beginning to end and is used for regular traffic, although there are some obstructions caused by sandbanks and other shoals along its meandering course. The route along the Ussuri is the best developed by communications, since both the main railway line and the motor road run along it in the same direction.

Navigation along the Amur is mainly by small steamers with an average indicated horse-power of 500 and a net displacement of 250 tons. However, in more recent times numerous larger vessels have been specially built for these waterways and put into service. Goods transport is generally by flat wide barges, which have a displacement of up to 800 tons and are usually coupled together for towing. In the 1930's there were more than 200 river craft and tugs, a number which probably has increased in the meantime. Apart from these commercial craft there exists an Amur naval force having its base at Khabarovsk and composed of river gunboats of up to 1,000 tons gross.

*The Selenga* river system drains the main parts of western Transbaikalia. The river rises in Mongolia, where it is formed from the two rivers, Eder Gol and Mure Gol; it is 790 miles long, and its river-basin covers an area of 197,400 square miles. It enters Transbaikalia near Kyakhta, and flows on from there for another 260 miles, being 700–1,500 feet wide in this part, with an average depth of 5¼ feet, and an average velocity of 3½–5¼ miles per hour. There are no large obstacles here, apart from a barrier in front of the mouth which makes entrance into the river difficult, and in this section the Selenga can certainly be considered navigable. Occasionally during the high-water season in the summer smaller steamers can travel another 300 miles into Mongolia. The navigation season lasts for exactly six months, during which time the water-level varies on the average by about 6 feet. The regular steamship service goes as far as Ust Kyakhta, and there is traffic, when the need arises, along the tributaries, the largest of which are: the Chikoy, which is more than 460 miles long and navigable for 154 miles, the Khilok, which is 460 miles long, and the Uda, which is 250 miles long. The centre for all water traffic is Ulan-Ude, where there is a shipyard for steamers and barges. The Selenga is connected with water traffic on Lake Baikal and along the Angara as far as Irkutsk. In 1930 there were altogether eighty-seven steamers and 185 barges, compared with thirteen steamers and eighteen barges in 1912.

The importance and efficiency of the water traffic on the Amur are many times greater than that on the Selenga, as is shown by the comparisons given in the following table:

### Water-borne traffic in 1939

(in 1,000 tons)

| | Total | Petroleum | Timber | | Grain | Minerals, Building Materials | Salt |
| | | | Per Ship | Per Raft | | | |
|---|---|---|---|---|---|---|---|
| Selenga . | 200 | 7 | 7 | 91 | 45 | 14 | 1 |
| Amur . | 1,305 | 191 | 11 | 645 | 186 | 65 | 13 |

### Air Traffic

In order to overcome the great distances, air traffic was introduced at an early date throughout the whole of the Far Eastern territories. The main route, originating in Moscow, leads via Chita and Khabarovsk to Vladivostok, serving the following places along the line: Ulan-Ude, Chita, Nerchinsk, Mogocha, Skovorodino, Tygdinsk, Svobodny, Arkhara, Birobidzhan, Khabarovsk, Bikin, Iman, Voroshilov, and Vladivostok. From Ulan-Ude an important line leads to Ulan-Bator in the Mongolian

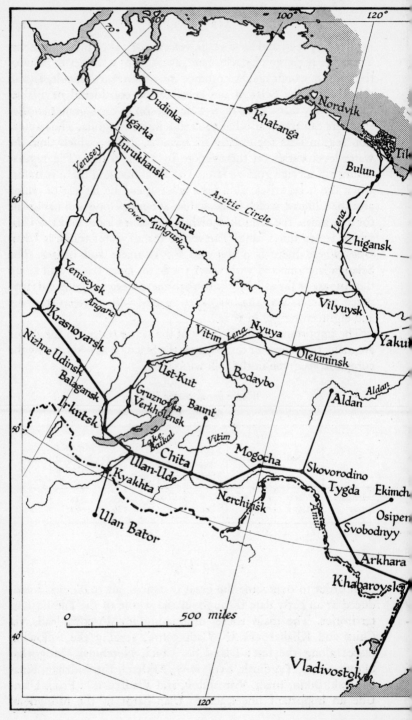

24. THE SOVIET FAR EAS

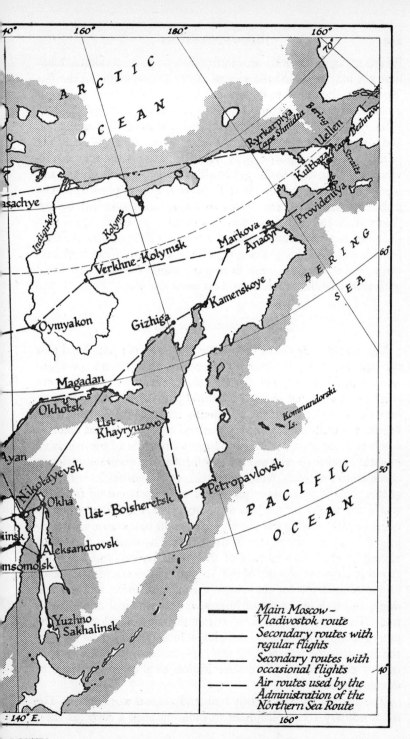

People's Republic, with an intermediate stop at Kyakhta. Khabarovsk may be called the special centre for air traffic in the Far East, since the routes to the north start from here. There is a regular air service to Komsomolsk, Okha, and Aleksandrovsk on Sakhalin, extending to Ayan, Okhotsk, Petropavlovsk on Kamchatka, and Anadyr in the extreme north-east. There are air services for purely commercial purposes as well, for example the regular service from Ulan-Ude to the gold-fields on the upper Barguzin, and from Chita to the gold-fields at Tsipikan on the upper Vitim. The polar stations along the Arctic coast are also supplied by air. Apart from the regular services there are occasional flights into the most remote areas; during the summer flying-boats are used for this purpose, flying along the rivers where they can land anywhere and at any time, while during the winter the planes are fitted with skis, enabling them to land on snow and ice.

## Communications in the North

The whole wide north is so large and so thinly populated that the building of roads seemed unnecessary, apart from a few highways, and the whole area may be called generally roadless. There is traffic to a limited extent on natural paths through the forests, on narrow tracks across the mountains, and anywhere on the open tundra across the wide plains. Overland communications come to a halt at many places during the summer because of the excessive moisture and the very swampy conditions, and communication is confined to the rivers, which offer their best possibilities for traffic at this time of year. Many places are completely cut off from the world for weeks or months at a time. The transport of goods occurs mainly during the winter, which is the best season for travelling throughout the whole of the north. The roadless areas start already in the northern part of the Amur region, and reach the Amur itself in the vicinity of the Amgun. The characteristic means of communication for these areas are sledges, using reindeer and dogs, and to a lesser extent horses, as the principal draught animals. These are the means of communication developed by the native Tungus and Palaeo-Asiatics, which must also be used by the Russians for transporting their goods, because of the absence of any other means of communication in the present stage of development.

The sledges are very lightly built and are real works of art. The extraordinary accomplishment in building such a *narte* (as these sledges are called) is that the only tool used in their construction is a knife. No nails or glue are used, simply straps and carved wooden pins. This enhances the extraordinary elasticity which is innate in the birch wood—their principal building material. The 'dog *narte*' is usually 9–10 feet long, 20 inches high, and 2 feet wide. On each side there are three or four wooden posts fixed into the runners, the latter being 4 inches wide and $1\frac{1}{4}$–$1\frac{1}{2}$ inches thick. The posts are connected across the width of the sledge by wooden ledges, on top of which are fixed thin wooden boards running lengthwise to form the floor of the *narte*. The ends of the runners are turned upwards, both at the front and the back, and are tied to a horizontal wooden bar which is bent in an oval shape and fixed at the same height as the floor-boards to form the outer frame of the *narte*. The traces are fixed to the front bow of this frame. The traveller either sits on the *narte* with his legs hanging down sideways, or lies down on the sledge and stretches his legs out towards the back. The sledge is drawn by eleven to fifteen dogs— always an uneven number—with a lead dog at the head who is intelligent and understands his master's orders. His sense of orientation is remarkable, and safety from danger in this broad wilderness often depends on this dog. The other dogs are tied in pairs to the traces, with the harness fixed round their necks, but in such a way that the pull comes on their chests. The straps are bound with fur to prevent chafing. To make it impossible for the individual dogs to break out at the side, they wear collars which are tied to the traces by light chains or leather straps. A cargo *narte* can carry a load of 2–$4\frac{1}{2}$ cwt. but the lighter *nartes* which are more often used for passenger traffic cannot as a rule carry a load heavier than $2\frac{1}{2}$ cwt., including the weight of the passengers. With a cargo the sledge can usually travel at $2\frac{1}{2}$–$3\frac{1}{2}$ miles per hour, but with only one passenger and a team of thirteen or fifteen good dogs it can achieve 6–7 and sometimes as much as 10 miles per hour. If the dogs are well looked after it is possible to travel for 300 miles with the same team without it being necessary to break for a long rest. Castrated dogs are used as a rule and rarely bitches, because the latter often become ill and have less staying power.

The sledge-driver—the *kayur*—is of the greatest importance for the accomplishment of a journey. He is not a coachman in the ordinary sense of the word. Either he stands with one leg on the runner, leaving the other dangling in the air, or he runs constantly alongside the dogs, rearranging their harness or assisting them in pulling the *narte* up a hill. He is continually talking to the dogs,

who love this, urging them on either by flattering them or by
scolding them. The *kayur* knows his dogs and they know him, and
it is very difficult for him to travel with strange dogs.

The dogs are controlled only by the words of the driver or by
the *ostol*—a birch-stick 3–5 feet long. This stick is very rarely used
for driving the dogs on; sometimes it is needed to support the
*narte*, sometimes to brake the sledge in order to prevent a collision
with a tree. In the woods, the *kayur* must always be on the look-
out for any birds or wild animals which might leap forward from
the trees and frighten his dogs, since if they should rush ahead and
cause the traveller to fall out of the sledge, he would be lost in this
vast wilderness.

The reindeer sledge of this eastern coastal area is similar in its
construction and lightness to the dog sledge, but it is higher,
wider, and shorter. It is more lightly built and very different from
the clumsy heavy sledges of the Samoyedes. For easy journeys it
is usual for only two reindeer to be used, and the traces are not
actually tied to the front arch of the sledge, but are only pulled
through, so that both animals must use the same amount of
strength to pull the sledge. A *narte* with two reindeer can carry a
load of 4–5 cwt. Larger *nartes* are used for the transport of *yourtes*
or heavy loads; these are pulled by three or four or even more
reindeer and can carry loads of 8–10 cwt. Other factors being
equal, reindeer are generally preferred to dogs for the longer journeys, since during the trip the former can forage for themselves,
while food for the latter—usually fish—has to be taken along.

Riding a sledge is very difficult when the snow is loose and
deep, since the animals sink into it and cannot pull ahead. If this
happens the *kayur* goes in front of the sledge on wide Koryak
skis, treading a path for the animals, whether dogs or reindeer.
Riding in a *narte* is not nearly as pleasant as a European imagines it
to be, thinking of a ride in a proper sledge. The journey is extremely trying when the ground is uneven or when the wind has
caused hard ridges of snow to form on the plain; the *narte* often
overturns, the *kayur* falls down in trying to help, the dogs whine
and yelp because they get caught underneath the *narte*, and the
traveller suffers from headaches and sickness because of the sway-
ing and the hard bumps.

Pack-animals come into their own in the mountainous areas,
where there are only narrow and often steep paths. It is mainly
horses that are used; reindeer are hardly ever used for this purpose,
since their backs are too weak to be suitable. Reindeer are also

seldom used for riding, except by the *Lamutes*, who place the saddle well forward, so that the rider sits directly above the animal's front legs. On Kamchatka in more recent times, as well as on the Okhotsk coast, the horse has become more and more common as a draught animal, and has started to replace the dog in several areas.

Throughout the whole of the north in the summer there is traffic into the interior from the places on the coast served by coastal steamers. Distances are thereby considerably reduced, and the use of the rivers makes it possible to penetrate into the interior. In this latter respect the Kolyma is of special importance, since this river is used regularly every summer for supplying the gold-fields. However, the navigation period lasts for only three months, and in the winter, when the coast is covered with ice and large parts of the sea have changed into an icy waste, the old means of communication—the dog and reindeer sledges—become as important as ever, even today.

## Sea Communications and Coastal Conditions

The extensive coasts of the Far Eastern territories are dependant above all on sea communications. This applies particularly to the whole of the coast north of the mouth of the Amur, along which most settlements possess a very limited (sometimes almost non-existent) economic hinterland, and are therefore totally dependant for their development, and for at least some of their supplies, on the sea routes, which represent for most of them their only communication with the outside world. The coastal settlements of the Sikhota-Alin are also without any properly built-up roads which would give easy passage across the mountains to the thickly populated Ussuri–Khanka plain, so that here, too, any exchange of goods is possible only by sea. Since these sea communications are of such decisive importance, it is understandable that the Soviet Union is making the greatest efforts to extend and develop them. Unfortunately, as mentioned above, the climatic and other natural conditions are not very favourable for shipping along the whole of the Far Eastern coast. The sea routes can be used for only a very limited period because of the ice barriers which form in the winter. In the area of the Sea of Japan, and everywhere along the Soviet Russian coast north of the 42nd parallel, the coast is covered with ice, and the rivers are frozen over comparatively early because of the cold winds coming from

the continent. The port of Vladivostok, however, can be used all
the year round. The 'Golden Horn' freezes up during the second
half of December and this ice-cover remains until the second half
of March, but the ice never becomes too thick for the ice-breakers
to cut a channel for incoming and outgoing ships, although even
here the undisturbed ice becomes as much as 3 feet thick.

Conditions are much less favourable in the Gulf of Tartary,
which separates Sakhalin from the mainland. In the southern part
the changing distribution of the ice, depending on the prevailing
winds, influences the accessibility of the coast. When there are persistent north-west winds the ice accumulates along the west coast
of Sakhalin, while with east and south-east winds it is driven towards the mainland coast. North of the 51st parallel the surface ice
becomes thicker, so that for about 125 days of the year the gulf is
covered with an uninterrupted sheet of ice, through which passage
is impossible until the beginning or middle of May. The individual
bays on which the coastal settlements are found are ice-bound
much earlier and remain so for an even longer period. For example, at Nikolayevsk the Amur is covered with solid ice for an
average of 184 days. More details about these conditions are given
in the appendix to this chapter.

The Sea of Okhotsk comes under continental influence early in
the year, because of the north-west winds which have set in
already in September and are particularly noticeable in October.
Ice starts to form along the north coast at the end of October and
in the first half of November, growing thicker until March, keeping its thickness throughout April, and starting to thaw only in
May. The break-up occurs almost simultaneously, first at the
mouths of the rivers and then along the coast. This break-up con-
tributes to the destruction of the solid coastal ice, which now becomes further broken up by the wind and the waves, and is carried
by the current towards the west and south-west. It piles up in
Udskaya Bay and in front of the Shantar Islands in the south-west
corner of the Sea of Okhotsk, where it thus remains longest, and
where it is still possible to find large ice-fields in July. Between
July 20th and 28th, 1916, the steamer *Tula* ran into extensive
fields of drift-ice between the mouth of the Amur and Ayan. The
steamer could neither get into Udskaya Bay nor to Nikolayevsk
on the Amur, and, being thus unable to reach her destination, she
had to return with her cargo to Vladivostok via the Straits of La
Pérouse. The fact that on January 20th, 1940, the merchantman
*Igarka* could reach Ayan unhindered and without the help of ice-

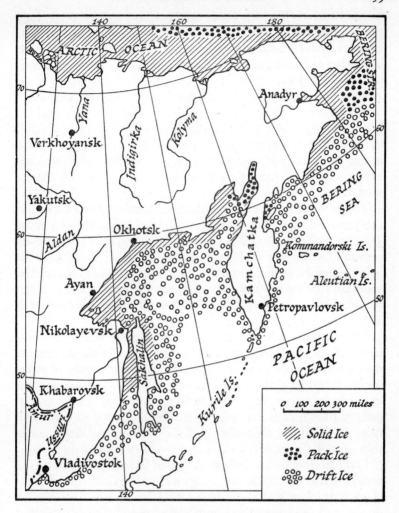

25. MAXIMUM EXTENT OF COASTAL ICE

breakers is thus all the more remarkable. It was the first successful attempt at passing through this area in winter, but on her return journey the vessel got stuck in heavy ice and had to be freed by the ice-breaker *Krassin*. In June the Sea of Okhotsk is usually free of ice except for the south-west corner and the northern bays. From the end of November the bays of the northern coast are generally covered with an uninterrupted sheet of ice, which then spreads along the coast and out into the sea. An exception to the general case is Penzhina Bay, where the tidal currents and the tidal range of up to 40 feet prevent the formation of a continuous ice-sheet. However, heavy masses of pack-ice pile up here instead, and both in this bay and in the neighbouring Gizhiga Bay the ice stays until the middle of July.

Ice conditions seem to be most favourable along the west coast of Kamchatka, because of the north-east and east winds which break up the ice near the coast and drive it out into the sea. Even in the middle of winter a narrow strip of the sea next to the coast is free from ice, although farther away from the coast there are heavy masses of ice which remain stationary throughout the winter.

The passages and coasts of the Kuriles, between Kamchatka and the Japanese island of Hokkaido, are blocked by drift-ice from January until the end of March (while west and north-west winds prevail), but otherwise these waters are passable, the conditions being easier the farther south one goes. Pack-ice from between the southern Kuriles is often driven far into the Pacific, where it can be found as late as May, and even in June after a particularly hard winter.

The east coast of Kamchatka bordering on the Pacific is not subject to any ice formations hindering the passage of ships. There is drift-ice everywhere, but it accumulates as large masses of pack-ice only on the sandbanks near the coast. Solid sheets of ice form in the bays (e.g. in Avachinskaya Bay, where Petropavlovsk, the principal town of Kamchatka, is situated), but the ice lasts only from the middle of December until the beginning of April, and is thin enough for ice-breakers to keep the bays open all the time.

In the Bering Sea the difficulties caused by ice increase along the coast towards the north. In the bays and on the coast the solid ice-sheet is thicker, and the drift-ice lasts longer and increases in density and thickness. The Count Litke Strait, between the island of Karaginski and Kamchatka, is blocked by drift-ice from the end of December until the middle of May, but it very rarely freezes solid. One such occasion was in 1918/19, when the Koryaks, together with their herds, crossed to the mainland at the beginning of March, when fodder for the reindeer became too scarce on the island. Korff Bay, where coal is extracted, is blocked by ice from the beginning of December until the end of April. Between Olyutorskaya Bay and the Gulf of Anadyr a belt of solid ice and pack-ice generally surrounds the coast from November until May. The Gulf of Anadyr proper freezes over in the second half of

November and is blocked until the beginning of May, with the drift-ice remaining even longer. In Provideniya Bay the first ice appears as early as September, but it is not until the beginning of November that a solid ice-sheet is formed, which during the course of the winter reaches a thickness of 10–13 feet.

In the open northern part of the Bering Sea light drift-ice appears about the middle of October, and according to American whalers a solid ice-sheet is formed round the St Lawrence Islands by the end of December. Drift-ice has been found here as late as the end of July. In the southern Bering Sea obstruction by ice is rare, and as a rule the area round the Kommandorski Islands does not freeze over. The northern Bering Sea is generally navigable from the end of May until the middle of October, but the Bering Straits are open as a rule only from the middle of June until the beginning of October. The sea near the Bering Straits is covered by thick pack-ice at the beginning of November, and according to some reports the sea between Cape Deshnev, the Diomede Islands, and Cape Prince of Wales is frozen to such an extent from February until March that communication is possible across the ice between the Chukchen peninsula and Alaska.

Ice conditions along the northern part of the East Siberian coast are most favourable for navigation during August and September. The greatest difficulties are generally met in the western part of the Chukchen Sea and in the eastern part of the East Siberian Sea, that is, the area along both sides of the Long Straits. The formation of ice begins at the end of September or the beginning of October, starting first in the areas near the coast where the salinity of the water is lowered by the inflowing rivers. The ice grows out into the sea from the coast, forming an uninterrupted ice-sheet by the end of November or the beginning of December. During the winter this solid ice extends roughly to the 25-metre underwater contour line (approximately 12 fathoms), the belt of ice thus varying in width according to variations in the depth of the water. Around the New Siberian Islands the ice stretches out from the mainland coast beyond these islands and out into the sea for a distance of 220 miles or more—the largest expanse of ice in the Arctic. The first signs of thawing become evident at the beginning of April, and cracks form rapidly in May and June. As the season advances the large ice-fields become smaller and smaller, until there remain only isolated floes between which there is room for ships to pass. Farther to the east the ice begins to crack later, and in the Chukchen Sea it is generally delayed until July. The deeper

Q

parts of the North Polar basin are covered with Arctic pack-ice, from 10 to 11½ feet thick towards the end of the winter, decreasing to 6½–8 feet during the summer. The action of tidal currents, surface currents, and wind creates tensions and pressures that cause the ice to pile up and form pack-ice, which reaches a thickness of 35 feet or more in some places. Since the movement of water along the continental shelf is usually directed towards the east, while the movement in deeper waters is towards the west, the ice in the boundary zones is constantly loosened and large cracks are formed which are temporarily navigable. These cracks, which are called *polynia* (ice-free spots) by the Russians, occur in a zone stretching from west to east across all the various Arctic seas. In the Chukchen Sea this zone often comes very close to the coast. The ice-free areas disappear completely when there is a north wind, and the Arctic pack-ice then becomes one with the solid ice of the continental shelf; when the wind changes, the pack-ice is driven towards the north and the *polynia* reappear.

Ice conditions vary a great deal throughout the whole of the Far Eastern coastal area between one year and another and even within the year, as is shown in the table at the end of this section. The parts of the sea which are endangered by ice could be made much more accessible by the use of ice-breakers in association with a well-built-up network of meteorological stations coupled with a news service about ice conditions, and the Soviet Government has done some most remarkable and excellent work in this respect.

*Distance by coastal steamer from Vladivostok*

|  | Miles |
|---|---|
| Sovietskaya Gavan . . . . . | 670 |
| Aleksandrovsk (Sakhalin) . . . . | 830 |
| Nikolayevsk (mouth of the Amur). . . | 980 |
| Okhotsk . . . . . . | 1,990 |
| Petropavlovsk . . . . . | 1,730 |
| Anadyr . . . . . . | 2,880 |
| Mouth of the Kolyma . . . . . | 3,220 |

The centre of all coastal communications is Vladivostok, the starting point for all the coastal routes. The heaviest traffic takes place along the southernmost part of the coast, as far north as Nikolayevsk at the mouth of the Amur, but places situated farther north are also called at several times during the year. The longest line goes as far as the mouth of the Kolyma, which is visited by one ship, or sometimes by a group of ships, once a year. The coastal traffic accounts for 864,000 tons out of the 2,021,000 tons (1935) total turnover of the port of Vladivostok. The foregoing table of distances may help to explain the situation in respect of coastal communications.

### Data about the freezing up and the breaking up of the sea along the coast

| | Final Settling of the Ice | | Final Freeing from Ice | | Average Number of Days with Ice [1] |
|---|---|---|---|---|---|
| | Earliest | Latest | Earliest | Latest | |
| **1. Sea of Japan and Gulf of Tartary:** | | | | | |
| Bay of Peter the Great at Cape Gamor . . | 19. 1 | 18. 2 | 3. 3 | 29. 3 | 72 |
| Bay of Peter the Great at the Askold Island . | 19. 12 | 3. 2 | 26. 2 | 24. 3 | 59 |
| Golden Horn . . | 10. 12 | 30. 12 | 15. 3 | 24. 3 | 90 |
| Amur Bay . . . | 18. 11 | 30. 12 | 11. 4 | 28. 4 | 130 |
| Ussuri Bay . . . | 27. 12 | 15. 1 | 14. 3 | 30. 4 | 85 |
| Sea along Cape Povorotny | 1. 2 | 4. 2 | 26. 2 | 14. 3 | — |
| Olga Bay . . . | 17. 12 | 4. 1 | 27. 3 | 12. 4 | 100 |
| De Castri Bay . . | 16. 11 | 15. 12 | 25. 4 | 21. 5 | 152 |
| Gulf along Cape Pronge . | 24. 10 | 22. 11 | 30. 4 | 29. 5 | 185 |
| Amur at Nikolayevsk . | 30. 10 | 27. 11 | 10. 5 | 25. 5 | 184 |
| **2. Sea of Okhotsk:** | | | | | |
| St Nicholas Bay . . | 5. 11 | 17. 12 | 27. 5 | 25. 7 | 190 |
| Shantar Islands . . | 10. 11 | 31. 12 | 25. 5 | 20. 7 | 174 |
| Udskaya Bay . . . | 20. 11 | 18. 12 | 27. 4 | 10. 7 | 178 |
| Sea at Ayan . . . | 25. 11 | 22. 1 | 20. 5 | 26. 2 | 164 |
| Sea at Okhotsk . . | 27. 11 | 26. 1 | 19. 3 | 18. 5 | 117 |
| Yamskaya Bay . . | 12. 11 | 18. 12 | 21. 5 | 28. 6 | 185 |
| Gizhiga Bay . . . | 27. 11 | 30. 12 | 25. 3 | 2. 6 | 136 |
| Penzhina Bay . . | 9. 11 | 12. 12 | 5. 5 | 2. 7 | 188 |
| **3. Bering Sea:** | | | | | |
| Avachinskaya Bay . . | 20. 11 | 7. 1 | 10. 3 | 9. 5 | 115 |
| Side Bay of Avachinskaya | 19. 11 | 16. 12 | 11. 5 | 5. 6 | 170 |
| Ukunskaya Bay . . | 14. 11 | 8. 1 | 15. 3 | 22. 6 | 128 |
| Korff Bay . . . | 15. 11 | 30. 12 | 18. 4 | 16. 6 | 160 |
| Olyutorski Bay . . | 25. 11 | 30. 12 | 10. 4 | 10. 6 | 149 |
| Deshnev Bay . . | 8. 11 | 25. 12 | 29. 4 | 15. 6 | 170 |
| Anadyr Gulf . . . | 12. 11 | 5. 12 | 29. 4 | 9. 7 | 190 |
| Holy Cross Bay . . | 30. 10 | 18. 12 | 25. 4 | 18. 7 | 195 |
| Provideniya Bay and Emma Harbour . . | 24. 10 | 26. 11 | 2. 6 | 16. 7 | 220 |
| Cape Chaplin . . | 27. 10 | 8. 11 | 20. 6 | 15. 7 | 240 |
| Sea south of Markovskaya Bay . . . . | 25. 10 | 28. 11 | 12. 6 | 27. 7 | 230 |

[1] The average number of the days with ice includes pack-ice and settled ice.

# Part II

# DETAILED STUDIES

1 Baïkalian Dauria
2 Nerchinsk Dauria
3 Vitim Plateau & northern Forest Regions
4 Olekma Mountain Region & the Olekminsk Stanovik
5 Oldoy-Seya Mountain Region
6 Seya-Bureya Plain
7 Bureya Mountains
8 Amur Plain
9 Sikhota Alin
10 Ussuri-Khanka depression
11 Sakhalin
12 Amgun and Ud Region
13 Okhotsk Coastal Region
14 Regions of the extreme North-East
15 Kamchatka Peninsula

26. THE REGIONS

# The Individual Regions

*

## THE GENERAL PICTURE

The preceding general survey has shown that the geographical conditions themselves lead to a large-scale division of the whole area into separate natural regions. In the sections which follow, these regions have been subdivided into smaller units, mainly based on the relief. The size of these units makes it obvious that each contains many local differences in addition to the characteristics common to the unit as a whole, which would make it easy to introduce a further subdivision. However, for reasons of clarity this possibility was deliberately rejected.

It has not been possible to deal with each area in the same detail in this work, because of the varying amount of knowledge available about the different natural regions and their subdivisions. It can be noted again and again while studying the Russian literature that, apart from the well-known areas, there are still vast regions in need of accurate survey. Compared with the individual research which was prevalent during the time of the Tsars, Soviet Russian science has introduced a more systematic investigation, but the size of the country is so great that there is much still to be done.

Transbaikalia is divided by the Yablonovy range into two natural regions, which according to Obruchev are called the Western or Baikal Dauria and the Eastern or Nerchinsk Dauria. Towards the north the individual ranges merge to form an area of extensive plateaux, of which the Vitim plateau is a part. The latter can be considered as a separate unit, together with the adjoining forested mountain areas, which have the same harsh climate. The mountain area between the Vitim and the Olekma rivers forms, together with the Olekminsk Stanovik, the area of transition to the Amur region proper, where the Seya and Bureya highlands enclose the economically important Seya–Bureya plain. The plain of the lower Amur merges with the Amgun river-basin. The Sikhota-Alin and the Ussuri–Khanka depression form separate natural units within the Ussuri region. The delineation of the remaining regions follows naturally: the island of Sakhalin, the basin of the Amgun and the Ud, the coastal area of Okhotsk, the natural regions of the extreme north-east, and the peninsula of Kamchatka. (See map.) A short section on Lake Baikal is included here before beginning the detailed examination of the individual regions.

## LAKE BAIKAL

Lake Baikal adjoins Transbaikalia in the west, and is one of the most interesting lakes in the world. It has an area of roughly 12,200 square miles, extending over a length of 394 miles and a maximum width of 49 miles, with a volume of water of approximately 9,600 cubic miles. The lake narrows between the mouth of the Buguldayka and the delta of the Selenga to a minimum of 15 miles. From an average water-level of 2,375 feet above sea level, the bottom of the lake drops by 5,745 feet to reach a depth of 4,250 feet below sea level, making Lake Baikal the deepest lake in the world. Close to the water's edge the mountains rise to a height of more than 6,600 feet, so that there is a total difference in height of more than 12,300 feet in a very limited area. These figures of the different heights indicate the tectonic structure of the lake-bed, which apparently was formed by the collapse of four adjacent troughs and their slight shifting so that they merged into one another. The most south-westerly of these four troughs has a Sayan strike-line, while the others have Baikalian strike-lines, which accounts for the long curved shape of the lake-basin. The formation of Lake Baikal is connected with the subsidence of the Transbaikalian troughs, and must therefore have taken place in the Middle Tertiary era. It received its present form and appearance in the time between the Pliocene period and the beginning of the Quaternary era.

The temperature of the water is unusually low and in the open lake never rises above 48–50° F., even in August, when the temperature is at its highest. Near the lake-shore the surface water is slightly warmer, but it is only in a few bays in specially favoured positions that the temperature of the water rises as high as 60°, or at the most to 68°. Below a depth of 140 fathoms the water temperature remains constant. Measurements show it to be 38·3° at 140 fathoms, 38·1° at 495 fathoms, and 37·4° at a depth of 880 fathoms. The main reason for the low temperature of the surface water is the frequent very strong winds which continually toss up the water. On the other hand, these winds also prevent Lake Baikal from freezing over before the beginning of January. On the average, taken over many years, the lake is covered for 116 days each year by a firm sheet of ice which may reach a thickness of up to 4 feet.

The fauna of the lake is very remarkable, having a unique collection of endemic forms; of the 1,000 species discovered up to now, about 75 per cent are peculiar to the lake. Here in the middle of the continent a type of seal (*Phoca Siberica*, called the *'nerpa'* by the Russians) has been found which belongs to the same family as similar types found in the northern Arctic (*Ph. Hispida*) and in the Caspian Sea (*Ph. Caspia*). The small viviparous spider-fish (*Callionymus Baicalensis*), whose family (Comephoridae) is found only in Lake Baikal, should also be mentioned. There is an abundance of molluscs, of which eighty-five different varieties have been established; of these, two endemic families—the Brachipods Benedictiidae and Baicaliidae—are typical examples of fresh-water fish. The great age of the Baikalian fauna, which was forced to develop in isolation, is proved by the presence of the mollusc Baicalia in the fresh-water deposits of the Lower Cretaceous period in Transbaikalia.

Lake Baikal offers very good possibilities for water traffic, because of its depth and its favourable natural landing-places. A regular steamer service connects all the larger settlements and also handles the transport of goods, the latter consisting mainly of timber (40 per cent), with stones and building materials in second place (30 per cent), and then fish, salt, flour, &c. Timber is usually floated down the rivers to the lake, and then towed by steamer to the mouth of the Angara, where it is transferred to the railway at the station of Baikal, which is equipped with mechanical loading facilities. Minor quantities of timber are floated right down to Irkutsk. On the Transbaikalian side the timber comes mainly from the river-basins of the Barguzin and the upper Angara.

Fishing, too, is of economic importance, and takes place in the open lake as well as in the bays. The catches consist principally (58 per cent) of a kind of salmon called the Omul (*Coregonus omul* Pall. or *C. migratorius*), and kindred fish. Different kinds of carp take second place (22 per cent), and are caught mainly in the coastal lagoons and neighbouring lakes. The seal already mentioned above is also of some importance, as shown by the catch of 1,380 animals in 1948. Fishing is organized both by the State and by the fishing *kolkhozes*, the former being responsible for 32 per cent of the catch in 1949, and the latter for 68 per cent. On the Transbaikalian side within the area of the Buryato-Mongolian ASSR,

65,000 lb. of fish are caught yearly, and as much as 70,000 lb. in a good year. A number of fishing settlements enliven the Transbaikalian edge of the lake, the most important of which are the following: Nizhne Angarsk, situated in the extreme north-east corner of the lake; Ust-Barguzin, at the mouth of the river bearing the same name, where there is a factory for tinned fish; and Goryachinsk, towards the south, which apart from its fishing industry is of growing importance as a spa because of its warm springs.

## BAIKAL DAURIA

The Baikal Dauria region starts in the west with the *Khamar-Daban mountain range*, the large massif which rises to 7,272 feet and runs parallel to the southern edge of Lake Baikal, forcing the Baikal Railway to circle round following its sinuous line. This mountain massif forms a fairly unbroken mass, showing predominantly gentle forms with rounded and only occasionally rocky heights. These heights, as Prassolov describes them (160), give the impression of flat steps, one piled on top of the other, easy to climb from the south, but dropping steeply towards the lake. Sharp crests and pointed pyramid-shaped peaks appear, however, in the western part, especially in the area of the upper Temnik and the Snezhnaya. Here the greatest heights are to be found, alpine in character, with numerous gorges and other traces of former glaciation. The main body of the mountains is 25–45 miles wide and rises to between 3,900 and 5,200 feet, with the saddles and passes only 650 feet lower. Outcrops of the bed rocks, mainly gneiss and granite, are to be found mostly along the lower slopes. The southern and eastern parts show a more varied geological picture. Here are found primarily crystalline limestone and other metamorphic rocks, as well as porphyry and basalt. Radioactive ore has been discovered in the Khamar-Daban, in addition to other minerals. The main part of the range is covered with dense forests, the tree-line being broken by only a few bare *golzy* in the east and by alpine formations in the west. The composition of the forests is strongly influenced by the local climatic conditions. On the cool and humid slopes, inclined towards Lake Baikal and exposed to the north-west winds, is found the typical Siberian taiga, including cembra pines, fir trees, and larches, while on the dry south-east slopes the fir is predominant. The flat ridges are covered with shrubs and dwarf timber.

In the south the valley of the River Temnik (which flows into the Selenga) separates the Khamar-Daban from the *Borgoyski Mountains*. These mountains run parallel to the Khamar-Daban Mountains and are generally of a similar character, except that they are more broken up towards the south. The mountains drop down to the extensive valley of the Dzhida. Compared with the tangled forests of the Khamar-Daban and Borgoyski Mountains, which are forbidding and difficult to get through, the valley of the Dzhida is fairly well opened up as a result of its valuable mineral resources. In addition to coal, the area round the upper reaches of the river contains rich supplies of wolfram and molybdenum, the deposits of the latter being regarded as the richest in the Soviet Union. A small industrial area is therefore springing up here in the middle of this remote wilderness. Its centre is Gorodok, which already has more than 10,000 inhabitants, and is based on a large wolfram–molybdenum *kombinat* comprising modern mines and dressing-plants, truck-lines and suspension railways. The slopes of the valley are still overgrown with dense taiga, but towards the east the forest is receding from the lower slopes. These slopes spread out and give way to an extensive grassy steppe which merges without a break into the steppe of the Selenga. In the south, the valley of the Dzhida is flanked by the mountains of the same name (the Dzhidinsky Mountains), with the Mongolian frontier running along the watershed.

The Khamar-Daban continues morphologically and geologically towards the east (its dimensions constantly decreasing), but the narrow valley in which the Selenga breaks through is generally considered to be the eastern boundary. The Selenga flows around the eastern part of the Khamar-Daban and then into Lake Baikal, where its mouth forms a wide delta.

The *Selenga delta* is an alluvial plain at an average height of 23–26 feet above the water-level of Lake Baikal, and dropping down towards the lake in terraces. The lower terrace, which is composed of lacustrine deposits, is completely flat, while the other parts are gently undulating. Numerous channels of the Selenga (some now dry) cross the present delta proper in the north-east, while in the south-west there are several small rivers coming directly from the Khamar-Daban. The character of the delta is that of a dry steppe with swamps occurring in all low-lying areas and depressions. It is fairly densely populated by Russians and Buryats who are engaged in fishing and in agriculture, using artificial irrigation. The centre is Kabansk, where the railway coming from the west reaches the Selenga for the first time. Here the catches of fish are delivered

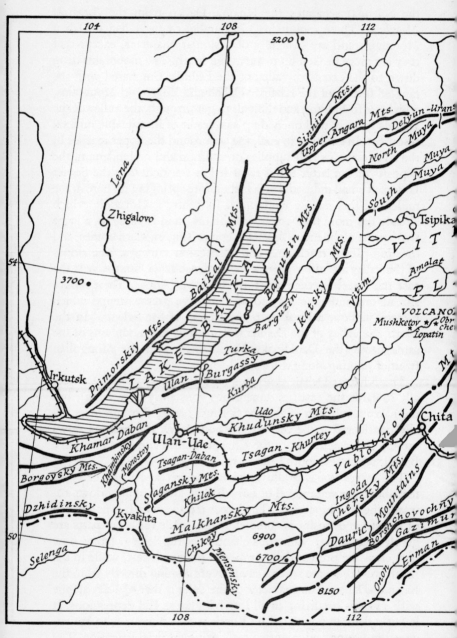

27. THE MOUNTAIN RANGE

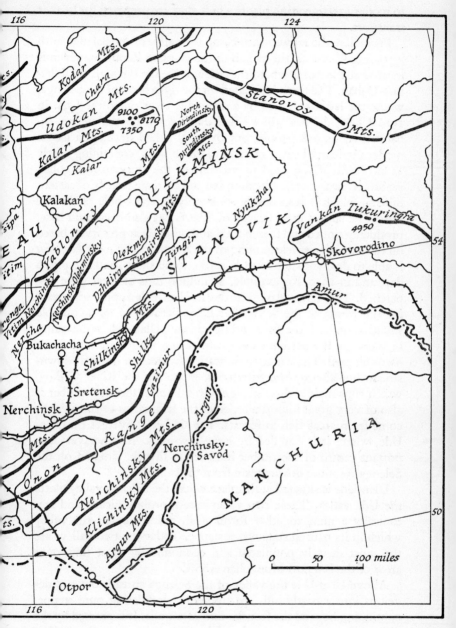

TRANSBAIKALIA

to modern refrigerating plants where they are prepared for further transport.

From here the railway runs along the valley of the Selenga until it reaches *Ulan-Ude*, the capital of the Buryato Republic, which is located at the point where the Selenga breaks through the Khamar-Daban. The town is situated on the right bank of the Selenga, where the latter is joined by a navigable river called the Uda. In 1926 Ulan-Ude was still a small dusty town on the steppe, inhabited by 29,918 people, but by 1939 it had developed into a modern industrial town of 129,419 inhabitants, containing nearly 25 per cent of the total population of the Buryato-Mongolian ASSR. It has the largest locomotive and carriage factory of eastern Siberia, which is responsible for supplying the whole of the Far East. The largest meat factory of Siberia has also been built here, producing tinned and frozen meat and other meat preserves, based on the extensive stock-farming of the Buryats. The meat *kombinat* is able to deal with 400 head of cattle, 1,000 sheep, and 250 pigs a day, and in 1940, for example, 25 million tons of meat were dispatched. Two large glass factories in Ulan-Ude supply glassware for the whole of the Soviet Far East. Because of its favourable situation on both the river and the railway, Ulan-Ude is the centre of traffic on the Selenga, and steamers and barges are built in its own shipyard. There is communication by steamer not only downstream but also up the tributaries, including the River Chikoy, which runs mainly through agricultural areas. Floating timber is also of very great importance, since the tributaries of the Selenga come from areas rich in forests. The timber converges on Ulan-Ude, where it is handled by large saw-mills. Another very important centre of the timber industry is Iliynsk, situated on the Selenga, 35 miles downstream from the capital.

Ulan-Ude is situated at the place where the Selenga valley meets the Uda valley. These two valleys are morphologically and tectonically a unit, together forming an uninterrupted rift valley which in its natural state was a steppe. Today the two valleys are the most densely populated and economically most important areas of the Buryato-Mongolian ASSR.

Above Ulan-Ude the valley of the Selenga spreads out and develops into a partly hilly, partly gently undulating pure steppe, continuing beyond the frontier into Mongolia. It is crossed by the old caravan route connecting Ulan-Ude with Ulan-Bator (formerly Urga), the capital of the Mongolian People's Republic. The route crosses the frontier at Kyakhta (about 10,000 inhabitants),

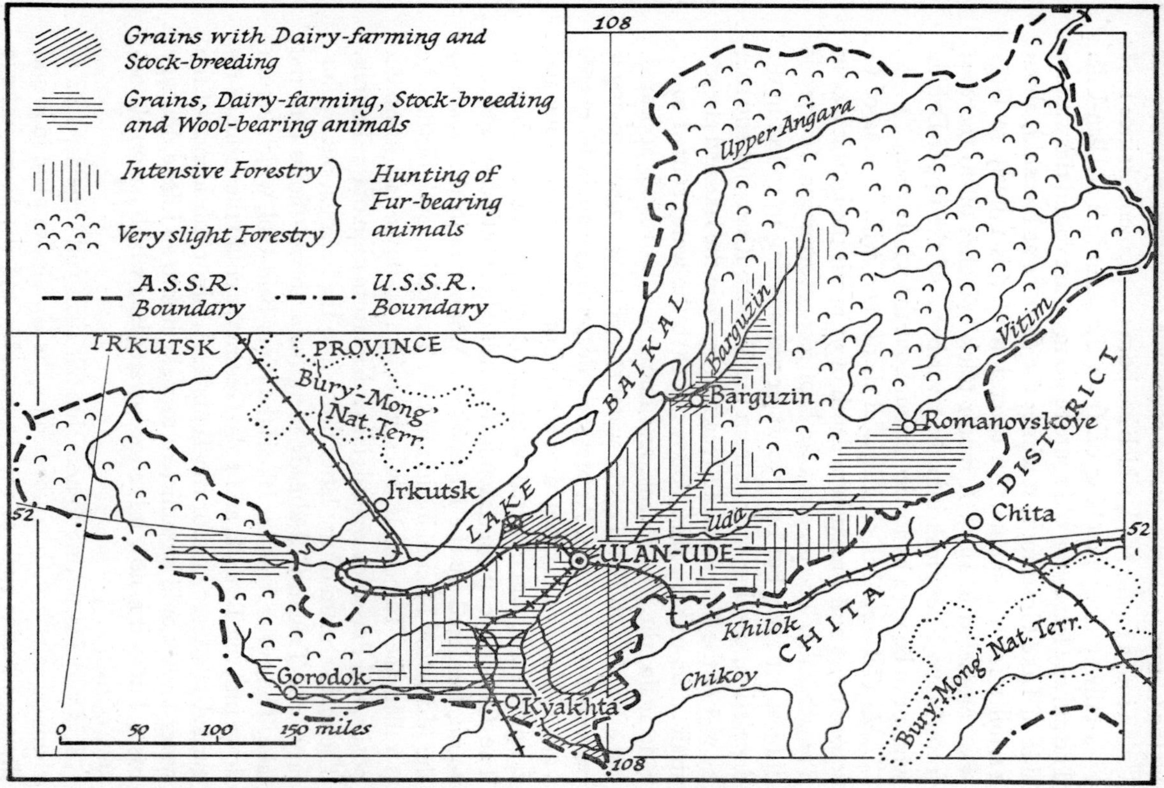
Grains with Dairy-farming and Stock-breeding
Grains, Dairy-farming, Stock-breeding and Wool-bearing animals
Intensive Forestry
Very slight Forestry
Hunting of Fur-bearing animals
A.S.S.R. Boundary
U.S.S.R. Boundary
108
52
IRKUTSK PROVINCE
Bury'-Mong' Nat. Terr.
Irkutsk
LAKE BAIKAL
Upper Angara
Barguzin
Barguzin
Vitim
Romanovskoye
DISTRICT
Chita
Uda
ULAN-UDE
CHITA
Khilok
Chikoy
Bury'-Mong' Nat. Terr.
Gorodok
Kyakhta
0 50 100 150 miles

28. LAND UTILIZATION IN THE BURYATO-MONGOLIAN ASSR

opposite the Mongolian town of Altin-Bulak (called Maimachen by the Chinese). This overland route was converted by the Soviet Union into a motor road, which has been supplemented since 1938 by a railway line branching off from the main line at Ulan-Ude. The railway leaves the old route to go in an arc round the western side of Lake Gussinoye, reaching the frontier at Naushki, about 12 miles from Kyakhta. An extension of this railway to Urga was completed in 1949. A motor track branches off to the west from Novo Selenginsk into the river-basin of the upper Dzhida which can be used by lorries throughout the whole year.

*Lake Gussinoye* has an elliptical shape, and with its area of 64 square miles and a maximum depth of 92 feet is the largest lake in Transbaikalia. The present lake is of recent formation. In 1720 it did not yet exist, but by 1730 water was starting to collect in the depression, coming mainly from the Temnik River and entering by way of the Tsagan-Gol River, and by 1800 the lake had already attained its present size. Following 1810 the water started to recede again, the lake shrank, and numerous flat islands appeared, but after 1865 the level of the water started to rise again, giving it back its former shape. At present a decrease can again be noted. Lake Gussinoye is situated in a basin of Jurassic sandstone and conglomerate, interspersed with layers containing brown coal. The Gussinoye plain extends towards the north-east and the south, bordered by the Khambinski Mountains in the west and the Monostoy Mountains in the east. The plain south of the lake is called the Tamchi. It owes its origin to fluvio-lacustrine deposits, and Prassolov regards it as a delta formation of the Temnik. The main stream of the latter flows into the Selenga, but a tributary—the Tsagan-Gol already mentioned above—flows into the lake. The outlet from the lake is the River Bain-Gol, which in turn flows into the Temnik, and Lake Gussinoye could therefore be regarded as a reservoir for the Temnik. A minor subsidence of the water-level would be sufficient to make it into an inland drainage basin, but as it is now it is a fresh-water lake which has an abundance of fish.

It is very interesting to note that salt lakes and large deposits of chemical salts have been formed on the Gussinoye plain in inland drainage basins such as the Tsagan-Nor and the Selenginskoye Osero, the latter being nine-tenths of a mile long and up to 6 feet deep. The hot summer favours the concentration of the salts in these lakes, and the lakes proper are often situated in elongated depressions embedded in thick layers of salt deposits, so that at

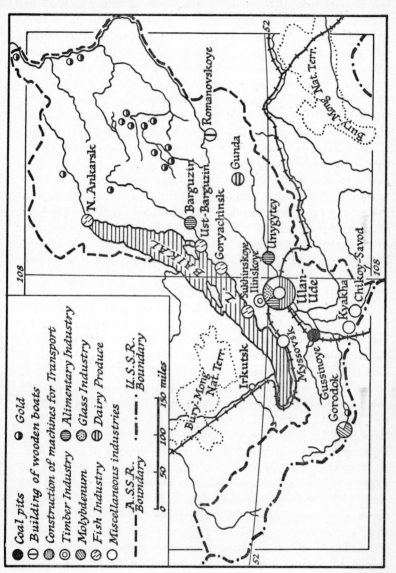

**Legend:**

- ● Coal pits
- ● Gold
- ⊕ Building of wooden boats
- ⊙ Construction of machines for Transport
- ⊘ Timber Industry
- ⊕ Alimentary Industry
- ⊙ Molybdenum
- ⊛ Glass Industry
- ⊘ Fish Industry
- ⊖ Dairy Produce
- ○ Miscellaneous industries
- — · — A.S.S.R. Boundary
- — · · — U.S.S.R. Boundary

Scale: 0 50 100 150 miles

**Place names (map labels):**
Romanovskoye, Gunda, Barguzin, Ust-Barguzin, Goryachinsk, N. Ankarsk, Unygytey, Sukhinskoye, Ilinskoye, Ulan-Ude, Kyakha, Chikoy-Savod, Myssovsk, Gussinoye, Gorodok, Irkutsk, Bury-Mong. Nat. Terr., Buri-Mong. Nat. Terr.

29. INDUSTRY IN THE BURYATO-MONGOLIAN ASSR

R

present only the deepest parts are filled with water. It can therefore be concluded that processes which are still taking place at the
present time must have been more intense in the past. The water-
basins are interesting examples of salt lakes of continental origin,
which neither in the more recent nor in the more distant past have
had any connexion with the sea. One group of these lakes has collected the salts which were freed by the chemical decomposition
of crystalline rock, while another group has leached out the salts
with which the continental sediments had been enriched in an
older geological era. For this reason the individual characteristics
of these lakes depend on the rock in which they are embedded. If
they are found within igneous rock the lakes are generally alkaline,
in the sense that they contain and deposit soda (e.g. Lakes Doroninskoye, Ononskoye, and Borgoyskoye). In the dry winter climate, soda crystals form on the icy surfaces of the lakes, and are
lifted by strong winds which deposit them on the adjacent and
more distant surroundings, thus furthering the mineralization of
both the ground and surface waters. The soda crystals, which
appear as a whitish efflorescence on the ice, are swept together for
the extraction of the soda, yielding 8–10 tons of highly concentrated soda-lye for each acre of the icy surface. The crystallization
is encouraged by breaking up the ice so that the water of the
lake can rush up under its own pressure and flood the surface.
In the case of the lakes embedded in Jurassic sediments it is
generally sulphates (particularly mirabilite) which are formed.
There is a layer of Glauber salt several metres thick, amounting to several thousand tons underneath Lake Selenginskoye,
and Lake Alginskoye also belongs to this group of lakes. The
railway from Ulan-Ude to Naushki is meant to facilitate the
opening up of the large salt deposits in the vicinity of Lake Gussinoye, making use of the brown-coal deposits in the same area.
One large sulphate plant is already in working order, and the
once small and unimportant settlement round the station of
Gussinoye Osero has already developed into a town of more
than 10,000 inhabitants. There are coal-mines here which supply
the railway, and in addition there have sprung up saw-mills,
brickyards, dairy farms, and a factory for tinning the fish caught
in the lake.

The *steppe areas in southern Transbaikalia* vary considerably in
their economic importance. In the southern parts Artemis steppe
extends over a wide area, covering not only the valley floors but
also the slopes, and even the tops of the mountains, which are

generally not very high. In its driest parts the ground has a vegetation cover of only 40–50 per cent; grass grows no higher than 6–8 inches, and pastures are poor. Towards the north the vegetation cover thickens and the grasses increase, gradually changing into an Artemis grass steppe in which grasses grow to a height of 14–16 inches. The steppes are used as pastures in the spring and in the first half of the summer, as long as the ground is not parched by the summer heat. Both types of steppe contain salt-pans, and both have developed on chestnut-coloured soil. Farther towards the north the soil becomes darker, its humus content increasing to 3–5 per cent. The soil changes into the so-called southern black earth, which is rather thin with a carbonate horizon lying close to the surface. The vegetation here is more abundant and covers the ground more thickly, providing pastures suitable for sheep and goats, although not adequate for cattle. For the latter only the meadow steppes which often occupy large areas along the rivers, are suitable. The Selenga steppes, and the valley floors of the Dzhida and the Uda, belong to this category. A similar change in the character of the steppes also takes place towards the various mountain ranges, the different types of steppe spreading upwards around the mountains, running parallel with the contour lines.

The principal importance of the Selenga steppes lies in the fact that cattle-raising has been intensified through concentrating on particularly valuable breeds of cattle, principally in the areas left of the Selenga and in the valley of the Dzhida. The old *yurtes* of the Buryats have disappeared and have been replaced by long rows of small, sober, solidly-built timber houses, which surround the *kolkhoz* buildings of the centralized stockyards. However, in the less favourable pasture-lands, such as the Kundara steppe east of Kyakhta, the traditional life of the Buryats has been retained. On the middle Chikoy a fairly large leather factory called the Chikoyski Savod has been built, mainly for processing local skins but also drawing some of its raw materials from Mongolia. In the remaining areas on the right-hand side of the Selenga, particularly on the lower Chikoy and the lower Khilok, agriculture again predominates.

The wide steppe valley of the Uda is the second most important stock-farming area of the Buryato-Mongolian ASSR, mainly because many Russians have settled here as stock-breeders. Along the upper Uda, in the region of the Yeravninsk plain with its rich endowment of lakes, there are numerous Russian villages where excellent dairy-farming is carried on, in addition to arable farming on a minor scale. The largest places in this area are Gunda and Sossnovo-Oserskoye.

East of the Selenga delta rise the *Ulan-Burgassy Mountains*, forming the watershed between the Uda and the Turka, the latter flowing into Lake Baikal. The Ulan-Burgassy range is wider than the Khamar-Daban and has a distinctly plateau-like surface, which is covered with boulders and overgrown with shrubs, and surmounted by only a few rocky mountain tops 5,300 feet high. The greater part is covered with thick taiga. Towards the north-east the Ulan-Burgassy range gives way to the *Ikatsky Mountains*, which merge into the Vitim plateau.

To the west of the Ikatsky Mountains, and separated from them by the wide depression of the Barguzin valley, rise the *Barguzin Mountains*, which run alongside Lake Baikal as far as its northern end. This range differs distinctly from the other mountains of Transbaikalia because of its alpine shapes and snow-covered tops. Some individual peaks rise more than 7,500 feet above the Barguzin valley, reaching altitudes up to 8,860 feet. In many parts of the mountains, particularly in the north, are found traces of former glaciation, such as U-shaped valleys and numerous lakes of fjord-like appearance from which erratic blocks protrude. The mountains slope down gently towards Lake Baikal, but break off sharply and steeply towards the Barguzin valley, where the mountainous character is most pronounced. Steep rocky walls rise almost vertically here, reaching above the tree-line, while the lower slopes are covered by typical taiga with very dense undergrowth. For all these reasons the Barguzin Mountains are extremely inaccessible, and one or two of the passes can be used only by experienced walkers. It is therefore not surprising that it is in these mountains that unspoiled nature has been best preserved. They still possess an abundance of valuable fur-bearing animals, and even the much-hunted sable has found a refuge here too. The southern part of this range adjoining Lake Baikal, near the village of Sosnovsk, has been declared a National Park.

The picturesque *Barguzin valley* runs for roughly 190 miles between the Barguzin Mountains and the Ikatsky Mountains, and at some places reaches a width of almost 20 miles. Three different types of landscape can be recognized. Dense taiga and numerous clearings covered with tall grasses spread over the alluvial flood-plain in the upper part of the valley, which extends as far as the mouth of the Garga. The middle section, as far as the town of

Barguzin, has an irregular sandy surface broken by dunes, in which are embedded numerous bogs and lakes, with various rivers forming a network of tributaries. The vegetation here is extremely poor, and of steppe character. Rocks rising above the sandy plain show traces of desert erosion, complete with typical sand abrasion and other forms of wind erosion usually characteristic of dry climates. Numerous warm springs flow from the foot of the Ikatsky Mountains containing predominantly sulphates, and there are also mineral lakes to be found in basins containing Glauber salt deposits of great thickness similar to those of Lake Alginsk. Below the town of Barguzin the mountains close in on the river to form the end of this extensive river-basin. This marks the beginning of the third part of the valley, the gap in which the Barguzin breaks through to reach Lake Baikal. On the right-hand side the mountains come very close to the river, producing a picturesque and attractive landscape, but on the left-hand side the mountains recede somewhat to make room for flat banks. The lower Barguzin runs through this latter type of landscape for about 25 miles. The Barguzin valley is thus made up of a strange mixture of landscape types: magnesium sulphate salt lakes between alluvial marshes, a valley floor containing both lakes and rivers and flowing abundantly with water, highly-developed sandy areas with dunes and steppe vegetation and traces of desert-like erosion, permanently frozen subsoil, warm springs, dense taiga all round, and snow-covered mountains in the background—all this is a collection of contrasts such as is rarely found anywhere in the world.

Apart from its gold-bearing alluvial sands, the basin of the upper Barguzin is used only by the Tungus reindeer-breeders. The rest of the river-basin is occupied by settlements which give the impression of islands in the middle of deserted mountain forests. In addition to stock-farming, many Russians and Buryats make a good profit from tilling the soil, with the help of irrigation drawn principally from the lateral tributaries flowing down from the mountains. The centre of the principal area of settlement is the village-town of Barguzin, which is situated on the river and has several thousand inhabitants. The river starts to become navigable here and represents the town's only connexion (via Lake Baikal) with the outside world.

Just north of the mouth of the Barguzin is the *Svatoy Nos peninsula*, which has the form of an island 34 miles long, crossed by two mountain chains rising up to 5,205 feet, which only recently became connected with the mainland by a flat isthmus. The material for the isthmus came from the Barguzin, the currents and waves of the lake being responsible for the drifting of the deposits and their accumulation here. The original idea that the peninsula was a continuation of the island of Olkhon, as had been maintained by Busch, has proved to be incorrect. On the contrary, Olkhon Island runs to the north-west of the peninsula as an underwater ridge, separated from the peninsula by a channel. On the other hand, the Ushkani Islands to the north-west of Svatoy Nos rise from this underwater ridge and are of the same geological formation as Olkhon Island.

South of the Uda depression, parallel to one another and following the Baikalian strike-line, are the following mountain ranges: first, the ridge of the Tsagan-Daban and Khudunsky Mountains; then in the west, starting at the Khilov River, the Saganski and Tsagan-Khurtey Mountains, which are bordered in the south by the wide valley of the Khilok (followed by the railway in its upper reaches); finally, rising between the Khilok and Chikoy rivers, are the Malkhanski mountains, which merge with the Yablonovy range in the east. All the river valleys (such as the Uda, the Khilok, and the Chikoy) are very broad in the west, where they merge with the Selenga steppe. Towards the east their character changes considerably, the difference in height between the valley floors and the crests diminishing, the slopes becoming gentler, and the shapes of the mountains becoming rounder, with watersheds which are frequently almost level. The valley floors are 2,800–3,100 feet high, the passes from 3,300 to 3,800 feet, and the summits from 3,900 to 4,600 feet. The climate shows more obvious contrasts and becomes more humid towards the east, and as a result the valley floors show signs of increasingly swampy conditions. Settlement is limited almost exclusively to the valley floors, and therefore decreases correspondingly towards the east. The valley of the Khilok is relatively more thickly populated than the others because it is served by the railway line, and here the town of Petrovsk-Sabaikalski should be mentioned. It is situated on the railway line which comes from Ulan-Ude through a gap between the Saganski Mountains and the Tsagan-Khurtey Mountains, and it possesses the only major iron and steel works of Transbaikalia. The iron ore is supplied by the mines of Balyagansk, north-west of Petrovsk, and the coal comes from Tarbagatay and Khalyarta in the Khilok valley. All three places are situated near Petrovsk and are connected by rail with the main line. The valleys of the upper Khilok and the Chikoy differ from the other areas of Transbaikalia in that they grow summer rye for bread, while elsewhere predominantly wheat is grown.

Eastwards from Petrovsk-Sabaikalski along the railway line, and still in the valley of the Khilok (which eventually flows into the Selenga), there are located (in addition to the mining centres mentioned above) the town-like settlements of Khokhotuy and Bada, and farther on Khilok and Mogson, all of which are known for their timber-mills. The last two also have food industries, and metal and machine factories. East of Mogson the railway crosses the Yablonovy Mountains and enters Nerchinsk Dauria.

## NERCHINSK DAURIA

The two Daurias are divided by the Yablonovy Mountains, which form one of the best-known mountain chains of Transbaikalia, and act as the watershed between the tributaries of the Amur and those of the Selenga, thus separating in the broadest sense the Pacific catchment area from that of the Arctic Ocean. However, the latter holds good only for the south-western part, because above the River Chita the mountains push between the Vitim and its tributary the Karenga, and farther towards the north-east they separate the river-basin of the Vitim from that of the Olekma, yet all these rivers flow towards the north, draining into the Lena. The Yablonovy Mountains also represent a noticeable boundary with regard to climate and plant geography. The influence of the East Asian monsoon penetrates as far as the mountain ridge, and it is therefore possible for deciduous trees (the representatives of a moderate climate) to grow here, whereas west of the ridge they do not appear. Since the mountains are of only moderate height it is surprising that they should exercise such a strong influence.

The height of the *Yablonovy Mountains* is generally only from 4,000 to 4,300 feet. The highest point (5,550 feet) is the Sarakan, situated north-east of Chita, which rises as a *golez* from the otherwise rather monotonous surface. The differences in height between the valley floors and the ridges are relatively small. The railway crosses the ridge west of Chita at the station of Yablonovaya, at a height of 3,470–3,530 feet. The actual pass lies only 350–410 feet above the valley of the Khilok in the north-west, but 1,010–1,070 feet above the valley floor of the Ingoda, the drop down into the latter being also shorter and steeper. This unsymmetrical structure, with its steep south-east slope and gentle north-west descent, is characteristic of nearly all the mountains of Transbaikalia. Obruchev explains this contrast as the effect of solifluction and stronger erosion induced by permafrost. The mountain ridge makes very little impression on the landscape, the slope rising slowly from the valley of the Khilok to the watershed, which has the appearance of a flat-topped wall. The ridge itself is a more or less wide plain covered with dense forest, with boggy saddle-like hollows from which the rivers generally spring.

South-east of the Yablonovy Mountains and their western continuation, the Malkhansky Mountains, runs the comparatively wide valley of the Chikoy and the Ingoda, which is inhabited mainly by Russians. Here the Russian villages stretch along the river like pearls on a string, while only a few miles away can be found the uninhabited mountains. The best way to reach these settlements is from the railway stations of Khilok and Mogson.

*Chita*, the capital of the region, is situated at the mouth at the confluence of the Chita and Ingoda rivers. Since the construction of the railway, Chita has developed from a small town into a city which already had 102,555 inhabitants in 1939 and by now has probably surpassed 150,000. The town is built in a dry and healthy area on both sides of the Chita River, on the two river terraces which rise like an amphitheatre towards the north to an altitude of 2,180 feet. Chita is the economic centre of the whole region. It is especially noted for its fur and leather products, and in addition the town possesses several flour-mills, saw-mills, and fairly large repair shops for locomotives and railway carriages. One of the most important coal districts of the area—the Chemovskoye Kopi —is within a few miles of the town, and natural calcined soda is extracted from Lake Doroninskoye, situated farther up the valley.

South-east of Chita, the Ingoda breaks through first the Cherski and then the Dauric Mountains and then, after turning back again in the Baikalian direction, finally follows the depression between the Dauric and Borshchovochny Mountains. Here the Ingoda joins the Onon (coming from the south) to become the Shilka, a left-hand tributary of the Amur.

About 35 miles below the confluence of the two rivers is the town of Nerchinsk (28,000 inhabitants), situated on the River Nercha, which flows into the Shilka from the north; a further 50 miles downstream is Sretensk. In this area, on the left-hand side of the Shilka, lying mainly between its two tributaries, the Nercha and the Kuenga, is the well-known *steppe-island of Nerchinsk*, the greater part of which is an almost perfect plain, the remainder be-

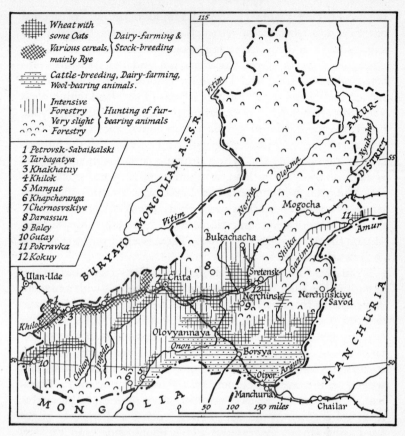

**30. LAND UTILIZATION IN THE DISTRICT OF CHITA**

ing gently undulating with a slight rise towards the perimeter. The steppe has a granite foundation with liparite and tuffs on top, superimposed by a thick layer of lacustrine deposits which hint at the fact that the steppe-basin had its origin in a former lake (Gladzin 69/174). Its present dryness is remarkable and in sharp contrast to the forest areas surrounding the steppe-island. Its situation as a low depression (2,030–2,230 feet above sea level) between the uninterrupted mountain chains may well be the reason for the remarkable climatic conditions which prevail here. The fertile steppe soil (often called 'black earth') has resulted in settlement so dense that the grass steppe in its natural state has now generally disappeared. The even surface of the steppe is interrupted only by shallow, mostly dry, valleys with gentle slopes. In the lower-lying places are found humid meadows, occasional marshes, and frequent salt-pans. Birches, willows, poplars, and shrubs grow on the north-facing slopes of the valleys, particularly where they are of gorge-like character, and the transition into forest-land is a quick one. The southern slopes, however, tend to remain unforested, often forming islands of parkland within areas generally dominated by uninterrupted taiga. Towards the Shilka, the steppe plain ends abruptly in a steep high terrace which is considerably dissected and when seen from the river gives the impression of a mountain area. Wheat-growing is the main agricultural activity on the steppe-island, in addition to dairy and stock farming. The economic centre is Nerchinsk, with its mills and distilleries, although Sretensk is more conveniently situated from the point of view of communications, since the regular shipping service on the Amur starts from there. There is a shipyard to the west of Sretensk at Kokuy.

From Nerchinsk the Transbaikalian Railway continues to run along the left bank of the Shilka as far as Kuenga, with a branch-line running from there to Sretensk. The main line (which from here on is called the Amur Railway) leaves the Shilka valley at Kuenga and circumvents the Shilkinsk Mountains in a large arc. Here to the north, in a side-valley of the Kuenga, are the coal-mines of Bukachacha, which are connected by a branch-line and which, on the basis of output, are the most important in Transbaikalia. Farther to the east, near the railway station of Mogocha, there are extensive gold-fields. Here a dense and sparsely populated taiga already covers the whole countryside, and the raw climate becomes very noticeable; the perennial ice-floor lies only 3 feet below the surface, the lower-lying places become more and more boggy, and more and more *golzy* are to be seen, either bare or covered with dwarf timber. All this indicates that this is an area of transition to the rough forest areas of the north.

The Baikalian *Chersky Mountains* lie to the south of the Yablonovy range and run parallel to it. In the south-western part the Ingoda valley separates the two mountain chains, and east of the Ingoda gap the wide, boggy valley of the Chita River forms the dividing line. Farther to the north-east the Chersky Mountains run into the almost unknown regions of the sources of the Nercha. According to Vosnessenski, the Krapotkin peaks (6,504 feet and 6,663 feet) are part of the Chersky mountain range. Adjoining the Chersky Mountains, and again following the same direction of strike, are the *Dauric Mountains*, the line of which has not yet

been completely established. Because the actual boundaries between the two mountain ranges are not clearly defined, some Russian authors refer to them collectively by either one name or the
other. However, in the vicinity of the Ingoda gap the two mountain ranges are recognizable as separate units. Two tributaries of
the Ingoda—the Olenguy from the right and the Kruchina from
the left—divide the whole massif. The Dauric Mountains remain
on the left bank of the Ingoda and the Shilka, until farther to the
east they cross the Nercha.

According to Gladzin, the *Shilkinski Mountains* could be a
continuation of the Dauric Mountains. Both mountain ranges
show by their gently undulating surface formations that they originally formed a peneplain, which through subsequent uplift and
its attendant erosion became more divided up and dissected by
valleys than the Yablonovy range. As a result its watershed follows a very meandering course and is sometimes divided up into
separate sections.

Lying to the south-east of the Shilkinski Mountains are the
*Borshchovochny Mountains*, which can be regarded as the last
typically Baikalian mountain chain. They start near the upper
reaches of the Ingoda and the Onon close to the Mongolian frontier, and stretch over almost 600 miles towards the east-north-
east. With these mountains, too, the eastern part of the range is
more clearly defined and better known than the western part. This
range forces the Ingoda (immediately after the river breaks
through the Dauric Mountains) to turn towards the east, so that
they then run parallel to the river. There is a gap in which the
Onon breaks through from the south, but the range remains on
the right-hand side of the Shilka, with the Gasimur River bordering it to the south. When the range reaches the Argun it meets the
outlying spurs of the Great Khingan Mountains—two clearly defined tectonic lines thus meeting here at a sharp angle. The surface
formations generally have the same character as the ranges described above. In the eastern part, along the Shilka and in that
general vicinity, the weathering into valleys is particularly marked,
since, in accordance with the usual Baikalian characteristics, the
southern slopes towards the Gasimur are short and sheer, and as
a result nearly all the rivers flow towards the Shilka. The vegetation cover of the Borshchovochny Mountains is still dense and
uninterrupted forest, except south of Chita, where the steppe
advances even on to the mountain ridge.

According to present knowledge, all three mountain ranges—

the Chersky, the Dauric, and the Borshchovochny—converge towards the south-west in the area between the longitudinal valley
of the Ingoda and the Chikoy on the one side, and the Onon on
the other. It is impossible to draw any definite boundaries, although the Borshchovochny Mountains represent the principal
chain, since they form the main watershed between the rivers
flowing south into the Onon and those flowing north into the
Chikoy and the Ingoda. The Chersky and Dauric Mountains, on
the other hand, are crossed not only by the upper Chikoy and the
Ingoda, but also by numerous tributaries, and are thus divided
into separate sections. The whole of the area of the upper Ingoda,
Chikoy, and Onon river-basins has its own physical–geographical
character, which differs from the rest of Transbaikalia. It is a
mountain area with numerous peaks which rise far above 6,500
feet. The best-known peak is the Sokhondo (8,226 feet), which is
situated on the main watershed of a mountain chain in which the
highest peaks all rise to between 7,360 and 7,650 feet. North of
this row of peaks other mountains have been found (as reported
by Gladzin, 69/169) which are of comparable altitude. The *golez*
Barun-Shebetuy (8,384 feet), situated between the Chikoy and its
tributary the Chikokon, surpasses even the Sokhondo, which until recently had been regarded as the highest mountain of Transbaikalia.

Because of their remoteness and inaccessibility these unpopulated areas are still very little known, but from the explorations of Dengin we get a general picture of the landscape, which
resembles the rest of Transbaikalia in its geological and morphological history. The Barun-Shebetuy and neighbouring *golzy*, as
well as most of the mountains of the Sokhondo range, have flat
tops and represent the remnants of a considerably uplifted peneplain. The present relief is the result of very strong erosion in
which the Quaternary glaciation played a vital part. The corries,
moraines, and U-shaped valleys found in the Sokhondo are evidence of this glaciation, which probably affected other mountains
of more or less the same altitude. Thus the morphology of the
area resembles that of the western Khamar-Daban and the main
part of the Barguzin Mountains: the uplifted peneplain has been
much more sharply eroded wherever the Quaternary glaciation
was effective, resulting in a mountainous landscape with typical
alpine formations.

Another matter of special morphologic significance for the area
around the upper reaches of the Ingoda, Chikoy, and Onon rivers

is the frequent appearance of intrusive rocks from the Palaeozoic to the Upper Mesozoic eras, as well as erupted material such as porphyry, dacite, andesite, and basalts of different ages, which, because of their different rates of weathering, have helped to produce an extremely varied relief. From all this it can be seen that, as the result of past and present processes of erosion, the present relief does not coincide wholly with the geological structure. As a rule the mountain slopes are covered with dense forest, and only on the southern slopes is treeless steppe to be found. This is, of course, particularly the case on the peripheral slopes facing towards Mongolia. The foot of the Sokhondo, for example, is covered with pure steppe up to an altitude of 4,000 feet. Birches and aspens, soon joined by firs, form the transition to the rough mountain taiga where larch and pines are prevalent. At 6,300 feet there begins the transition first to dwarf timber and then to mountain tundra. There is very considerable storm damage as the result of high winds. Russian settlers are to be found only along the outer edges of the area and on the floors of the main river valleys, while the whole of the vast interior is completely uninhabited.

The Manchurian Railway, which takes the direct route via Harbin to Vladivostok, branches off between Chita and Nerchinsk, at the station of Karymskaya. The last Soviet Russian station is Otpur, situated just outside Manchuria on the other side of the frontier. The railway runs directly to the south-east and, while doing so, crosses all the mountain ranges roughly at right angles. The Borshchovochny Mountains are followed by the Gasimuro-Onon range (which reaches the Argun south of the Gasimur River); then come the Erman, the Nerchinski, the Klichinski, and finally the Argun Mountains. All these mountain ranges run almost parallel to each other and follow the Baikalian direction of strike. The Gasimuro-Onon range runs along the north side of the middle Onon to the point where the river breaks through, and the range finally ends at the Argun River, between the Gasumir River to the north and the Uryumkan River to the south. These mountains do not rise higher than 3,300 feet. The Erman Mountains are divided into two parts by the Tarey inland drainage basin, and the other mountain ranges run only from the Tarey basin to the Argun River.

The landscape of the whole area shows a gradual change from north-west to south-east as well as from north-east to south-west. From north-west to south-east, that is moving in the direction of the Manchurian Railway, the ridges gradually become lower and the differences in elevation diminish. The pine-woods and bogs disappear, and there appears a striking abundance of birches which at first cover even the ridges, but farther on cover only the northern slopes. Finally the birches make way entirely for pure steppe, and salt-pans are found occasionally in the hollows. North-eastwards, in the direction of the Argun, all the mountain ranges increase in height, the Erman Mountains reaching up to 4,600 feet, the Nerchinski Mountains up to 4,300 feet, and the Argun Mountains up to 3,000–3,300 feet. In the areas which drain towards the Argun—particularly around the head-waters of the Gasimur, Uryumkan, and Urov—the mountains are of medium height with rounded tops, deeply-cut river valleys, and greater relative differences in height (700–1,300 feet). The young river-system, with its steep gradients and numerous stony rapids and waterfalls, indicates a recent uplift of these areas. This landscape can be called the Argun type. Towards the south-west the altitude of the mountain ranges decreases, the relative differences in height diminish (to an average of 350–500 feet), the valleys widen, and the rivers have large bends and numerous meanders. Lateral erosion is prevalent, and the ridges gradually change into hills. This land-scape, called the Gobi type by Presnyakov, forms the mountain steppes of the Onon and the Argun, and occupies all the southern part of the Argun region. The third type of landscape to be mentioned is the Tarey basin, also called the Onon plain by Russian geographers. It forms an internal drainage basin stretching over the Mongolian frontier as far as the Kerule River. In the centre are situated the Tarey lakes, some of which are very large (e.g. the Barun Tarey, 170 square miles; and the Sun Tarey, 120 square miles). The landscape is generally flat, and interrupted only by dry river valleys and lake-basins. The remnants of former lakes are situated 200–230 feet below the general surface level (at an altitude of 2,030 feet), but even so may still be up to 16 feet deep. There are clear signs that these lakes dried up fairly recently and there are still many places where there are surface springs which form the centres of human life. The steppe often assumes a desert-like character.

The boundary between steppe and forest runs from Aksha on the middle Onon, northwards via Ilinskoye to the watershed between the Aga and the Ingoda rivers, and then eastwards along this watershed to the mouth of the Aga. From here it forms an arc curving southwards around the Argun Mountains via Onon-

Borsya, Akatuy, and Algachi, and then north-eastwards again via Nerchinski-Savod to the Argun.

South-east of Chita begins the *steppe of Aginsk*, which is a genuine grass steppe covering the river-basins of the Aga and the middle Onon. This is the area of the National District of the Buryats, who have developed it into an important cattle-breeding region. Farther to the south-east the whole of the area is taken up by the Argun steppe, where cattle-breeding is again the predominant feature of the economy. However, here it is the Russians who work as cattle- and sheep-breeders on large, specialized farms owned by the State. There are also several State-owned farms for horse-breeding. In the northern part of both steppes the cultivation of grains (principally wheat) extends over large areas and is advancing on a wide front towards the south. A line of villages runs right through the middle of the steppe along the larger rivers, including the Argun. In spite of the often rather meagre steppe vegetation, the spread of cultivation is favoured by the existence of a soil horizon very rich in humus—a kind of black earth which has developed below the turf.

However, for future economic development the large quantities of mineral resources (especially iron and copper ores) are of much greater importance. The most serious difficulty impeding the utilization of this mineral wealth is the lack of communications in the area. Apart from the railway line from Karymskaya via Otpor to Manchuria, there are only country roads to be found. Even the important zinc–lead mines at Khapcheranga and Mangut, and in the Sokhondo, can only be reached from the station of Ulsutuy (west of Karymskaya) by an improved country road more than 200 miles long, along which the products of the area have to be taken by lorries to the railway line. However, since this route crosses several mountain ranges, people in more recent times have preferred the route along the Onon valley, which has smaller variations in height, and which leads to the station of Olovyannaya. The areas lying in the angle formed by the Manchurian branch of the railway and the Argun are also solely dependent on improved tracks and lorries. It seems that Borsya, which is situated on the railway line, will develop into a centre of communications in this area. A narrow-gauge railway leads eastwards from here to the copper-mines of the Argun district, and another leads south-west to Choy-Balsan in the Mongolian People's Republic. The town itself, situated in the middle of the Argun steppe, which is rich in cattle, possesses a large meat *kombinat*. In addition to

Borsya on the Manchurian branch of the railway is Olovyannaya (already mentioned above), which is of considerable importance and is known for its zinc *kombinat*. Most other places in the area have already been mentioned when discussing the mineral resources.

## THE VITIM PLATEAU AND THE NORTHERN MOUNTAIN FOREST AREAS

The Vitim plateau spreads out to the north of the Yablonovy range and east of the Ikatski Mountains, and adjoins several other mountain ranges in the north. The whole of this region has the difficult climatic characteristics of the mountain forest areas which hinder human settlement. Agriculture disappears almost completely and is limited to small sporadically scattered islands. Only a small number of Tungus hunters and reindeer-breeders, who lead a hard life, pass through the dense taiga. However, extraordinarily rich alluvial gold deposits are to be found in these barren areas, mainly in the central part of the Vitim plateau, and these deposits have given rise to an active gold-mining industry which has resulted in these parts becoming better explored and better known.

Since this area is the north-eastern continuation of Transbaikalia, the same characteristic morphological features are evident. The old peneplains have been divided up by faulting into horsts and troughs, resulting in wide, gently undulating plateaux surmounted only by residuals, as well as unbroken mountain ridges and wide valleys. The old fault-lines, following the Baikalian direction of strike towards the north-east, are also found here, and determine the principal boundaries of the morphological units. The metamorphic and igneous rocks of the Archaean era are already joined here by younger sediments, especially by numerous layers of basalt which have a decisive influence on the surface relief of some areas. In some localities the morphology has been influenced by the Ice Age, causing the accumulation of great moraines in the valleys. In general, the characteristic effects of frost and solifluction are much more apparent here than in the other parts of Transbaikalia.

*The Vitim plateau* is formed by the merging of the various Transbaikalian mountain ranges coming from the south-west. Most of the plateau is bounded by the Vitim River, which at first flows southwards, then turns abruptly towards the north-east, and

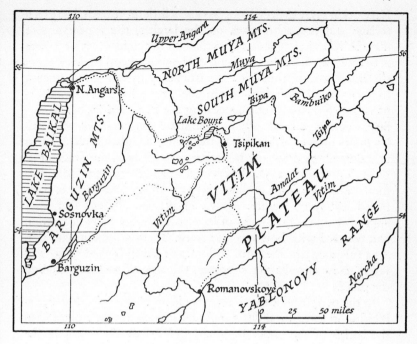

31. THE VITIM PLATEAU

finally towards the north-north-west. The interior of the plateau
is drained by tributaries of the Vitim, chiefly by the Tsipa and its
affluent, the Amalat.

   The plateau is a monotonous tableland crossed by gently sloping hills, between which are boggy plains covered with dense
larch taiga. These plains often stretch for more than 6 miles without the slightest change. The smaller rivers flow along flat, open
valleys, while the larger rivers have cut into the plains of the
plateau by as much as 130–160 feet. Along the latter, the undercut
bank is steep and rocky, while the slip-off slope spreads out as a
humid and marshy plain containing numerous small lakes. At present, lateral erosion is prevalent in all the valleys. The watersheds
rise 1,300–2,000 feet above the valley floors, but are situated at
great distances from them. The principal watersheds reach altitudes of 5,600–6,200 feet, while the passes are at 4,570–4,920 feet
(Gladzin, 69/151). The principal line of watersheds (between the
Tsipa and the Amalat) stands only 1,200–1,500 feet above the
plateau, and because of the gentleness of the slopes it is difficult to
distinguish even their highest points from the surroundings.
S

Kropotkin says: 'A little less grass and a little more moss, less green foliage and fewer branches on the larches, the appearance of dwarf birches in larger numbers than on the plain—that's all there is to indicate the higher position of the watershed.' In this respect the river-basin of the Tsipa is particularly monotonous, since it has only small variations in altitude over a large horizontal expanse, with dense woods concealing the irregularities of the surface, rounding off and softening the sharp contours. The wide valley floors merge so slowly into the gently undulating plateau that it is difficult to draw any boundary, especially as the gradient of most slopes is only 2–5°. However, here and there some individual mountains with sharp outlines rise from the general surface, composed mainly of granite. Above an altitude of 5,000 feet, they appear as enormous blocks of bare rock, without any vegetation and covered with boulders and scree. These are the usual *golzy*. As a rule they take the form of domes or hump-backed ridges and rarely show any sharper contours, the type of rock determining the relief.

In the peripheral areas the plateau is more strongly eroded, exhibiting in some localities a mountainous character, especially in the basins of the upper Barguzin and the upper Vitim. In the south-west the surface is of a more level and only slightly undulating character, as a result of the extensive basalt deposits superimposed everywhere throughout this area. Where these deposits do not exist, the relief is more varied and shows sharper contrasts. The distribution of the basalt flows is related to the distribution of the river-valleys, and there must be an orogenic connexion between them. In the west and south the boundary of the basalt flows lies along the Vitim, while in the north it runs along the Great Amalat to the point where it meets the Little Amalat, running southwards from that point towards the Vitim. The basalt layers occupy nearly the whole of the south-west corner of the area bounded by the Vitim. Three typical volcanic cones have been discovered here: first, the volcano of Mushketov; second, the volcano of Obruchev, opposite to the first on the right-hand side of the Vitim, near the mouth of the Kokyrtuya; third, the volcano of Lopatin, slightly higher up the river and again on the left-hand side of the Vitim valley. The three cones rise about 330–530 feet above their surroundings. Although these volcanoes may have played a part in forming the layers of basalt, most of the occurrences can be traced back to eruptions from fissures. These layers of basalt have helped to form and preserve the level character of the plateau, but wherever the rivers have managed to penetrate through the basalt (which is often as much as 60 feet thick) they have cut deeply into the plateau. Thus for the areas on the edge of the plateau, gorges and canyons are particularly characteristic, their rocky walls forming a sharp contrast to the otherwise flat surface.

The main drainage pattern of the Vitim plateau has developed in accordance with the structural lines of weakness. The Tsipa originates not far from the head-waters of the Barguzin, and flows north-eastwards at first along a broad valley containing many lakes. Then it suddenly breaks away towards the south, leaving the more north-easterly part of the valley to be used by the Bambuyko River, which in its turn flows along it for only a certain distance and then also breaks out towards the south, making room for the Tuldunin River, which flows along the last part of the valley and finally reaches the Vitim. The Tsipa and the source of the Bambuyko are separated by an area of low hills composed of alluvial deposits, with lakes filling the hollows. The Bambuyko originates from these lakes. It is presumed that there are older rocks underlying this barrier of alluvial deposits. The second barrier—between the Bambuyko and the Tuldunin—is formed by a granite ridge.

After the Tsipa has broken away towards the south, it flows through a narrow valley which in some sections is no more than a gorge. This valley later widens considerably, and the river continues south-eastwards, running almost parallel to the Vitim, but in the opposite direction, until it meets the Amalat, coming from the right. The latter comes from the south-west and flows north-eastwards along a wide valley, running almost parallel to the south-east edge of the plateau (which is followed by the Vitim in this area). Although the Tsipa has the greater volume of water, it adjusts itself to the line of the Amalat valley and follows the direction of this tributary towards the north-east until it reaches the Vitim. The Tsipa–Bambuyko and the Amalat–Tsipa valleys follow the Baikalian strike-line, which is crossed here by fault-lines running south-east to north-west, as indicated by the middle course of the Tsipa and the north-westerly direction of this part of the Vitim.

The valley of the upper Tsipa has been interpreted as being the structural continuation of the Barguzin valley. It becomes extraordinarily wide (up to 15 miles or more), and is actually the floor of a former large fresh-water lake, whose surface level is clearly shown by terraces to have been at an altitude of 3,725 feet. The present valley is covered mainly by peat bogs and heathland in which are found numerous lakes of different sizes which are remnants of a former large water-basin. The largest of these are the Baunt, Bussani, and Okunevski lakes. The Tsipa River flows through Baunt Lake, which is situated at an altitude of 3,270 feet, and a tributary of the Tsipa—the Tsipikan, whose source is near that of the Vitim—uses the south of this depression which is so rich in lakes. Towards the east the former lake-basin changes into a narrow valley, making it easy for the barrier of alluvial deposits to obstruct the course of the Tsipa and deflect it southwards. As mentioned above, however, this tectonically formed valley continues beyond the barrier towards the north-east, serving as the river-bed for part of the Bambuyko and for the whole of the Tuldunin.

The most important *gold areas* of the Vitim plateau are found slightly west of the centre, in the river-basins of the upper Tsipikan, the upper Vitim, and the upper course of the Little Amalat. The alluvial gold is found mainly in the areas of permafrost, and recovery of the gold is very difficult, even with the help of dredgers and washers. The provisioning of these areas is particularly difficult, since supplies have to be brought across the wide, empty wilderness of the taiga. Fish is provided by Baunt Lake, meat comes from the reindeer herds of the Tungus, and potatoes and vegetables are locally grown to a limited extent; but for everything else people are dependent on deliveries from the outside world. In this connexion the Barguzin valley is the most valuable, because from here the shortest (although difficult) routes lead to the gold districts. There are also overland connexions running southwards via Romanovskoye on the Vitim to Chita, and very recently a quick and permanent line of communication has been established by a regular flight service connecting Chita with Tsipikan, the centre of the northern gold district.

North of the Tsipi–Bambuyko valley rises the Muya highland, which is divided by the Muya River (flowing north-eastwards into the Vitim) into two elongated ranges—the South Muya and the North Muya Mountains. This highland's northern boundary is formed by the extensive valley of the upper Angara, flowing west-south-west to Lake Baikal.

The South Muya mountain range consists of an enormous and massive horst which forms the watershed between the Tsipa and the Muya. It has a rough and wild appearance, and its crest carries numerous *golzy*, several of which have snow-covered tops reaching heights above 6,500 feet. These mountains do not create a uniform impression, and a wealth of different shapes results from changes in the type of rock. The former peneplain, in spite of having been considerably eroded, is still recognizable. In the higher areas are found traces of a former glaciation, such as moraines and U-shaped valleys, corrie lakes, and bogs, and deposits of scree and drift. As the Muya valley lies at a comparatively low altitude (1,500–2,000 feet), the northern slopes of the South Muya Mountains are far steeper than the southern ones, which drop down to the Tsipa valley (altitude generally more than 3,000 feet). The passes are few in number and difficult, with altitudes from 4,800 to 5,600 feet. Thick taiga covers the slopes rising from the marshes at the foot of the mountains, and the ascent through the narrow valleys choked with thickets is particularly difficult. Only higher up, where the vegetation is sparser, does travelling become easier.

The valley of the Muya, which is the product of tectonic influences, reaches a width of 20 miles. A mixture of older and younger deposits gives the valley floor a rather varied character, containing a succession of hills, long mounds, and sand-bars interrupted by enclosed lakes, swamps, and moors. Terraces along the edges of the valley, and widely scattered lacustrine deposits, prove the existence of a former lake in the valley.

The North Muya mountain range, also a horst, is very similar to its southern partner. The valley of the upper Angara has a milder climate (being open to Lake Baikal), and there are therefore occasional islands of agriculture inhabited by Russians; otherwise the whole area is almost uninhabited, with the exception of a few hunters and reindeer-Tungus. This is also true of the mountain ranges farther north, such as the upper Angara Mountains, their southern continuation the Delyun-Uranski Mountains, and the Mama highlands. It is only far beyond this unpopulated zone, in the southern part of the Patom plateau on the lower Vitim, that there are some settlements worth mentioning, such as Bodaybo, Leninsk, and Artemovsk, which sprang up because of the abundance of gold in this district. However, all these areas are outside of Transbaikalia, and cannot be dealt with in detail. They belong to the sphere of influence of the Lena proper, and are drawn economically towards Irkutsk and Yakutsk.

# THE OLEKMA MOUNTAIN AREA AND THE
## OLEKMINSK STANOVIK

When we enter these regions we find large and, in the main part of the north, almost unpopulated areas which are generally unexplored, so much so that even the structure of the big mountain ranges has not yet been clearly ascertained. The southernmost area, which stretches as a narrow strip along the Amur and flows into it, is at present the best known. Thanks to the Amur Railway, which runs parallel to the river for a distance of 30–45 miles, this area has more of an economic life and is more open to human observation. The Olekma, its right-hand tributary the Nyukzha, and the Oldoy (a tributary of the Amur), together form the eastern boundary of this region. The western boundary is clearly marked only in the north, by the Vitim, whereas in the south between the south-eastern arm of the Vitim and the Amur it is not defined, because the mountains of Transbaikalia continue here without interruption into the Olekma region.

Between the Vitim and the Upper Nercha, the Yablonovy Mountains push into the region as far as the north-flowing section of the middle Olekma. Here the ridge runs along the north side of the upper Olekma and divides its tributaries from those of the Kolakan and Kalar, which drain into the Vitim. In this way the Yablonovy ridge divides the whole of the area into the mountain region of Olekminsk in the north, and the Olekminsk Stanovik in the south. If the Yablonovy ridge (which according to some geographers stops short at the Kironga, a right-hand tributary of the Vitim) is continued as far as the Olekma, so that it ends approximately opposite the mouth of the Nyukzha (as suggested by Obruchev), it still has neither any geological nor tectonic relationship with the Stanovoy Ridge, as is still wrongly shown on many maps. The Yablonovy ridge abuts on the Stanovoy range almost at a right angle, or at least at a sharp angle. The general strike-line of the Stanovoy range runs westwards towards the north end of the Lake of Baikal, and the range shows some connexion with the Mutya Mountains, but certainly none with the Yablonovy range.

From south to north within the *mountain area of Olekminsk* the following three ridges are named: the Kalar Mountains (north of the river bearing the same name), the Udokan Mountains, and the Kodar Mountains. While the latter two are separated from each other by the valleys of the Chara (towards the Olekma) and the Koyurla (towards the Vitim), the Kalar and Udokan ranges fuse in the east, almost midway between the Vitim and the Olekma, into a plateau at an altitude of more than 6,500 feet. Here on the top of the plateau, south of the sources of the Kalar, rise two enormous *golzy* to a tremendous height. They are the *golez* Skalisty (Rocky Golez), altitude 9,400 feet, and the *golez* Sneshny (Snow Golez), altitude 8,200 feet. According to present-day knowledge they are the highest elevations of the Olekma mountain area. More recent news tells us that a still higher peak has been discovered in the Udokan Mountains, with an altitude of more than 9,800 feet and named Typur, but no further details are known.

The Kalar, Udokan, and Kodar Mountains consist basically of Pre-Cambrian crystalline schists and gneisses, with many large granite intrusions. Younger formations separating the mountains are found only in the valley floors, e.g. the continental Jurassic formations of the upper Chara. Although the three valleys are in parts very wide and deep, the three mountain ranges are related symmetrically. The Kodar Mountains have a gentle slip-off slope in the north, and rise towards the south, where they break off steeply towards the Chara valley. The Udokan Mountains drop steeply towards both the north and the south, whereas the Kalar Mountains drop steeply towards the north and more gradually towards the south.

Seen from the Chara valley, the Kodar Mountains form a single unbroken mass, and the character of an upper peneplain is easily recognizable. Erosion has divided it into separate blocks, with the Quaternary glaciation helping to change and widen the valleys. The steep southern slope is the most heavily eroded. The *golzy* which rest on the surface of the massif reach an altitude of 6,500 feet.

The Udokan Mountains present a much more uneven landscape than the Kodar Mountains, since the original fold has been broken up into irregular sections which lie at different altitudes. Here, too, erosion has played a large part in the destruction of the original formation, the slope in the east towards the valley of the Olekma being the most broken up. The highest parts of the mountains, especially in the area where they meet the Kalar range, owe their present form to the Quaternary glaciation, the traces of which are visible everywhere and give this part of the mountains an alpine appearance. Apart from this area, the Udokan Mountains also contain flat plateaux in which the original shape of the Post-Tertiary peneplain is still discernible.

Except for those parts which adjoin the Udokan Mountains, there are generally more plateaux in the Kalar Mountains, with flat *golzy* whose slopes are covered with boulders and scree. The plateau-like character is much better preserved in this range, and towards the south the mountains slope down gently towards the middle and lower reaches of the Kalar valley.

Most of the Olekma range is covered with dense taiga. Only the high *golzy* tower above these forests and are covered with dwarf conifers and tundra, while the highest mountains are without any vegetation. Swampy conditions prevail, especially on the flat plateaux and the valley floors. The valley of the Chara is considered to be particularly bad, and in fact all the valleys which open towards the north suffer far more from excessive moisture than those with a southerly aspect. However, even here some lonely Russian settlements are to be found whose inhabitants are mainly farmers, and the Tungus reindeer-breeders are known to live in the valleys of the Kalakan and the Kalar. Alluvial gold is worked on the Ketemakhta, a left-hand tributary of the upper Kalar. Mountain paths which lead in the south to the station of Mogocha on the Amur Railway, form the connexion with the outside world.

The *Olekminsk Stanovik* includes the whole of the upper reaches of the Olekma, and forms at the same time the watershed of the Amur. The whole area is described as a forest-covered plateau whose average altitude lies between 3,100 and 3,300 feet, with deeply incised river-valleys which lie from 250 to 650 feet below the level of the plateau. The ridge between the Olekma and its right-hand tributary the Tungir is called the Dshaliro-Tungir-ski range, but apart from this no other individual names are known. The watershed of the Amur forms a flat ridge whose average altitude is only 2,600–2,900 feet, which changes very quickly towards the south into hilly country divided up by the broad valleys of the numerous rivers flowing into the Amur. The most important of these is the Amasar, the valley of which is used in part by the Amur Railway. Numerous deciduous trees on the slopes of the Amur valley give a much friendlier impression than the dense larch-woods which cover the main part of the Stanovik range. Gold is the most valuable product of the area. The river-valleys between the upper Tungir and the Amasar are rated as especially rich in gold, and are easily accessible because of their close proximity to the railway. The town of Mogocha, with about 30,000 inhabitants, which is situated on the railway on the left-hand bank of the Amasar, is the centre of the gold-mining area. The alluvial sands of all the small rivers flowing into the Amur carry gold, and therefore attracted a great number of people at an early stage. These have remained in the country, and as a result the whole stretch of land between the railway and the Amur is relatively densely populated. The valley of the Urusha is an important one, and where it is crossed by the railway there is a station of the same name. Lignite has been found in the vicinity of this station, and the presence of utilizable tin has been ascertained in the vicinity of Yerofei Pavlovich, a centre of 20,000 inhabitants farther to the west.

## THE OLDOY–SEYA HIGHLAND

East of the upper Olekma basin is the Oldoy–Seya highland, which is the beginning of the Amur region, and comprises the catchment area of the Oldoy and the upper and middle Seya.

It stretches from the Amur to the hinterland of Ud Bay on the Sea of Okhotsk, running northwards from the river at first and then turning towards the east, thus enclosing the lower-lying and mainly flat areas along the lower Seya and Bureya, which might be called the 'inner' Amur region.

The western boundary of the area is formed by the watershed between the big rivers Amur and Olekma, represented in this area by their tributaries the Oldoy and the Nyukzha. The northern boundary is formed by the watershed of the Aldan, which runs along the Stanovoy range. The eastern boundary is formed by the watershed of the Ud and the upper and middle Bureya. (The Turana range, and the mountains in which lie the sources of the upper Selemdzha, will be dealt with later in connexion with the Bureya Mountains.) The area comprises two wide and elongated mountain ranges separated by a depression which is almost as wide, and is thus characterized by large-scale relief which forms a marked contrast with the succession of small mountain ranges and valleys found in Transbaikalia. Nevertheless the Baikalian characteristics remain predominant, in particular the horsts and the plateau-like tops of the ridges. The structure of the area is thus as follows: the large and massive Stanovoy Mountains in the north, followed closely along their southern foot by the extensive plain of the upper Seya, which is then closed in on the other side by a

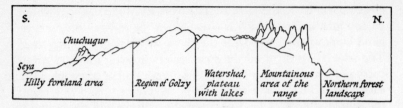

**32. MORPHOLOGICAL PROFILE OF THE STANOVOY MOUNTAINS**

*Taken from Bomnak on the Seya River to the Great Toko Lake, in the region
of the head-waters of the River Uchur (a tributary of the Aldan).
(After N. J. Prochorov.)*

long mountain range with a parallel line of strike. This mountain
range consists of three parts: the Yankan, the Tukuringra, and the
Dzhagdy (following each other in that order from west to east).
The Oldoy highland in the west, between the Yankan and the
Amur, must be added as a fourth distinct part of the area.

On the whole, the Stanovoy range has been very little explored
as yet. However, it is certain that the old idea of a mountain chain
acting just as a single watershed does not correspond to reality,
and that the range really forms a complete mountain system, with
an average width of 60 miles or more, stretching from the Olekma
almost to the coast of the Sea of Okhotsk. According to Tanfilyev
(207), the Stanovoy system can be divided into three parallel zones
of relief. On the northern edge, between softer formations, there
is a line of numerous sharply-defined *golzy* in groups and rows
consisting mainly of igneous rocks, and rising up as peaks with
very marked profiles. The middle range of the Stanovoy forms a
plateau-like uplifted ridge of great width. Groups of peaks are
very rare here, and the mountainous character is often completely
lost, especially in the eastern half. The traveller thus gets the impression of a wide undulating plain, an impression which is
strengthened by the very marshy character and the many embedded lakes. Most of the rivers start from this plateau, both those
draining northwards into the Aldan (the Lena system) and those
flowing southwards into the Seya. The watershed is therefore
very sinuous and not clearly expressed in the relief, and several
rivers flow locally in an east–west direction along the plateau (e.g.
the Tok, which follows this direction for more than 30 miles before running southwards into the Seya). The plateau-like ridge
generally lies at an altitude of 3,300 feet, with the highest points
reaching up to 4,300–4,800 feet. The northern edge rises slightly

above the general level of the plateau and is highest in its eastern part, north of the sources of the Seya, where the highest point is 8,140 feet. The southern edge of the plateau again has more of a highland character, but there are only groups of flat *golzy*, and the mountainous character is not developed everywhere to the same extent. As a rule, the southern slope is formed by individual flat sections of plateau sloping to the south and separated by quickly widening valleys; these slopes merge directly and without interruption into the basin of the upper Seya. It is characteristic of the whole structure of the Stanovoy Mountains (as reported by Ahnert (17), who crossed it at two places) that the central plateau descends both northwards and southwards in step-like sections running in a latitudinal direction. There are marked differences in landscape between the two outer zones. In the north the valley slopes are generally covered with woods, with the exception of the lowest parts and the heights; the former have mossy hillocks and bogs, while the latter are bare of trees, and are either covered with scree and boulders or consist of steeply-rising smooth bare rock. In the south, however, all the higher regions are covered by dense wood, and only the valley floors are devoid of woods because of the intense marshiness. In contrast to the rest of the Stanovoy Mountains, the watershed of the Seya is also mountainous in the south.

South of the Stanovoy range, at an altitude of 1,085 feet, is situated the rift valley of the upper Seya, filled with woods and marshes, which is joined by the much narrower valley of the Gilyuy coming from the west. Both belong to the richest gold areas of the Far Eastern territories, and are therefore fairly well known. The floors of the valleys as well as the gentle slopes of the plateau are mostly covered with a thick layer of moisture-soaked moss, while on the better-drained slopes and more elevated places grows a dense larch taiga. Deciduous trees are still very rare here. Moss hillocks containing a core of ice are often found in this area as a result of the prevailing permafrost. These often rise to a height of several metres, and where they become more numerous the landscape assumes almost the character of a hilly tundra. The traversing of these mossy marshes is made more difficult by gaps in the ice-floor, probably caused by warm springs, in which one can easily be drowned. As a rule wherever there is gold-mining the taiga has been deliberately burnt and destroyed, leaving an ugly ravaged countryside in its place. Numerous deserted and derelict huts, overgrown with bushes, add still further to the desolation of the picture. There are no large settlements in this area, although there are some villages in the centre of the valley, such as Pote-khino and Bryanta, where larger stores of provisions are kept in order to supply the widely scattered settlements of the prospec-tors. Gold-mining, which is now managed by the State, is very prosperous and has made the valley into one of the most important gold areas of the Far East. Alluvial gold is found along the Seya and also along the Gilyuy and its tributaries, but the extreme marshiness and the presence of permafrost cause great difficulties. Development is slowed down by the remoteness and inaccessibi-lity of the area, since there is only one gateway to the rift valley through the gap where the Seya breaks out towards the south. Up to the present, supplies have been sent by water as far as the village of Seya (the Seya River being navigable this far), and from there by vehicles alongside the river to places farther upstream. The Never–Yakutsk motor track runs through the upper Gilyuy basin, crossing the Tynda River (a tributary of the Gilyuy) at the village of Tynda. It is planned that the new Baikal–Amur Railway, com-ing from the Nyukzha valley, shall enter the valley of the Gilyuy at Tynda and follow the river as far as the Seya, in order to use the Seya gap as the exit to the south. From the building of this rail-way across the Seya–Gilyuy depression can be expected not only better opportunities for exploiting the gold-fields, but also for the utilization of the rich timber reserves of the forests, and eventually a more extensive colonization.

The watershed which closes off the upper Seya–Gilyuy depres-sion in the south (thus forming the large basin which has the Seya as its sole outlet towards the south) is a range of mountains which is regarded as a continuation of the Dauric and the Shilka Moun-tains. This mountain range stretches from Transbaikalia via the Olekminsk Stanovik to the plains of the Amgun (the left-hand tributary of the lower Amur) (207/250). According to Ahnert (17) the whole of this mountain chain came into being partly through folding, but mainly (particularly on the southern edge) through faulting. The mountain chain starts in the west (within the Oldoy–Seya highlands) with the Yankan Mountains, which are situated between the upper Oldoy and the Great Urkan. The Yankan Mountains form the eastward continuation, without any visible break, of the Olekminsk Stanovik, their transitional character being demonstrated by the gradual disintegration of the plateau-like surface, both northwards to the upper reaches of the Gilyuy, and southwards to the Amur. The Tukuringra Mountains stand much more on their own, since they form a divide between two strongly marked depressions—the basin of the upper Seya and the Gilyuy (already mentioned above) in the north, and the wide Seya–Bureya plain (which advances northwards here to the foot of the mountains) in the south. The Tukuringra Mountains consist mainly of metamorphic rock, and also partly of gneiss and crystalline slate. As a result of intense erosion, the range is very much dissected and divided up into individual massifs, but this can also be attributed partially to vertical dislocations. The surface is characterized by the usual plateau with conical peaks, and surmounted by *golzy*, the latter often standing closely together and forming, with their great differences in height, a mountainous area of moderate altitude. The general altitude of the plateau is 3,000–3,300 feet, with the peaks rising up a further 1,700–2,000 feet. The main part of the range is covered with dense taiga, and only the highest *golzy* are treeless. The different Siberian species are joined by numerous deciduous trees on the southern slopes, giving the countryside a more friendly appearance. However, at the same time, with the climatic conditions becoming milder, the undergrowth becomes extraordinarily dense, making it difficult for human beings to make their way through it. Thus, in spite of the more inviting appearance of the landscape, its resistance to cultural penetration remains. This is typical of all these mountain regions.

The continuation of this mountain range, starting from the River Dep (a left-hand tributary of the middle Seya), is called the Dzhagdy Mountains. A cross-connexion from these mountains northwards to the Stanovoy range forms the eastern boundary of the upper Seya basin, and also acts as the watershed between the Seya and the Ud. This remotely situated mountain range has been explored hardly at all, but its central part is supposed to rise to a height of 6,500 feet or more. The Dzhagdy Mountains continue generally eastwards, although changing their direction of strike several times on the way. They divide the catchment area of the Ud from that of the Selemdzha (the largest tributary of the Seya), and then merge into the Bureya highland, forming its northern rim.

The Oldoy highland is the smallest section of the whole region, and comprises the area between the Yankan Mountains and the Amur. Towards the south, around the head-waters of the Oldoy, the countryside already begins to get lower, breaking up into individual ridges, peaks, and valleys, which create the impression of a hilly or somewhat mountainous landscape. Towards the south-east, between the Urkan and the Amur, the broad hills disappear completely and the landscape merges into the so-called Amur–Seya plateau, which is already part of the wider Seya–Bureya plain.

The Amur Railway runs across the Oldoy highland in the north, and from Skovorodino (which has more than 20,000 inhabitants and is the seat of a managing board of the railway) a line branches off to the Amur port of Dzhalinda. This area is thus fairly well served with communications, and is the most densely populated part of the whole region. The alluvial sands of the rivers to the north of the Amur Railway are rich in gold, particularly in the valleys of the upper Oldoy and of the Great and Little Urkan. From the station of Never (about 10,000 inhabitants) the built-up motor-track already mentioned above crosses the Tukuringra Mountains and the western part of the Stanovoy Mountains, leading via the Aldan gold-fields to Yakutsk. This route is open all the year round and runs as far as Tynda in the basin of the upper Gilyuy. A railway line has recently been built along this very important route from Skovorodino to Tynda, and from Tynda there is a connexion to the all-important Baikal–Amur Railway (the BAM). This line was intended to be a direct cross-connexion between the shipping on the Amur and the BAM, as well as opening up new areas for settlement and serving as a pace-maker for denser agricultural settlement. Some arable farming is carried on in the less boggy valleys between the railway and the Amur River. A thriving foodstuffs industry has therefore been developed at Skovorodino (the centre of the Oldoy highland often mentioned above), in addition to an engineering industry and repair shops. Fuel is supplied by brown coal mined in the vicinity, and zinc has been discovered north of the town. A nearby airport connects Skovorodino with the great Moscow–Khabarovsk–Vladivostok airline.

## THE SEYA–BUREYA DEPRESSION

This area is the most populated, and economically the most developed, part of the Amur region. The easily accessible plains, the milder climate, and the fertile soil favoured the early settlement of a comparatively dense population, engaged in agriculture. The area is the granary of the Amur region, containing 80 per cent of its total arable land.

The area can be divided into two parts: the Amur–Seya plateau in the west, and the Seya–Bureya lowlands which stretch east of the lower Seya along the Amur, as far as the Bureya Mountains.

The *Amur–Seya plateau*, which takes up the western part of the area, lies between the Seya, its tributary the Urkan, and the Amur. The interior is generally flat, with only slight undulations, and declines slowly from north-west to south-east, while towards the periphery deep gorges have been cut by the rivers. The plateau breaks off steeply towards the lower Seya and the Amur. The right-hand bank of the lower Seya is 600–800 feet high, and when seen from the grassy western banks of the river has a mountainous character, due to its numerous gorges. Along the Amur the plateau is not more than 330–400 feet above the river, and rarely comes very close to it. Between Chernyayevo and Blagoveshchensk the Amur valley has four terraces. The lowest of these is visible only at low water, and from this there is a step of 13–20 feet (even 26 feet in some places) up to a meadow terrace built up from deposits of sand, pebbles, and silt. This meadow terrace is very much wider than the first, and is regularly inundated at high water. Then follows the 'middle' terrace, lying 35–65 feet above the normal water-level, rising up very steeply from the preceding one, and occasionally coming very close to the water where the bank is steep. Settlements are frequently to be found on this terrace. The fourth, or upper, terrace reaches a height of 160–200 feet and is less clearly defined.

The north-west part of the plateau is still densely covered with woods, containing a considerable proportion of deciduous trees. Towards the south-east the woods thin out and change slowly into a kind of forest steppe or parkland, characterized by small birch-woods, extensive marshes, and boggy meadows. The Russians who have settled here are mainly cattle-breeders, and only in the extreme south-east—in the triangle between the Amur and lower Seya—is arable farming found to any great extent. Outside the latter area there is a loosely scattered line of settlements running along the Amur and the railway.

The Amur Railway runs roughly across the centre of the plateau, following exactly the line of the watershed, since for obvious reasons this offered the best possibilities for its location. A branch-line 23 miles long runs from the station of Ushumun to Chernyayevo on the Amur. The latter is the centre of an area with good future prospects, since coal deposits have recently been discovered here, along the left-hand side of the Amur between its

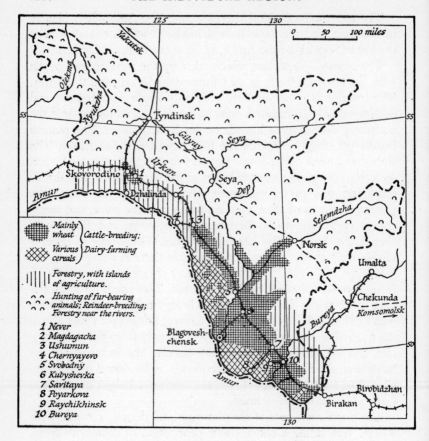

**33. LAND UTILIZATION IN THE AMUR DISTRICT**

tributaries the Urinda and the Magdagacha, roughly surrounding
the town. The coal is of Jurassic age, and lies in separate anticlines
which run towards the north-east. Although various samples indicate a very high ash content, the deposits are of the greatest
importance, since they are located in an area which was hitherto
dependent on very distant supplies of coal. At various places the
coal-bearing strata are interrupted by granite laccoliths and porphyry intrusions, around which the coal has been changed into
valuable semi-anthracite or anthracite. Nothing is known about
the total reserves of the 'Upper Amur Coal Basin', as it is called by
the Russians. Numerous outcrops occur along the Amur and in
some of the river valleys, and mining of the deposits has started
recently near Magdagacha.

The centre of the north-west part of the plateau is Magdagacha (about 10,000 inhabitants), while the south-eastern part is centred on Shumanovskaya (about 25,000 inhabitants). Both places are situated on the Amur Railway. The station of Tygda, between Magdagacha and Ushumun, is of some importance because of the road which leads from there via Ovsyanka (at the confluence of the Seya and the Urkan) to the place where the Seya breaks through the Tukuringra Mountains. This road is the shortest overland connexion from the Amur Railway to the gold-fields on the upper Seya and the Gilyuy.

East of the lower Seya begin the *Seya–Bureya lowlands*. Towards the east they spread over a wide area extending along the Amur and across the lower Bureya, until they are finally terminated by the wall of the Bureya Mountains, which here come very close to the Amur. Farther north, these lowlands extend over the river-basin of the Selemdzha towards the foothills of the Tukuringra Mountains. The main characteristics of this densely populated area are the vast wide plains (formed by Tertiary fresh-water deposits), the warm and humid summers, the extensive arable farming, and the numerous villages and small towns.

The southern part along the lower courses of the rivers is almost completely level and often covered with stagnant water, bogs, and lakes. There are also long, gently-undulating, dry islands, rising up between the rivers, but morphologically they are hardly noticeable in the predominantly flat landscape. However, the river-courses themselves bring some variation into the general monotony, since in this area they all possess well-defined right-hand banks which, although not high, are steep and heavily eroded. The left banks are mostly marshy meadow-land and rise slowly towards the watersheds. The Bureya retains this asymmetric formation of its banks far up into the highlands. North of the Tom (a left-hand tributary of the Seya) the relief changes, and gently undulating hills rise slowly towards the north. Here the unbroken meadow-steppe, still in its natural state (overgrown with the very tall grasses which have caused it to be called the 'Amur prairie'), comes to an end. Its place is taken by an extensive and unusual parkland, in which the hills and higher places take the form of islands covered with oak-woods or bushes, while in the lower-lying places the meadow-steppe continues. The dampness of the ground diminishes in this area, although boggy patches are found here and there on top of clay soils. Towards the north, where the land rises still further, the variations in altitude become

T

greater, and the valley floors become deeper and narrower. Pine trees are to be seen on the mountains, and the marshiness of the valleys increases again. Slowly the dark taiga takes possession of the whole countryside, while in the background the rocky peaks of occasional *golzy* rise from the otherwise unbroken green.

The reason for the importance of the Seya–Bureya plain is the great fertility of its soil, which has been investigated over a large part of the area by Tomashevski (219). In the south-west, over-lying a heavy clay subsoil, an intensely black-coloured soil has developed, covered with pastures and meadows containing tall grasses. The black colour was the reason why the first researchers put these soils into the category of the black earths, and even to-day the local people call them chernozems. However, these soils are not typical black earths, since the granular structure is missing and the accumulation of carbonates cannot be established. In summer the horizon of humus is soaked with water, and processes of re-generation take place in horizon B, often indicating light pod-solization. These semi-boggy 'meadow soils' (as Tomashevski calls them) are just as fertile as the black earths, and are capable of producing excellent wheat-crops year after year, without any manuring. They are generally found on higher spots at some dis-tance from the bottoms of the river valleys, and they cover more than 1¼ million acres. Another semi-boggy kind of soil (which the local people have characteristically called *myassigi* or 'kneading material') is found more frequently in the lower-lying areas and is less fertile. Here, too, the deep black upper horizon of the soil has developed over heavy clay, but signs of regeneration are more pronounced. During the humid summers, horizon B becomes tough and sticky, like thick dough, so that horses get bogged down and the soil is difficult to till. In their natural state the *myas-sigi* are covered predominantly with reeds (Calamagrostis) and moss (Polytrichum), and differ greatly in appearance from the re-latively drier soils. A large part of the Seya–Bureya plain, mainly towards the north and east, is covered by the lighter podsols. The natural vegetation on the heavier of these soils is white birches, while the lighter soils carry black birches and oaks. These trees served as indicators of soil quality to the first Russian settlers. The degree of leaching varies and is generally insignificant. It is said that the fertility of these soils is equal to that of the black earths, and they are easier to till, since their drainage is better.

During the dry season the Seya–Bureya plain is similar to the black-earth steppes of South Russia. However, during the rainy

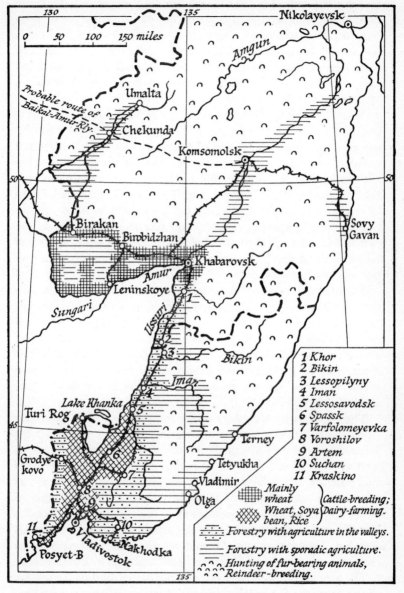

34. LAND UTILIZATION IN THE SOUTHERN PART OF THE DISTRICT
OF KHABAROVSK AND IN THE COASTAL REGION

season the picture changes completely; flat basins become lakes, valleys are inundated, and even on flat plains the water remains stagnant. Tomashevski is therefore astonished that it was possible for anyone to think that black earth had developed here. The black-earth areas of South Russia have a humid spring and a dry summer, while here it is the other way round, with a dry spring and a very humid summer.

Along the lower Bureya, red earth is found underneath the partially podsolized surface soils. These red earths are produced by the weathering of grey Tertiary slates, and owe their brick-red colour to the concentration of iron oxide. They prove that the climate in this area during the Tertiary period must have been much warmer than it is at present. The same Tertiary red earths have also been established along the lower Amur. According to Glinka (70), 'grapes, cork, oaks and tigers are the relics of the period when the red earth was being formed, while pines, firs and reindeer are in complete harmony with the present formation of podsols and boggy soils'.

The northern parts of the Seya–Bureya plain generally lie at altitudes of less than 1,600 feet, and slope down towards the lower Seya and the Amur, where the altitude is generally less than 700 feet. At Blagoveshchensk, for instance, the Amur is only 400 feet above sea level. The subsoil is exposed at several places by the emergence of rocks from the horizontal Tertiary beds. These rocks consist of granite, Jurassic conglomerates and sandstones, and even porphyry.

The high moisture content of the Seya–Bureya plain (resulting from the plentiful precipitation during the summer) produces many different kinds of landslip on the slopes of the hilly areas, as well as signs of soil-creep. This makes the construction of roads and railways particularly difficult, especially in the areas (such as the foothills) also affected by permafrost. To combat the danger of increasing marshiness, the peasant must drain his land continually, but in spite of these difficulties the arable area is constantly increasing. Every year turf-covered marshes are burned over to convert them, first of all, into hay-fields, and then into arable land.

The area is comparatively densely populated, and in the valleys of the Seya, the Selemdzha, and the Bureya, settlers are penetrating farther and farther into the interior. On the plain, it is frequently possible to see from one village to the next. The settlements do not differ in any way from those of the Russian homeland, and at the height of summer, when the fields of sunflowers

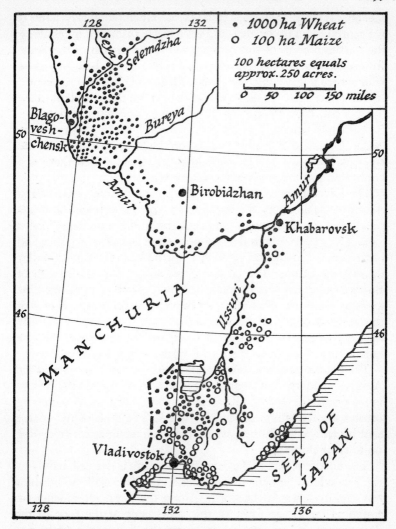

• 1000 ha Wheat
○ 100 ha Maize

100 hectares equals
approx. 250 acres.

0    50    100   150 miles

35. DISTRIBUTION OF WHEAT AND MAIZE IN THE AMUR AND
COASTAL REGIONS

are seen mixed with the golden yellow of the wheat-fields, it is
easy to imagine that one is in South Russia. An alien element is
introduced, however, by the cultivation of the soyabean and the
perilla, which occupy a considerable part of the arable land.

The railway crosses the Seya at Svobodny (10,000 inhabitants),
where a thriving timber industry has been developed. A branch-
line 67 miles long runs from Kuybyshevka (more than 10,000

inhabitants) to Blagoveshchensk (58,700 inhabitants). The latter is the central town of the area, and stretches for almost 5 miles along the northern bank of the Amur towards the mouth of the Seya. In this area the Seya is the wider of the two rivers, being $1\frac{1}{4}$ miles wide where it flows into the Amur. Blagoveshchensk is the centre of the whole agricultural area, and has several flour- and oil-mills. Timber products are also of considerable importance, using timber which is floated down to the town on both the Seya and the Amur. Opposite Blagoveshchensk, on the Manchurian side of the river, is the town of Heiho (Sakhalyan), from which there is a connexion to the Manchurian railway network.

The lower Bureya area shows the same landscape characteristics as the plain along the Seya, except for the frequent outcrops of bedrock resulting from the proximity of the mountains in this area. The area is just as densely populated as the Seya plain, and settlements are penetrating farther north along the Bureya valley into the highlands. The centre of the area is the small town of Bureya, situated where the railway crosses the river. A railway line 27 miles long branches off from here to Raychikhinsk, centre of the largest brown-coal deposits in the Amur region. Very recently the town of Savitaya has grown in importance because of the new railway line built from there to Poyarkovo on the Amur.

The brown-coal fields are situated between the railway and the Amur, extending over an area of 250 square miles from the Bureya in the east to the Savitaya River in the west. The main coal-mining centres are Raychikhinsk and Kivdinsk. The bulk of the coal is sent by railway to Bureya, where there are facilities for reloading on to river shipping.

The northern part of the Seya–Bureya plain is drained mainly by the Selemdzha. Settlement is limited to the river-valleys and thins out rapidly towards the north. Along the Seya, settlements are found as far as the town of the same name at the foot of the Tukuringra Mountains, while along the Selemdzha settlement generally comes to an end near Norsk. There is a regular steamship service along the rivers to both of the aforementioned places. The construction of the new BAM railway line running eastwards across the area from the middle course of the Seya, and crossing the Selemdzha at Norsk, opens up new possibilities for further development of areas which are suitable for settlement but until now have been too remote.

# THE BUREYA HIGHLAND

The Bureya highland occupies a central position in the Amur region. It forces the Amur to swing in a wide arc to the south, and only allows the river to escape eastwards through a narrow gorge at the point where the highland meets the Little Khingan Mountains. At the same spot the highland intrudes wedge-like into the extensive lowlands running along the Amur, separating the Seya–Bureya plain in the west from the lowlands of the lower Amur and Amgun.

The main part of the highland forms the inner catchment area of the Bureya, which is bounded by the two principal mountain chains of the highland—the Turana range in the west (also forming the watershed for the Seya) and the Bureya Mountains in the east (also forming the watershed for the lower Amur).

The Bureya Mountains represent the backbone of the highland. These mountains start on the Amur as a continuation of the Little Khingan Mountains, which run in a north-east direction across the river from Manchuria, and they are therefore also known by this name. However, Russian geographers generally call this range the Bureya Mountains, and this is the practice we shall follow here. Although there are local variations in the lines of strike, the range runs generally north-eastwards until it joins the Dzhagdy Mountains approaching from the west. Here in the north some of the different parts are known by special names, e.g. the Dusse-Alin, which forms an arc around the Levaya Bureya River (the left-hand source of the Bureya), followed towards the north by the better-known Yam-Alin, which converges with the Dzhagdy Mountains. These two ranges form the northern and eastern boundaries of the upper Selemdzha river-basin, an area rich in gold. From the southern part of the Yam-Alin, a great massif thrusts westwards, forming a divide between the Selemdzha and the upper Bureya. The highest elevations of the Bureya Mountains (as well as of the whole Bureya highland) are found in the northern part of the highland, where enormous high plateaux converge in a very restricted area. The Yam-Alin has several peaks with altitudes of more than 6,500 feet, the highest reaching 7,265 feet. The main divide, lying between the sources of the Selemdzha and the Bureya, has several *golzy* which are almost as high, with altitudes between 6,940 and 7,070 feet.

The source area of the Selemdzha is rich in gold, and has numerous gold-washing installations managed by the State, some of which are operated mechanically. However, the remoteness of the area causes great difficulties. The Selemdzha River serves as the main supply route. There is a regular steamship service as far as Norsk (often also called Norski-Sklad), which even extends as far as Selemdzhinskoye when conditions are favourable. From the latter there is a difficult track 150 miles long, which finally leads over steep slopes which must be climbed in order to reach the gold-fields.

From the huge complex of high plateaux surrounding the source of the Selemdzha, the highland descends slowly towards the south. Along the upper reaches of the Amur and the Tunguska (a left-hand tributary of the Amur), the general level of the Bureya Mountains is only 2,000 feet, with a few *golzy* rising up to 3,300 feet. The Lagaural pass, through which the Amur Railway crosses the mountains, has an altitude of only 1,492 feet, and along the Amur itself the highest mountains reach no higher than 650 feet. The mountains come very close to the river on a wide front, with the river breaking through between the Khingan and Bureya ranges in a narrow valley about 90 miles long, between Pashkovo and Yekaterino-Nikolskoye. Here the great volume of water is forced between steeply sloping and often bare rocks, which in some places form narrow passages with high, almost vertical, walls.

The general appearance of the Bureya Mountains differs very little from that of the Seya highland. Here, too, the basic plateau-like formation is recognizable everywhere, with numerous *golzy* rising from the surface. However, all parts of these mountains are more strongly eroded, probably because of the more plentiful precipitation. Nearly all the rivers (at least in their upper reaches) flow in narrow and deeply carved rocky gorges, as long as they remain within the area of the former plateau. Then the valley floors quickly start to widen and run between the gentle inclines of the marshy plateau. Even here the valleys are often character-ized by steep and rocky precipices, and the lower parts of the plateau area are still surmounted by occasional dome-shaped peaks standing in isolation.

The vegetation of the Bureya highland has an unusually great variety. Apart from the richness of the variations in relief, the reason for this can be found chiefly in the fact that three different types of plant communities meet here—the East Siberian, the Okhotsk, and the Manchurian. In the northern parts of the high-land, at an altitude of 2,000–3,000 feet, dense forests are found on the mountains and higher slopes, consisting mainly of the Ayan pine (*Picea ayanensis*) and the white-barked fir (*Abies nephrolepsis*). A small number of birch trees are found interspersed among the other species. These forests have a very strange appearance as the result of the prevalent low temperatures, cool mists, and the strong humid winds blowing in from the sea during the summer: long lichen covers the twigs, looking like beards, and moss grows on the tree-trunks right up to the branches, while a thick layer of moss spreads over the ground, from which water wells up at every step. On the middle and lower parts of the mountains the forests change slowly into pure larch-woods, which advance far towards the south and fill the valley floor of the large rivers as far down as the middle reaches. The principal reason for this is that the cold air masses flow down the valleys and prevent the spread of other species of trees. Deciduous trees appear only along the lower reaches of the rivers flowing towards the south. Commercially, the larch forests covering the main part of the Bureya highland are the most valuable.

The valley of the Niman once belonged to the most famous gold-fields of the Far East, but the deposits are already exhausted. Nowadays they have been replaced by the gold-fields of the upper Bureya basin, but these cannot compete with the much more productive Selemdzha gold-fields. The Bureya valley serves as a communication route to the gold-washing centres. When the water level is favourable, the Bureya is navigable for 215 miles as far as Chekunda, and occasionally even as far as Umalta. The increased gradient of the river from Chekunda onwards pulls so strongly against upstream shipping that boats are usually drawn by horses from here. The last part of the route is covered either on horseback, or by using horse-drawn vehicles. An extension of this route, over a pass more than 3,300 feet high, leads to the gold-fields on the upper reaches of the Kerbi River, a tributary of the Amgun, and therefore already part of the lower Amur river-system. This old and once very active Bureya gold route has now lost most of its former importance, especially since the discovery of rich coal and molybdenum deposits in the valley of the upper Bureya and the building of a railway there.

Molybdenum is found in the valley of the Umalta, a left-hand tributary of the upper Bureya, and at Ust-Umalta a large molybdenum *kombinat* has been created. The hard-coal deposits can be divided into two parts—the upper Bureya deposits and the Tyrma deposits—separated from each other as a result of tectonic

movements and subsequent erosion. To provide access to these deposits, a railway line has been built from Isvestkovy (situated west
of Birakan on the Amur Railway) across the Bureya Mountains to
the upper reaches of the Tyrma, and then following this river as
far as its confluence with the Bureya. In 1942 this railway had been
completed as far as Ust-Tyrma, and since then its construction has
been continued parallel to the course of the Bureya, via Chekunda
as far as Umalta. A connexion southwards to the Amur Railway
has thus been opened up for the Bureya coal, although the route
along the Bureya is also still in use, and work for the improvement
of this waterway is in progress. Also crossing the same area is the
Baikal–Amur Railway, which leaves the Selemdzha at Norsk,
crosses the Turana range, and reaches the middle course of the
Bureya at Chekunda, continuing from there across the Bureya
Mountains to Komsomolsk.

In the Bureya mountain region these two railways are primarily
of industrial significance. Apart from coal, the most important
product which is carried out from these regions is timber, while
the carrying of food supplies is the railways' main task on the return journeys. In this latter respect the Bureya is also of some importance, since (according to several reports) loads of wheat are
transported upstream continuously during the navigation period.
The Bureya valley itself is most unsuitable for agricultural settlement, and the food supply of the new Bureya coal districts must
therefore be secured from outside. The whole of the Bureya in this
area has the characteristics of a mountain river. Between Ust-
Umalta and Ust-Niman its valley is up to 2 miles wide, but the
river, which is here very wild, rises regularly above its banks,
creating large marshy areas. From Ust-Niman to Chekunda the
right bank is steep and rocky, while the left, although level, is
occupied by almost impassable marshes. The valley narrows below
Chekunda, and rocky heights close in on the river from both sides
as far as the settlement of Paykan. It is only shortly before emerg-
ing from the mountains that the valley widens into a plain suitable
for settlement. The prospects for agricultural settlement in the
vicinity of the Bureya valley are therefore not very good, and it
will require many years of arduous cultivation before any self-
sufficiency in food can be achieved in these new coal-mining
areas.

Surveying the whole of the Bureya highland, it can be said that
most of the area is practically unpopulated, with the exception of
the following areas: first, the gold districts in the north, where

there are some widely scattered settlements; second, the Bureya
and Tyrma valleys, where limited areas are now filling up with
people; third, the more densely populated southern parts of the
highland, where we find unbroken belts of settlement along the
Amur Railway as well as along the Amur River. The settlements
along the river are purely agricultural, but those along the railway
in the vicinity of the Bureya Mountains are also partly industrial.
There is coal-mining at Bira, and to the west of Kimkan there are
iron-ore deposits, as well as deposits of magnesite, manganese, and
fluorspar, which have been discovered in the areas adjoining the
railway. In addition, gold is extracted from the alluvial gold deposits of the Sutar valley. This southern part of the Bureya highland belongs to the Autonomous Region of the Jews, which will
be dealt with in the following section.


## THE AMUR PLAIN

This region stretches from the eastern slopes of the Bureya
Mountains to the bank of the lower Amur, and forms a wide plain
constituting a meadow steppe covered with steppe grass scarcely
less abundant than the rich grass cover of the Seya–Bureya plain.
The average altitude of the plain is 150 feet. Several mountain
ranges run parallel to the plain on the eastern side of the Bureya
Mountains, but only in rare cases (for instance, in the Badzhalsky
Mountains) are they higher than 3,300 feet.

The Amur plain is regarded as a continuation of the Ussuri–
Khanka plain, and forms a rift valley which is embedded between
the Bureya Mountains in the west and the Sikhota-Alin in the east.
The plain itself is divided into the flood-plain (which can be up to
12 miles wide) and the plain proper, which begins as a river terrace. Only the edge of the plain is cut into by rivers; otherwise it
is generally completely flat, changing slowly into hilly country towards the mountains. Below the mouth of the Ussuri the right
bank of the Amur is given more varied character by the foothills
of the Sikhota-Alin; it lies generally at a higher altitude, and the
surface varies between gentle undulations and actual hills.

Although the appearance of the Amur plain closely resembles
that of the Seya–Bureya plain, it differs considerably from the latter
because of its much greater marshiness, which is attributable to
the more humid climate and also to the large masses of water from
the Amur, the Sungari, and the Ussuri, that flow together here.
Furthermore, the water-table is very high, because the plain is at

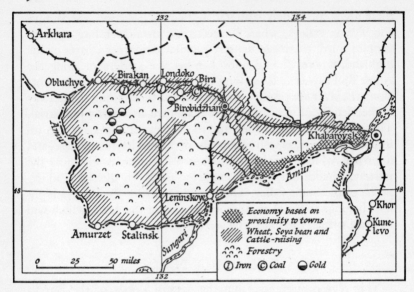

36. THE AUTONOMOUS AREA OF THE JEWS

such a low level in relation to the water-level of the rivers. Marshiness is also encouraged by the lacustrine deposits lying in the subsoil of the plain and generally forming firm and impermeable layers of clay. A further difference between the two plains lies in the degree to which the countryside has been developed. In comparison with the densely populated and intensively cultivated Seya–Bureya plain, the Amur plain is only inhabited to any appreciable extent in the southern part—along the railway and the Amur River—and even there only in certain tracts. Over the greater part, particularly in the area below Khabarovsk, only sporadic settlements are found, and these almost disappear here in the wide open spaces.

After the Amur breaks through the Bureya Mountains, which restrict its width in some places to no more than 1,600 feet, it widens again and develops into a typical lowland river. Its banks become low and recede, and numerous islands (often very large ones) begin to appear, dividing the river into many branches. The normal width often increases here to as much as 1–3 miles. The Sungari joins the Amur here from the right-hand side, coming from the distant south of Manchuria and bringing warmer water into the Amur. Thus, below its confluence with the Sungari, the Amur becomes ice-free sooner and stays open longer. Twenty-eight miles above Khabarovsk and the principal mouth of the Ussuri the Amur is joined by the Kasakevichevsk, which is the first branch of the Ussuri coming from the south.

Spreading out opposite the mouths of the Sungari and the Ussuri is the plain of Khabarovsk, overlying thick impermeable layers of clay which induce a strong tendency towards marshiness. Consequently the areas nearest the river are the least suitable for arable farming, which is found only higher up, where the soil is better drained. Thus, in contrast to the Seya–Bureya plain, extensive areas have remained in their original condition as boggy grasslands, used as pastures or hay-fields. However, in the centre of the plain there are dry ridges and groups of mountains, composed of Palaeozoic carboniferous strata and covered with forests. The mountains often rise to altitudes of about 1,600 feet.

The whole area inside the bend of the Amur, from Pashkovo to the mouth of the Ussuri, belongs to the Jewish Autonomous Republic, the northern boundary of which lies to the north of the railway. The republic has an area of 25,100 square miles and a population of 108,400 people (1939), about one half of the latter being Jews. This area is drained by the Bira (the upper valley of which is crossed by the railway) and by the Bidzhan, both of which flow into the Amur along wide valleys largely given over to arable farming. The region and the capital have both often been called Birobidzhan, after these two rivers. The capital is situated on the railway where it crosses the Bira, and had 30,000 inhabitants in 1939. It contains a large clothing and underwear factory, which is worth mentioning since it is the only large one of its kind in the whole of the Far East. The western part of the region, which has already been mentioned when dealing with the Bureya highland, is rich in several different kinds of mineral wealth. The development of a local heavy industry is planned on the basis of the Bira coal deposits and the Kimkan iron ore. The Jews work in all trades and professions, including agricultural work.

In the western part of the region it is mainly wheat and soyabeans that are cultivated, while in the smaller eastern part (influenced by the proximity of the large town of Khabarovsk) it is mainly potatoes and vegetables, in addition to dairy-farming.

Khabarovsk, situated on the right-hand bank of the Amur below the mouth of the Ussuri, is the administrative and economic centre of the whole Amur region. Its favourable position with regard to communications, at the centre of a large system of rivers and at the terminus of the Amur–Ussuri Railway, has made the town grow very quickly. The population quadrupled from only 52,045 inhabitants in 1926 to 199,364 in 1939, and by now it may well have surpassed 300,000. This rapid increase in the population can be attributed mainly to the introduction and development of industries, the most important of which is the engineering industry, particularly for agricultural purposes. The other more important industries which are concentrated in extensive plants are metal and timber manufacturing, and a large foodstuffs industry. Since the town is the centre of shipping on the Amur, it has a large shipyard which also builds coastal steamers. A modern cracking plant has been added to the older oil refinery which was already in existence, in order to refine petroleum from Sakhalin. There are several airports at Khabarovsk, which is the centre of all air traffic in the Far East, and there are also factories for the construction of aircraft and motor cars. Agricultural development in the vicinity of Khabarovsk closely resembles that usually found near big towns, specializing in dairy-farming and the cultivation of vegetables.

Below Khabarovsk the Amur plain spreads out towards the north, and it is only here that the Amur begins to attain its true size. Close to the town the water-level varies between 78 and 132 feet above sea level, and only a short distance below the town the river spreads beyond its normal boundaries by as much as 5–10 miles in some places at high water. The river flows along, forming bends and meanders as much as 6 miles long, where a straight channel would be only a fraction of this length. Numerous branches and stagnant pools accompany the main stream. The Tunguska River (which derives from the confluence of the Kur and the Urmi, and flows into the Amur from the left-hand side) was until recently a branch of the Amur in its lower reaches. It now shares the same river valley, flowing parallel with the Amur for the greater part of its course. However, at high water the upper reaches of the Tunguska are connected directly with the Amur. Lower down the Amur is forced into a narrower bed by the hills which come right up to its banks, but time and again the river spreads out over plains embedded between the hills, creating numerous branches and small lakes along its course. At Lakes Kisi and Kada the river comes within a few kilometres of the sea. It is possible that the mouth of the Amur may once have been located here, and that an emergence of the coast barred its exit, thus forcing the water to find its way farther to the north across a hilly and sometimes mountainous area until, after collecting the waters of the Amgun, the present outlet was found. Lake Kisi (which is joined to the Amur by a natural canal) lies only 9 miles from the Straits of Tartary, and is separated from De Kastri Bay by a range of low hills no higher than 510 feet. At this point the route to the sea along the Amur could be shortened by roughly 175 miles by cutting a canal from Marinsk on the Amur to De Kastri Bay. The construction of such a canal has been planned several times.

Along the lower reaches of the river the Amur plain continues northwards in the same monotonous way, except that running streams and lake-filled depressions are much more predominant here than in the plain of Khabarovsk. However, the monotony of the countryside is relieved by heights and hollows which lie alongside the river. These heights look like elongated hills or mounds, often as much as 6 miles long, and are former river-banks generally situated 46–53 feet above the normal water-level. There they are out of reach of flooding. Willows sometimes grow at the foot of these hills, or they may be covered with sparse grassy turf. Where the latter has been destroyed, loose sand is exposed and is blown into dunes by the wind. The banks of the river are flat, and are overgrown by willows which are submerged by high water without coming to any harm. The terraces comprising the former river-banks are of the greatest importance for settlement, and as a rule the wider hill-tops are ploughed up or used for vegetable gardens. The areas subject to flooding serve as pastures or as hay-fields. Every so often the whole plain is narrowed down by the encroaching mountains, while in other places it becomes very wide and merges with neighbouring depressions. The very shallow Lake Bolon (460 square miles in extent) occupies such a depression in extensive boggy surroundings, and is connected with the Amur by a wide channel. The water-level of the lake is governed by that of the Amur, and at high water a reflux has been noticed. At Komsomolsk, the hills come very close to the river on both sides, forcing it into a single undivided bed. Here the un-broken expanse of the Amur plain proper, with its extensive gentle relief, comes to an end and is replaced by a landscape made up of more irregular forms. The general appearance is greatly enlivened by numerous chains of hills and mountain ranges with heights up to 1,600 or even 3,000 feet. The general character of the considerably dissected Amur plain is frequently determined by the tributaries of the river, which flow towards it from both sides in long and sinuous wide valleys which add still further to the dissected character of the plain. Nevertheless the Amur itself

continually regains its predominance and spreads out over extensive flood-plains, forming numerous pools and islands, and filling
up the neighbouring old river-beds and stagnant pools to form
elongated lakes. The valley of the Gorin (which is perhaps the
most prominent of the tributary valleys) expands into a wide depression in the hinterland, in which is situated the large lake of
Evoron. Farther downstream are the plains of the Limuri and the
Pilda, the upper reaches of which have become known for their
auriferous gravels. Finally there is the vast valley of the Amgun,
which is more than 500 miles long.

Towards the north there is very little change in the landscape,
although the ground becomes progressively damper and marshiness increases. Meadow-steppes with tall grasses are still typical,
and broad-leafed deciduous trees appear in the wooded areas, giving rise to typically mixed forests in the hills and low mountains.
The deciduous trees disappear with increasing height in the direction of the Bureya Mountains, and on the mountains themselves
the Siberian taiga (with some of the characteristics of the Okhotsk
taiga) advances to the south, resembling in this respect the whole
of the Bureya highland. In the Amur region proper the mitigating
influences from the south cease with the end of the unbroken
plain: climatic conditions become less favourable, getting cooler
and more humid, and the Sea of Okhotsk starts to make its influence felt. The meadow-steppes change into mossy and treeless
marshes; coniferous forests bearing the characteristics of the Okhotsk type of vegetation cover the hills, and here and there the
beginnings of sphagnum moors can be found. These are all typical
signs of the northern coastal mountain areas, to which this region
already belongs. It will therefore be treated as a separate region,
together with the catchment area of the Ud.

In the region of Khabarovsk the Amur plain is still densely
settled. Wheat, barley, and rye are grown, and yield good harvests.
Towards the north the cultivation of potatoes and vegetables increases, corresponding with the decrease in the yields of grain due
to the greater moisture content of the soil. With sufficient drainage
it would be possible to make large areas suitable for grain, but at
present the excellent natural pastures are used for cattle-raising.
The density of population decreases rapidly towards the north,
and beyond the Mukhen (a right-hand tributary of the Amur)
settlement is limited to the banks of the rivers, where small villages or isolated settlements of Russians or of the native population are found at distances of 5–10 miles apart. Most of the settle-

ments lie on the right-hand bank of the Amur, since it is higher than the left-hand bank, where settlements would be endangered by the high waters which appear at regular intervals. At some favourable places larger settlements such as Troitskoye (with roughly 4,000 inhabitants) have developed, but generally the settlements are small. The Russian villages are to be recognized by their timber houses, while the Gilyaks and Goldes, and occasionally Chinese and Koreans, frequently still live in mud huts copied from the Chinese *fanses*. Agriculture decreases towards the north, along with the decrease in population, while fishing becomes more and more important, developing into the main occupation along the lower reaches of the Amur. Here settlements become more frequent again, and a specialized fishing industry has developed as a result of State organization. These settlements are attracting many immigrants, and their population is growing quickly, but they remain dependent on outside supplies for their general provisions.

All the other areas, away from the Amur, are almost unpopulated and are often unknown as well. In addition to the Golde and Gilyak fisher-folk who have their permanent dwellings mainly along the Amur and its tributaries, the only other inhabitants are the Samogir reindeer-breeders, who wander across the region of the Gorin, a smaller number of Nigidals who live in the Amgun area, and the Olches who live on the right bank of the Amur. In recent times gold has been found along nearly all the left-hand tributaries of the lower Amur and has stimulated a certain amount of settlement in this area, as for example along the Limuri, the Pilda, and the Bichi, and also on Lake Orel and along the lower Amgun.

The most important places on the lower Amur are Komsomolsk and Nikolayevsk. Komsomolsk is situated in a wide, lonely, and unpopulated area on the left bank of the Amur. The town developed only after 1926 from the small fishing village of Permskoye, and was founded by the Communist Youth (*Komsomoltsy*), from which it received its name. By 1939 it already had 70,000 inhabitants, and today it is estimated to have more than 150,000. The town has a large river-port with an important shipyard where ocean-going vessels also are built. The largest works are the 'Amur Steel' steel-works and rolling-mills, and there are plans to enlarge these still further by the erection of three blast-furnaces with a yearly capacity of 500,000 tons of pig iron. The existing oil refinery has been enlarged by the addition of a cracking

U

installation. A second power-station is under construction to increase the supply of electricity, and a large hydro-electric power-station has been completed recently. In addition to the above, there are about twenty other industrial enterprises in the town, which promises to develop into the economic centre of the whole lower Amur region. Several years ago the town was already connected with the Amur Railway by a railway line starting at Volochayevka, west of Khabarovsk, but to avoid the difficulties of railway construction in the damp Amur plain, the line has been shifted to the western edge of the plain, thus also by-passing Lake Bolon on the western side. By taking this route, new and dry areas are made accessible for agriculture, and the rich timber reserves of the forests can be reached and utilized more easily. Above all, the great importance of Komsomolsk lies in the fact that it is the terminal of the BAM, and thus provides large areas of the northern Amur region with their shortest route to the sea. However, because of the unfavourable conditions at the mouth of the Amur, an extension of the BAM has had to be built via the Sikhota-Alin to Sovietskaya Gavan, which is the best natural harbour along the coast of the Gulf of Tartary. For part of its route this railway runs along the middle reaches of the Khungari, a right-hand tributary of the Amur, where there are extensive Tertiary brown-coal deposits which were discovered in 1932 and which are to be used for the operation of the railway. This rail line is already of great importance for the transport of timber from the Sikhota-Alin to Sovietskaya Gavan, where it is processed for export in the *kombinat*.

Nikolayevsk, with its 30,000 inhabitants, is the economic centre of the area round the mouth of the Amur. It owes its importance mainly to the wealth of fish in the adjoining coastal waters and in the river, on the basis of which it has developed into one of the biggest centres of the fishing industry. However, Nikolayevsk could never develop into a major sea-port because of the severe climatic conditions and the fact that the ice-free period is no more than 160 days. The mouth of the Amur is blocked by a massive sandbar, over which ships drawing more than 12 feet of water are unable to pass. It must also be noted that the 'Amur *Liman*' itself is very flat and contains many shoals, so that sea-going vessels are limited to a few natural channels. Only small coastal steamers can get into the Amur, while the bigger sea-going vessels have to unload into river-craft on the open sea. Attempts have been made for many years to build a proper navigation channel into the Amur, but it seems that the difficulties are too great, mainly because of the natural shifting of the harbour bar which again and again defeats all human endeavours.

## THE SIKHOTA-ALIN

The Sikhota-Alin Mountains occupy the whole of the area from the mouth of the Amur in the north to the steep cliffs of Peter the Great Bay in the south. Running along the western foot of this vast range lies a narrow depression which spreads out into wider plains only in the south. This depression might seem to be of only minor importance, especially since the outliers of the Sikhota-Alin sometimes advance almost as far as the Ussuri, and because the plain is further interrupted by residual horsts from the marginal fault-block which runs the whole length of the Sikhota-Alin Nevertheless, this fairly small depression is of the utmost importance because most of the population lives here, and the main food-growing areas of the whole of the Ussuri region are situated here. The result is a marked contrast between the almost virgin landscape of the Sikhota-Alin and the cultivated countryside of the Ussuri–Khanka depression.

The Sikhota-Alin belongs to the younger peripheral structures of the Asiatic continent, and represents the uplifted eastern edge of a submerged fault-block. It lies between the Sea of Japan and the Straits of Tartary on the one side, and the depressions of Lake Khanka and the Ussuri and lower Amur rivers on the other. It consists of a row of up to eight parallel ranges with strike-lines running towards the north-north-east. Their average height varies between 2,300 and 3,300 feet. In the northern part some of the peaks reach a height of 4,300 feet, and near the head-waters of the Bikin and the Iman some of the mountains reach altitudes of more than 5,000 feet. In the southern part, the greatest height measured so far is a peak of 6,050 feet in the vicinity of the upper Ulukhe, although according to a new publication of Suslov the *golez* Komarov near the source of the Koppi has now been established as the highest mountain, with an altitude of 6,360 feet.

The watershed between the Ussuri and the ocean has shifted very much towards the latter, although the mountain ranges which serve as watersheds are by no means always the highest. The head-waters of the Ussuri and its largest tributaries—the Iman and the Bikin—are located quite close to the coast. In the middle and northern parts conditions are much more complicated, since there is no single mountain chain which forms the watershed throughout. The latter shifts continually and irregularly from one ridge to the next, with the result that rivers in this area frequently have their sources on the side of a mountain range facing away from their ultimate destination. (This applies both to those flowing into the sea and those flowing into the Ussuri and the Amur.) The rivers run at first along the longitudinal axis of the Sikhota-Alin and then break through transversely into the next valley, this sometimes happening several times before a river finds its final exit from the mountain system. The strange courses of these rivers are influenced by the geology as well as by the relief of the area, both being responsible for the broken lines of the river-courses which are characteristic of the whole of the Sikhota-Alin. Correspondingly, the rivers often change their whole character, a quiet course being followed by a break-through into gorge-like valleys with waterfalls and rapids, followed again by another calm and peaceful stretch of water. The result is a generally ungraded and irregular drainage system.

The whole of the interior is occupied by mountain massifs which run uninterruptedly towards the sea, where they end abruptly in terraced cliffs dropping down to the coast. Near the coast the ranges have been so strongly eroded and altered that, seen from the sea, they give the impression of high mountains. This is the result of strong weathering by the raw and humid climate, and by the powerful erosive action of the rivers flowing to the coast. The latter are short with steep gradients, and profiles which have been changed several times by vertical movements. The interior, on the other hand, is very monotonous. Looking from one of the higher mountains, perhaps from the watershed area, the eye encounters a vast sea of mountain ranges of various lengths, running mainly in a north-north-easterly direction. These consist of almost endless rows of low domes, generally covered with dense forest and only rarely bare. Nowhere do these reach as high as the permanent snow-line, and it is only in protected depressions under the umbrella-like roof of the taiga that the snow may occasionally remain as late as August or even September. The mountain chains often become disrupted, with transverse ranges connecting the various parts of the main chains and running in all directions. The picture is quite different again in those areas where basalt and other igneous rocks have come to the surface, as, for example, in the vicinity of the Soviet harbour—Sovietskaya Gavan —and in the central area along the upper Bikin. In these areas the eruptive rock often covers many square miles and results in an almost flat relief. The valleys are deeply incised, often forming canyons, and the valley sides are steep and often terraced. The plateau comes to such an abrupt end that the unexpectedly steep terminal wall is visible from many miles away, often dropping several hundred feet and giving the impression of a narrow valley from a distance. There are steep slopes in other areas as well, and the ascent to the passes and high plateaux is usually very difficult, being particularly arduous from the coast and less difficult from the west.

The land-forms produced by erosion are generally striking and demonstrate the effect of the monsoon climate, particularly in the south. The monsoon influence is especially evident in the spheroidal weathering of a great number of mountains in the Sikhota-Alin. These are mostly residuals, found on the Murayev-Amurki peninsula, where they consist of porphyry and porphyrous tuffs, rising as isolated peaks from the Lower Jurassic sediments. The ruthless felling in former times of the woods next to the cultivated zone, which laid bare whole regions of the mountains, has contributed to the intense erosion. In addition, the typhoon-like storms which blow across the south of the Sikhota-Alin often destroy the timber cover over large areas, thus strengthening the effects of the rainstorms on the slopes and adding still further to the destruction of the prevailing landscape. The extensive slopes covered with scree and boulders are particularly striking. Some of them may represent prehistoric formations having their origin in earlier eras when the climate was different, but they are mainly due to the intense erosion and great humidity of the present monsoon climate. Along the upper reaches of the rivers are valleys taking the form of narrow deep ravines, their steep slopes completely covered with scree. Some of these valleys are ill-famed for their falling stones and their landslides, one step often being sufficient to send the scree rolling down into the valley. It frequently happens that these narrow gorges are completely filled with boulders and broken timber, so that in their upper reaches many springs and rivulets flow invisibly underneath the debris, appearing at the surface to start forming their own beds only at a later stage in their courses.

The valley cross-sections vary greatly, showing all the different stages of development from the narrow gorge to the wide valley floor extending over several miles. Only the glacial forms are missing, since glaciation did not affect the Sikhota-Alin. Because the basalt-flows in this area occurred more recently than the formation of many of the older valleys, some of these valleys were dammed up by streams of basalt and then subsequently broken open again. Hanging valleys and river terraces appear quite frequently, caused by uplifting and headward erosion. The principal valleys are extremely wide, and the erosion here could not keep up with the recent uplifting, so that the lower reaches are generally characterized by strong rapids, often stronger than those of the upper reaches. However, in other cases the lower reaches have become silted up to a large extent, and consequently boggy, which is also a result of the extremely irregular water-level arising out of the monsoon climate. During the rainy season the main arteries are not capable of holding the volume of water accumulating from hundreds of tributaries, and they often inundate the whole of the valley area with full force, and with catastrophic effects on the inhabitants. All the settlements along the lower reaches of the rivers originating in the Sikhota-Alin suffer from these floods. The continental winter here produces all the characteristics of hard frost which are typical of Siberia. Along the rivers, water which is forced upwards through the ice-cover freezes again, and thus forms superimposed layers of ice, which often stretch for several miles. Where the water is forced out from below the scree, the boulders become covered with concentric layers of ice up to a thickness of 4 inches. The boulders and pieces of rubble become frozen into a completely solid mass, only to start moving all the more easily when the thaw begins. (Arsenyev.)

Despite all the differences in the details of the landscape, the predominant impression of large mountains with rounded symmetrical outlines is generally maintained, the more so since the area is so well wooded. In spite of the ruthless felling of trees in the peripheral regions, there is still a tremendous wealth of timber, especially in valuable deciduous trees, which represent a still unexploited treasure of the Sikhota-Alin. However, the forests are not everywhere of the same quality, since growth is often inhibited by the great humidity, especially at the coast, where the trees are commonly stunted and covered with fungi. Here the undergrowth is much thicker and the wilderness all the more difficult to penetrate. In the interior the woods readily become marshy, and there are bogs even along the watersheds.

The present coast-line derives from a former considerably eroded landscape which became submerged by the sea. There is a striking difference between the characteristic Ria-coast in the south and the more regular east coast with its relatively few bays. Detailed research has been undertaken by Romer (168) and Novak (134) concerning the origins of these morphological phenomena, and they have proved in the first place that the explanation of the older Russian scientists—who maintained that the sole cause was the combination of strike-lines and tectonic disturbances—no longer holds good. Romer has shown that what is mainly responsible is the varying resistance of the rocks, combined with variations in the angle of inclination of the submerged slopes. The 200-metre line of depth runs along the east coast at a distance of 9–15 miles, but along the south coast to the west of Cape Povorotny it lies at a distance of 75 miles from the coast. Along the east coast the average gradient is 8–13 per cent, more than five times greater than the gradient of 1·6 per cent along the south coast. Thus, although the power of the breakers is roughly the same, the former Ria-coast in the east has been completely destroyed, apart from a few remnants, while the south coast has been preserved. The varying direction of the strike-line is thus of only subsidiary importance, the vital factor being the varying submergence of a strongly eroded landscape. This submergence took place before the lava-flows, and the uplifted basalt lavas in the vicinity of the coastal town of Sovietskaya Gavan are covered with marine sediments, which indicate that the uplift here must have been very recent.

The young post-Quaternary vertical movements played a most important part in the detailed development of the coastal landscape, particularly in the valleys through shifting of the valley floors. These movements are characteristic of a large part of the East Asiatic coast. There is evidence of this uplift in the beach-drift, terraces, coves, and bays, the remnants of former cliffs, and the deposits containing young fossils which are found at various altitudes of the present-day relief. According to the work of Dunikovski (57) and Romer, there were five stages in this movement: (1) uplift of more than 650 feet above the present sea level, (2) subsidence of 1,650 feet, (3) uplift of 500–650 feet, (4) uplift of 350–500 feet, (5) recent subsidence. The last phase affected only the extreme south coast, where even today it is still continuing. On the east coast, however, uplifting still seems to be taking place, and deltas are forming at many of the river-mouths.

Numerous spits have been formed along the coast, all pointing towards the south, as a result of the south-running coastal current. The deltas are situated mainly to the left of the rivers, thus indicating the deflection of the rivers towards the right, which is also shown by the undercutting of the right-hand banks. Along the extremely irregular south coast the ocean current is weaker and more variable, allowing spits and promontories to extend here in all directions.

The most important bay along the east coast is Olga Bay, which was discovered in 1787 by La Pérouse and forms one of the best natural harbours on this coast. The small, rocky islands of Chikachev lie across its entrance. The bay itself has a diameter of nearly 2 miles and an average depth of 80 feet, although in the past it was at least three times this size and reached much farther inland towards the west. At present the valley floors of the rivers flowing into the bay are boggy, and when there is a strong east wind a flow-back into the rivers can be observed. The old marine erosion terraces are very well preserved in the surrounding mountains, at heights of 80, 100, and 400 feet. The low mountains surrounding the bay consist of granite, quartz, porphyry, and sedimentary rocks, which contain mainly iron in addition to lead ores rich in silver and copper. Magnetite containing about 50 per cent iron is mined here. The port of Olga itself has several thousand inhabitants, and Russian peasants have come and settled in the hinterland.

Tetyukhe Bay is of greater economic importance, since the largest deposits of zinc–lead–silver ore in the Soviet Far East are to be found here, only 22 miles from the coast. A narrow-gauge railway connects the mines and ore-dressing plants with the port, which was recently equipped with modern loading facilities. The port has several thousand inhabitants, and here, too, agricultural settlements are found in the hinterland.

The third bay to be mentioned is Vladimir Bay, situated between the other two, and surrounded on all sides by granite mountains up to 750 feet high. The bay has a depth of up to 7 fathoms, and it, too, must have been larger in the past, judging by various nearby fresh-water lakes and marshes. The bay is enclosed by two rocky protruding peninsulas. Vladimir is known for its factories for the extraction of iodine from sea-weed.

Among the more favourable bays along the northern part of the Sikhota-Alin coast is the bay on which is situated the port of Sovietskaya Gavan. This natural harbour, which possesses favourable landing conditions, has a wide flat hinterland fairly densely covered with agricultural settlements. Since the construction of the railway connexion with Komsomolsk, the place has quickly developed into a town of more than 20,000 inhabitants and has been provided with a modern port. Its economy is centred mainly on the timber industry, but there are shipyards as well. The port has a floating dock for ships of up to 5,000 tons gross.

In addition to the places mentioned above, there are several small Russian fishing-places along the coast, usually situated at the mouths of the rivers. Recently noticeable progress has been made in the development of these settlements, as the result of the consolidation and extension of the fishing industry. They are supplied by coastal steamers. Russian settlers are found only where wider bays and broader valleys are conducive to settlement, but in some places they have already advanced 30 miles or more into the country.

The extensive mountain massif of the Sikhota-Alin proper is very sparsely populated, and large parts remain completely empty. It is still possible to come across Tungus Oroches and Olches in the pathless interior along the upper reaches of the Bikin and the Khor, and also along the Mukhen, the Anyu, and the upper Khungari. These peoples are nomads, who live in their pointed tents and depend exclusively on hunting and fishing for their livelihood. Their numbers are constantly decreasing. Otherwise, only a few Russians and Chinese pass through the wilderness of these lonely valleys and mountains, hunting for fur-bearing animals and for the *panten* of the Isyubr deer. There are very few opportunities for agriculture and cattle-breeding, since suitable conditions are found only in the wide valley floors of the main rivers. However, Russian settlers are slowly advancing towards the interior from the valley of the Ussuri, particularly in the valleys of the Khor, the Bikin, and the Iman, along which they have already advanced far into the mountains. It is impossible to say how far the collectivization of agriculture has contributed to the further opening up of the country, or to what extent these measures have helped to keep people on the land already gained.

In these areas, however, it is the natural resources which offer the greatest rewards for human activity. In spite of the ruthless felling of trees in the peripheral areas, the Sikhota-Alin can still be considered rich in forests, and planned utilization has not even begun. Of still greater importance for the future is the abundance of mineral wealth, especially in the south-eastern Sikhota-Alin, which seems to be very richly endowed. Many of these deposits have not yet been adequately explored. The prospects for developing industries based on mining are very favourable, but the area must first be made accessible by the development of better communications.

The extreme south of the Sikhota-Alin is comparatively densely populated, and is also more readily accessible from Vladivostok. This area is so closely connected, both culturally and economically, with the Ussuri–Khanka valley that it will be dealt with together with the latter in the following section.

## THE USSURI–KHANKA PLAIN

An extensive depression runs along the western foot of the Sikhota-Alin for the whole of its length, stretching for more than 800 miles from the Bay of Peter the Great to the mouth of the Amur. Its greater—southern—part is formed by the Ussuri–Khanka plain, which has a total length of 430 miles from its southern end to the mouth of the Ussuri. In contrast to the Sikhota-Alin, it represents the subsided parts of a fault-block, and is joined in the west by the elevated fault-block of the East Manchurian Mountains. According to Ivanov (83), the whole depression was flooded by the sea during the Tertiary era, leaving the Sikhota-Alin showing above the water as a long, narrow island. So far it has been possible to substantiate this only for the southern part of the depression.

The main part of the depression is part of the catchment area of the Ussuri. This part is terminated by a flat watershed (altitude only 630 feet and hardly noticeable from the ground), which separates it from the other part of the depression draining southwards to the river-basin of the Suifun.

The Ussuri originates in the southern Sikhota-Alin, its two sources being the Daubikhe and the Ulakhe. At first it runs entirely within Russian territory, reaching the Manchurian frontier at the mouth of the Sungacha, which comes from Lake Khanka. From here until its confluence with the Amur, the Ussuri forms the frontier. It meanders slowly along the plain with an average velocity of only 1 mile an hour and an average width of more than 1,400 feet. The lower course often divides into many channels, and becomes more than half a mile wide. Navigation is obstructed by many sandbanks, but a regular shipping service is maintained as far as Iman, where the pier is connected with the Ussuri Railway by a branch-line 1 mile long. When water conditions are favourable even the Daubikhe is navigable for about 60 miles, as far as Lasarevo. However, the volume of water is generally very irregular, even during the high-water season in the summer. There is a difference of 30 feet between the extreme water-levels. Heavy downpours of rain often cause the river to rise very quickly, with unforeseeable and disastrous floods as the consequence. Berg (27) gives figures indicating the tremendous amount of water which commonly comes down in such a cloudburst during the summer monsoon. The normal rainfall for September in Voroshilov (the former Nikolsk-Ussuriisk) is $4\frac{1}{4}$ inches, yet in one day of the same month a single enormous downpour once brought down $4\frac{1}{2}$ inches. On August 9th–10th, 1927, at the same place, a cloudburst associated with a typhoon produced $4\frac{3}{4}$ inches of rain within twenty-two hours.

The Ussuri plain stretches along both sides of the river for the whole of its course, merging with the Amur plain towards the north. Compared with the Russian side of the river, the Manchurian side seems to be at a disadvantage. It is lower-lying and has a much larger boggy area than the east side in Russia. The latter also has a very boggy zone running along the river which is exposed to flooding and hardly suitable for agriculture, but, in contrast to the west side, it is narrow, and widens only slightly at the mouths of the tributaries. Moreover, this boggy zone is completely missing where the spurs of the Sikhota-Alin come close to the river. In addition to these spurs there are also hills and ridges which often rise above the alluvial plain. These form patches of drier, usually arable, land where woods and villages are to be found. Consequently, few settlements are located along the river itself in those regions which are affected by flooding. For the same reason, the main zone of cultivation (which starts in the north at Khabarovsk) always avoids the river-bank, keeping to the higher ground. The Ussuri Railway does the same. In the cultivated zone the forests and parklands have been cleared to a width of 60 miles to make room for cultivation, which spreads out even farther along the lower reaches of the Khor, the Bikin, and the Iman. The most important places in the latter three plains are Kondratyevka on the Khor, and Bikin and Iman on their respective rivers. All three places are situated where the rivers are crossed by the railway. In the south the Ussuri plain merges into the agriculturally important Khanka plain.

Lake Khanka lies at an altitude of 227 feet, and has a maximum length of 50 miles and a width of 25–55 miles, covering an area of about 2,000 square miles. At its northern end a narrow sandy headland separates the Little Khanka Lake from the main body of water. The frontier crosses Lake Khanka south of this headland (apportioning roughly a quarter of it to Manchuria), while to the east the frontier follows the Sungacha. Lake Khanka is generally very shallow, with a maximum depth of only 30 feet. It is surrounded by large moors and marshes covered with reeds, and is rapidly being silted up. The western shores consist of Tertiary clays, and are therefore hilly and irregular, with numerous bays and peninsulas. Here, to the west, are found the most favourable agricultural areas in the vicinity of the lake. The flat moors and marshes which surround its other sides extend northwards for 6 miles, and towards the east and south for as much as 20 miles, thus giving an indication of the former size and position of the lake. Where the marshes surrounding it become somewhat drier, they change into meadows covered with high grasses, resembling the Amur prairies of the Seya and the Bureya. The soils in the Ussuri plain and the Khanka plain also resemble those of the Seya and Bureya. Here again it is not chernozem, as is still so often reported, but mainly boggy moors near the lake, surrounded by a wide zone of half-boggy meadow-land, followed by a zone of slightly podsolized soils. The two latter zones are tilled nearly everywhere, and their yields compare favourably with those of the true chernozems. As a result of these conditions, the zone of settlement in the east and south-east starts only at some distance from the actual lake. The reason for the hard struggle that the farmer has to put up here, as well as throughout the whole of the Ussuri region, lies not in the soil but in the climatic conditions, mainly because of the great amount of precipitation during the summer. The winter is very cold, and produces only a thin layer of snow, so that the ground freezes to a great depth. Berg (27/372) states that in Voroshilov the ground freezes to a depth of 6 feet, and at Grodyekovo the frost even penetrates down 8 feet. It is not advisable, therefore, to sow winter grains or clover and lucerne. There is always a certain risk involved in the cultivation of winter grains in this area, although farther south, in the Suifun plain, winter rye can be cultivated without danger. Since the frost penetrates to such a great depth, the ground thaws only at a very late date, but there are no areas of permafrost in the whole of the Ussuri region. Summer wheat is sown from the middle of April until May, and is harvested in the middle of August. Oats are sown two weeks later than the wheat, but are harvested at the same time, while millet is sown still later, but harvested only in the middle of September. The rapid ripening of the grain is indicative of the favourable con-

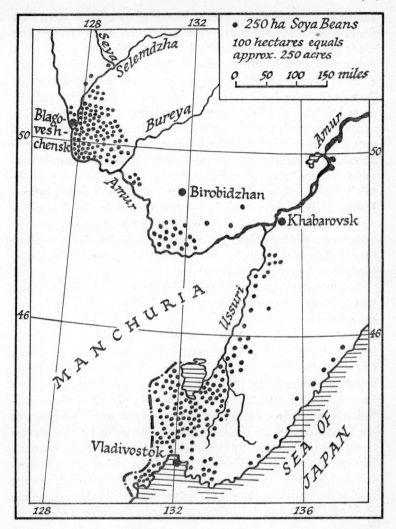

37. THE DISTRIBUTION OF SOYABEANS IN THE AMUR AND COASTAL
REGIONS

ditions for the growth of vegetation in general. The European
varieties of grain sometimes suffer from the strong winds and lack
of moisture at the time of sowing, while in the summer there is
an excess of moisture, hindering fertilization during blossom-
time, and endangering the complete ripening of the crops. However, the indigenous plants grow all the better under cultivation,
and with the right methods even the growing of European plants

can be very successful. Recently throughout the Far Eastern territories wherever there are very humid summers, the Soviet Government has started to introduce new machinery for sowing and cultivation, these machines being adapted for all the special conditions of these areas. The extension of the arable land devoted to growing soyabeans, rice, beans, and millet shows that recently there has been a switch-over to the cultivation of these crops, in accordance with the natural conditions. The noxious fungus, from which the European grains (such as wheat, barley, and oats) suffer particularly, has already been mentioned above. This plant disease appears in the damp, hot areas, especially in the years of unusually heavy rainfall. Arved Schultz (181) has observed that it is characteristic of the Korean and Chinese peasants' fields that they suffer less from the disease than do those of Russian peasants, a difference which presumably is not accidental. The Soviets have taken up the fight against parasites, of which altogether twenty-two kinds have been established so far.

In contrast to the eastern and southern sides of Lake Khanka, which are only sparsely populated, the Tertiary hill-country west of the lake is densely populated and is one of the best agricultural areas. A railway line 80 miles long leads from the Ussuri Railway into this region and has its terminal at Turi-Rog on the north-east corner of the lake, near the frontier. The zone of cultivation, which continues without interruption from the north, runs from the east side of Lake Khanka in a broad strip along the Ussuri Railway, with large extensions spreading out into the valleys of the Daubikhe and the Ulakhe, and also eastwards into the mountains. South of the lake this zone occupies the whole area from the Manchurian frontier to the foothills of the Sikhota-Alin and extends southwards, maintaining roughly the same width, via the Suifun depression to the coast, where it reaches its most southerly limit on the coastal plain along the west side of Peter the Great Bay.

The watershed between the Ussuri and the Suifun is almost flat and morphologically hardly apparent. The Suifun itself crosses the frontier from Manchuria almost exactly on the 44th parallel of latitude, and then immediately turns southwards towards the sea. The river-valley is generally flat and is lined on both sides by a row of dome-shaped hills from 160 to 320 feet high. There are also some steeply rising hills in the valley itself. Towards the east, irregular, gently undulating Tertiary hills form the transition to the foothills of the Sikhota-Alin. South of Lake Khanka, and also

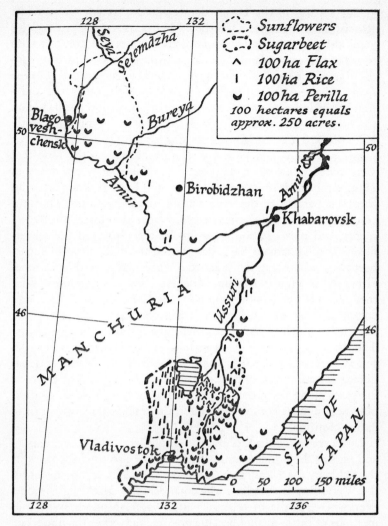

38. THE DISTRIBUTION OF VARIOUS CROPS IN THE AMUR AND
COASTAL REGIONS

in the Suifun basin, numerous oak-woods have been preserved,
giving the landscape a varied and friendly character. The best
agricultural land of the whole area is found in the Suifun basin,
owing to the good drainage conditions. However, agriculture also
makes good progress in the hilly countryside of Tertiary origin,
which includes the most densely populated parts of the Coastal
Region, as well as the whole hinterland of Peter the Great Bay.

The settlers in the Ussuri depression are mainly from White Russia. Their colourless weathered log houses are typical of this area, although the flatter roofs form a noticeable contrast with those of their homeland. The slope of these roofs is probably indicative of the smaller amount of snow they have to carry. In the fields, wheat, oats, and barley are predominant, but maize and a number of indigenous plants such as soyabeans and perilla are on the increase. The settlers in the Khanka plain are predominantly Ukrainians. There are historic reasons for this (as has already been mentioned above), since it was mainly men from the Don that were called upon when the Ussuri Cossack units were raised in 1862. Even so, it is strange that it should be the Ukrainians who form the majority of the settlers in this treeless country. The light colour of their whitewashed clay cottages dominates the settlements, and maize is commonly to be seen between the wheatfields. The Ukrainians have also started the cultivation of sugar-beets here, following the practice of their native land in Europe. However, in a few individual settlements and village communities there already appears the yellow of the Chinese and Korean clay cottages, often enclosed by the traditional clay wall, and in the flat irrigated fields can be seen the light green of the rice-plants. The latter predominate in the vicinity of Lake Khanka, where the soil is very moist. Farther south towards the coast the national differences are not so apparent, although the number of Koreans increases along the coast. They often wear Russian-style clothes, but are still more commonly seen in the traditional white of their native costume.

Cattle are raised throughout the whole area, with cows, horses, and pigs as the principal animals. Cows are also used for work in the fields by the Ukrainians, Koreans, and Chinese, but never by the White Russian settlers. The small Chinese black pig is found everywhere, but is of relatively little value. Modern systematic methods of cattle-raising became possible only after the import of valuable breeds by the Soviet *kolkhozes* and *sovkhozes*.

Melioration works have been carried out under the Soviet regime in the Ussuri region and in the vicinity of Lake Khanka, and further drainage schemes have been planned. Much has been done to improve agricultural methods through the introduction of agricultural machinery, for which this area is particularly suitable. In recent years the cultivation of rice, soyabeans, and sugar-beets has been specially encouraged, the latter having been introduced as a new crop by the Soviet authorities. It is not possible to

THE USSURI–KHANKA PLAIN 321

say anything about the collectivization, which was introduced later in the Far East than in the European part of the Soviet Union, and was carried out very slowly here. Nor can anything be said about the type of organization used in this area, which is occupied by so many different kinds of people.

Voroshilov is the centre of this important agricultural region, and is located where the Ussuri Railway meets the Manchurian Railway, the latter re-entering Russian territory here after leaving Transbaikalia and running across Manchuria. The town lies 100 feet above sea level, and at a distance of 63 miles from Vladivostok. It has 70,600 inhabitants (1939) and is the centre of an active foodstuffs industry. It possesses a large oil-and-fat *kombinat* for the processing of soyabeans, which also has associated with it a soap-boiling factory and a cosmetics factory. The town is of special importance as the site of the two earliest and largest sugar refineries of the Soviet Far East. The next most important place after Voroshilov is the town of Spassk (about 30,000 inhabitants), situated south-east of Lake Khanka, which has the largest cement factory of the Soviet Far East, in addition to flour-mills and oil refineries. The town of Grodyekovo (about 10,000 inhabitants) must also be mentioned as being the last place on the Manchurian Railway before the frontier. The town is already within the western mountains, but in spite of its proximity to the frontier its wooden houses impress one as being typically Russian.

From Voroshilov the railway first runs southwards through hilly country, then crosses some low ridges of the Sikhota-Alin (about 20 miles from Voroshilov) and enters the peninsula of Muravyev-Amurski, terminating at Vladivostok—the principal town and the most important Pacific port of the Soviet Union.

Vladivostok was founded in 1860; in 1872 the base of the Russian Pacific Fleet was moved here from Nikolayevsk, and since then it has been the centre of the country's military power on the Pacific. Economic development, on the other hand, has been slow. In 1882 the population was only 5,000. It was about this time that regular shipping services were established between Vladivostok and the Russian ports on the Black Sea, but the rise of the town to its later position as economic centre of the region began only after the construction of the Ussuri–Manchurian Railway. It was because of this railway that Vladivostok developed into an important Pacific port, handling mainly goods in transit, and providing this service for the whole of northern Manchuria as well. Its growth as a distribution centre has been paralleled in more recent

x

times by the growth of local industry. The population was 21,000 in 1897, 59,000 in 1914, 107,980 in 1927, and 206,400 in 1939, while at present it probably numbers more than 300,000.

The town lies on the deep and well-protected bay of the 'Golden Horn', at the southern end of the Muravyev peninsula, opposite the large and heavily indented Russki Island. The peninsula is separated from the island by the 'Eastern Bosporus', which runs from Amur Bay in the west to Ussuri Bay in the east. The bay is unique and is one of the best natural harbours in the world, as is indicated by its various names. The 'Golden Horn' penetrates northwards into the Muravyev peninsula and then turns almost in a right angle towards the east (see map). The north–south part forms the outer harbour and is just under 2 miles long, while the east–west part forms the inner harbour and is 2 miles long. The width of the 'Golden Horn' is 2,600–3,300 feet, the depth being 5 fathoms in the inner bay and 15 at the entrance. It is surrounded by hills which rise to 150–300 feet (even on the Shkota peninsula, which separates the outer bay from Amur Bay), thus protecting the harbour from the cold west and north-west winds. In spite of this the harbour is ice-bound for three to four months every year, and three ice-breakers are in operation all the time during the winter to keep the harbour and the entrance free from ice. The commercial port occupies mainly the outer harbour and the western part of the inner harbour, while the innermost part of the latter has been made into a naval port which is closed to commercial shipping. There are additional port installations on the 'Eastern Bosporus' and on the outer side of the Shkota peninsula. The following separate installations are found in the harbour:

1. The Krestovaya Docks, stretching along the foot of the Krestovaya Mountain (310 feet high), which has quays 1,600 feet long and is of special importance in the winter because it is easiest to keep the water open in this part.

2. The 'Egersheld', which also serves as the quarantine port. The quays here are 3,150 feet long, and the busiest season is the summer. These docks were specially constructed to handle the transhipment of grain, and they possess the most modern grain elevators and loading installations.

3. The docks of the 'Volunteer Fleet' (Dobrovolny Flot). The name derives from the organization of the 'Volunteer Fleet', founded in 1870, which was the first to establish communications between the motherland and the Far East.

39. VLADIVOSTOK AND THE SOUTHERN COAST

4. The customs pier and the so-called 'Broad Jetty', which occupies the north-west corner of the 'Golden Horn'.

5. The commercial docks, including the 'Broad Pier' (Shiroki Pir) along the south side of the bay, with extensive shunting yards and the largest warehouses. The quays here are over half a mile long.

6. The timber docks, situated slightly more to the south on Cape Churkin.

7. The Ussuri Railway Docks, on the west side of the Shkota peninsula, with extensive facilities for handling mineral oils and petroleum.

8. The Semyonovsky Basar, also situated on the Amur Bay side of the peninsula, serving mainly coastal traffic.

Altogether the quays have a length of more than $2\frac{1}{2}$ miles, and the network of tracks which encompasses the harbour and all its installations is 220 miles long (1937). The harbour was developed still further in the years between 1933 and 1939, and is now capable of handling the transhipment of 4–5 million tons a year. In the early years of its development, Vladivostok had difficulties with its water supply, but these have now been met by the erection of a large reservoir on the so-called 'Second Small River' (Vtoraya Rechka), and by the construction of a filtration plant holding 100,000 tons of water which is situated on the inner shore of Ulis Bay and is supplied with water from the small River Lipovi.

Vladivostok is built on a narrow site, stretching along the 'Golden Horn' and also along the shores of Amur Bay, with one district of the town lying on the northern tip of Russki Island opposite the entrance to the 'Golden Horn'. The hills rise quickly from the coast, and the rows of houses mounting up the slopes give the town an almost southern appearance. The main thoroughfares generally run parallel to the coast, and the side streets are often so steep that they make all vehicular traffic difficult. In contrast to the close-packed nature of the town, with the monotonous blocks of flats and business premises pressed so closely together, the varied green surroundings adorned by lovely summer-houses in beautiful settings strike one as particularly inviting. Most of the people are Russians, but the proportion of Chinese and Koreans is quite large. Out of a total population of 107,000 in 1926 there were 23,400 Chinese, 7,000 Koreans, and 600 Japanese. As a rule the Chinese are unmarried, and prefer to work as dock labourers.

Vladivostok is now an industrial town as well as a port. The fishing industry takes first place, and is distributed among numerous

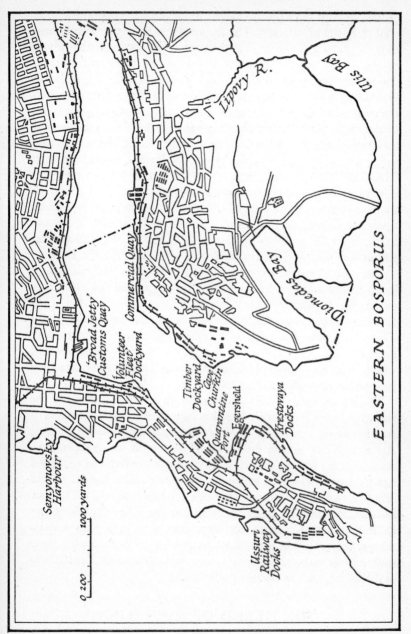

Semyonovsky Harbour

'Broad Jetty' Customs Quay

'Volunteer Fleet' Dockyard

Commercial Quay

Timber Dockyard

Cape Churkin

Quarantine Port

Egersheld

Krestovaya Docks

Ussuri Railway Docks

1000 yards

0 200

Lipovy R.

Ulis Bay

Diomedas Bay

EASTERN BOSPORUS

40. THE HARBOUR OF VLADIVOSTOK

centres in both the immediate and more distant surroundings, as well as in the town itself. The industry's main activity is the tinning of crabs and fish collected at many places along the whole of the south coast. The most important of these are situated either on the coastal bays or on the islands, the largest being Nakhodka (the terminus of a railway from Suchan), Sarubino, and the islands of Popov, Reineke, and Putyatin. In second place is the timber industry, which utilizes the valuable deciduous timber and produces furniture, plywood, and matches. Besides these two major industries, the town has rice-mills, leather works, and soap factories. Vladivostok is of great importance as a naval port and dockyard, and it also possesses aircraft factories. A mineral-oil refinery supplies the whole of the town's industry and transport. Foremost among the numerous scientific institutions in Vladivostok is the local branch of the Academy of Science, which has been responsible for much of the exploratory work in the Far East.

The area round Vladivostok is also richly provided with other industries in addition to the fishing industry, and here, too, it is the timber industry which is particularly noteworthy. It is concentrated mainly at Shkotovo (about 10,000 inhabitants) and Tigrovka (about 5,000 inhabitants), both situated on the railway line to Suchan, as well as at Okeanskaya (about 2,300 inhabitants), which is situated north of Vladivostok and has a large timber *kombinat* producing plywood for export.

The industries in Vladivostok and throughout the whole of the southern Ussuri region are based on the plentiful local supplies of coal in the region. Apart from several small coal-mining centres, Artem and Suchan are the principal centres of production. Production at the former was three times that of the latter in 1938, and has increased still further in the meantime. The Ugolnaya and Trudovaya coal deposits are part of the Artem coal-field. The new railway line running along the west coast of Peter the Great Bay to Posyet and Kraskino connects the most important coastal places, where fishing is the main occupation. There are also some deer-raising *sovkhozes* in the same general area, near Pestshanaya and Krabbe, and on Gamov peninsula.

## THE ISLAND OF SAKHALIN

Sakhalin became part of Russia by the treaties of Aigun (1858) and Peking (1860), but until 1875 Russia had to share the possession of the island with the Japanese, who in earlier times had erected numerous factories on the southern part of the island. Later as a result of the unfortunate Russo-Japanese War, Russia lost the southern part to Japan, and the 50th parallel was fixed as the frontier, but the end of the Second World War brought Russia renewed possession of the whole island.

Sakhalin covers an area of 30,000 square miles, and extends in an almost meridional direction for roughly 600 miles. Formerly dreaded as a penal settlement of the Tsarist Empire, the island is also ill-famed for its rigorous climate. The famous Russian writer Chekhov writes: 'Sakhalin has no climate at all; there is always just bad dull weather.' The island owes this unfriendly reputation to the influence of the cool Sea of Okhotsk, which has most of the island completely at its mercy. The greater part of Sakhalin is covered with dense forests reminiscent of the Siberian taiga. Along the coast there are extensive moss steppes of a tundra-like character which give the countryside an almost Arctic appearance, but it has a milder character locally in the south. Following the recent discovery and exploitation of rich coal and mineral-oil deposits, the island is becoming more and more a centre of economic interest, with the population growing quickly and settling down. The bad reputation of the island is consequently beginning to disappear.

According to its relief, Sakhalin can be divided into two parts: a larger mountainous area in the south, and a smaller, gently undulating or hilly area in the north. The mountainous south consists of two mountain chains which run lengthwise along the island and are separated from each other by a rift valley, which is drained to the north by the River Tym and to the south by the Poronay.

The eastern mountains, with Nevelesky (6,603 feet) and Lopatin (5,510 feet) as their highest peaks, are dissected to a greater extent than the western mountains, which are generally lower, with the highest peak—Aimi Yama—reaching only 5,382 feet. In external appearance the eastern mountains have more of a definite crest. They consist mainly of metamorphic rocks, slate, sandstone, and a marble-like limestone—the same rocks which appear in the mountain ranges along the edge of the continent. There are intrusions of syenite, diabase, andesite, and basalt at numerous places in the sedimentary rock, but there is no granite. Most of the sediments of the eastern mountains are considered to belong to the Palaeozoic era, with Mesozoic strata less developed and represented only locally. In the western mountains the situation is quite different. Apart from some older rocks, these mountains are composed mainly of rocks of Tertiary age, with a large proportion of Jurassic and Cretaceous rocks. The latter appear mainly in the south-western part and become more common in the former Japanese territory. Weathering is very rapid because of the humid climate, and is particularly marked in the treeless parts of the mountains. The sharper outlines and greater variety of relief in the western range are attributable mainly to the varying powers of resistance of its constituent rocks, the quickest to weather being the flinty and loamy slates.

The Tertiary deposits (which are very widespread all over Sakhalin) and the Cretaceous sediments have been considerably faulted. The mountain-building processes which determined the present relief began after the deposition of the most recent Pliocene formations, and finished before the formation of the horizontally bedded marine sediments deposited in Quaternary times, when the sea covered large parts of this area. However, the present mountains of Sakhalin cannot be traced back solely to Tertiary dislocations because, in some as yet undetermined period of the earth's history, the older strata were already folded to form mountain chains with the same strike-lines as today. It was therefore only a secondary folding that occurred during the Tertiary era. The post-Pliocene inundation by the sea separated Sakhalin from the continent and flooded all the low-lying parts of the island. It even penetrated between the two mountain ranges so that these rose above the sea as two large and lofty islands (207/265). A series of uplifts which followed later, possibly interspersed with a series of slight subsidences, caused the island to rise from the sea in its present form. These movements have not yet terminated, as is indicated by the earth-tremors which have continued to occur up to the present time. No traces of glaciation have been found anywhere.

The valley between the two mountain chains is a rift valley 3–20 miles wide, which is covered with post-Pliocene marine deposits over the whole of its length. The watershed which separates the north-flowing Tym from the south-flowing Poronay lies at an altitude of only 500 feet. The valley floor is mainly level and covered with fertile clay. Because of the protection afforded by the two mountain ranges, the valley has a more continental climate, with the warm summers which accord with its southern position. Many Russians have therefore settled here in a number of villages.

Towards the north both mountain ranges recede from the coast and change into gently undulating hilly country, which fills the northern part of the island and never rises above 1,600 feet. The island's two main ridges and the intervening rift valley still stand out as features of the relief far towards the north. The coast itself lies beside a wide plain consisting of recent as well as post-Pliocene deposits, and covered mainly by tundra vegetation mixed with bushes. The plain varies in width, the widest part being in the north round Sakhalin Bay, and it is terminated by a sharply defined terrace 7–20 feet high which marks the beginning of the hill country. As a rule the latter is covered with dense taiga composed of pines and larches. The watersheds hardly show up in the relief, but are marked by the growth of taller and denser forests. In some places the foothills come very close to the coast and form a steep cliff 50–85 feet high (207/266). In these places the taiga comes very close to the sea.

The Schmidt peninsula, which bears this name in honour of the famous Sakhalin explorer, forms the extreme northern tip of the island. This peninsula represents on a small scale a true copy of the geological and tectonic structure of the southern part of the island, even the intrusive rocks being the same. Here, too, we find eastern and western ranges of mountains separated by a depression. The eastern mountains reach an altitude of 2,323 feet in the 'Tri Brata' ('Three Brothers') peaks. This range generally slopes steeply down towards the sea, and in the north forms the rocky Cape Elizabeth—the northernmost point of Sakhalin. The western mountains also drop down steeply towards the sea, but this range reaches a height of only 1,332 feet. The intervening depression terminates in the north with a lake, which is separated from the ocean by a narrow headland. The most productive oil-fields in Sakhalin today lie on the isthmus which connects the Schmidt peninsula with the main part of the island.

Generally speaking, the coast of Sakhalin is little indented, the west coast being the most regular. In contrast to the latter, the north and east coasts form typical emergent coasts, with numerous barrier beaches. Baikal Bay in the north is formed by the largest of these bars, and is navigable by coastal shipping drawing up to 12 feet of water. On the east side of the bay is the oil-port of Moskalvo, which is connected by rail with the oil-fields on the eastern side of the peninsula. The characteristic features of emergent coast-lines are even more pronounced along the east coast, where the spits and bars are almost continuous. The lagoons which are thus formed are extremely narrow, but are often up to 100 miles long and, in contrast to the rough sea, permit well-protected water-borne traffic along the coast. Sandbanks or dunes are seldom found here. Wide tundra-like moss-steppes spread out along the lower reaches of most of the rivers, particularly on the Tym; they consist of layers of peat up to 50 feet thick and are the favoured pastures for reindeer (as they are also on the west side of the island).

The differences between the west and east sides of the island in the formation of the coast-line are attributable mainly to the prevailing ocean currents. On the east side the current runs southwards along the coast, while on the west side there is a southflowing current along the continental coast inside the Bay of Tartary, and a north-flowing current along the Sakhalin coast. The latter, however, does not flow regularly, since it varies in relation to the tides (as proved by Zhdanko (188)) and erosion of the coastline has therefore only just begun.

Climatically the low-lying northern part of Sakhalin is at the greatest disadvantage, because it is completely open to the raw influence of the Sea of Okhotsk. The Dauric larch and the Ayan fir are therefore equally common here. Towards the south are deciduous trees of the same kind as found in the Sikhota-Alin, intermingled with the taiga. As a result of the humid climate, mossy areas appear near the coast, as well as meadows in the more sheltered flood-plains of the rivers. These support a very strong growth of grass which reaches a height of 10–13 feet in some places, the principal species being *Senecio cannabifolia* and *Petasites iaponicus*. In the mountains the characteristic trees are firs and pines, with the stone birch (*Betula ermani*) found at higher altitudes. In the sheltered valleys pure deciduous forests are fairly common. The appearance of the wild Kurile bamboo (*Sasa Kurilensis*) is worthy of notice, although it is limited to the western mountains. In some places it forms thickets of almost tropical density through which it is very difficult to pass. This is the only region of the Soviet Union where bamboo grows wild.

The indigenous population of North Sakhalin is small in numbers, consisting of several thousand Gilyaks and Oroks. The former are found mainly at the mouths of the rivers along the coast, and live by fishing and hunting. The Oroks (known as Olches on the mainland) are mainly reindeer-breeders, and here, too, they live as nomads, although only within a limited area, moving between the moss steppes where they spend the summers and the edge of the taiga where they spend the winters. There are only modest numbers of reindeer.

The Russian population in North Sakhalin has greatly increased during the last three decades. In 1926 the Russians were estimated to number 20,000, but before the Second World War they had already increased to more than 100,000, and since then they have increased still further. They are concentrated mainly in three areas: first, Aleksandrovsk and the western coastal strip, which is important economically because of its coal-mining; second, the petroleum areas in the north and along the northern part of the east coast; third, to a smaller extent, the valley of the Tym and the Poronay. In the latter the population is mostly agrarian, although arable farming is generally still little developed in Sakhalin. In recent years the Soviet administration has taken great pains to secure the food supply for the industrial population in both the coal and petroleum districts, relying at least partly on local resources. The total area under grain has been increased, particularly in the sheltered longitudinal valley, where there are quite a number of *kolkhozes* and *sovkhozes*, although even here grain production yields only small surpluses. In the other areas climatic conditions are too unfavourable to encourage large-scale grain-growing. With regard to the production of potatoes, cabbages, and other vegetables, the position is quite different; remarkable results have been achieved, the high yields of potatoes being especially noteworthy. Recently, as a result of this experience, a systematic increase in potato production has been initiated, in order to make possible the large-scale breeding of pigs (in addition to ensuring supplies for human consumption). Numerous reports indicate that this scheme has proved successful.

The capital of North Sakhalin is Aleksandrovsk, and the district capital is now Yuzhno-Sakhalinsk. The former has about 20,000 inhabitants, and is the port of export for the coal-mining areas. The port has recently been extended and provided with modern loading equipment, the installations extending far out into the sea because of the flat bottom of the Bay of Tartary. Okha, with about 25,000 inhabitants, is the second most important town, and is the most important centre of the petroleum area on the north-east coast. During the last war the town acquired its own harbour, which is said to be open throughout the whole year. South of Okha lies Ekhabi, which has been frequently mentioned recently because of its rising petroleum output. A railway and an oil pipe-line run from Okha to the oil-port of Moskalvo, which is situated on the east side of Baikal Bay in the northern part of the island. Numerous permanently inhabited fishing-bases have been built during recent years along the coast, enlivening the coastal scene. The greater part of the interior is still undeveloped, having been left up to now to the indigenous peoples and their primitive economy.

In South Sakhalin (known by the Japanese as Karafuto) the natural regions continue in accordance with the general description given above for the north. The western mountains (rising up to 4,500 feet) form the backbone of this part of the island and stretch southwards beyond the 46th parallel, while the eastern mountains already come to an end north of the 49th parallel. The Poronay valley ends even earlier, after having attained a width of as much as 20 miles.

As in North Sakhalin, here, too, the greater part of the country is covered with indigenous forests. They are composed of the same species as in the north, but the proportion of deciduous trees is larger, increasing particularly on the lower slopes and on the terminal spurs of the western mountains. Tundra-like moss steppes appear here, too, in spite of the milder climatic conditions resulting from the more southern position. The indigenous peoples—the Oroks and Tungus—continue to be reindeer-breeders even today.

The population of South Sakhalin amounted to 332,000 in 1936, and 412,000 in 1940, the increase being attributable mainly to immigration from Japan. Of the original indigenous peoples there are barely 2,000 left; among these the Ainos, numbering 1,500, are the largest group, the remainder being composed of Gilyaks, Oroks, and other Tungus tribes.

The economic importance of Sakhalin is based on the timber reserves of its forests, its coal deposits, and the abundance of fish in the coastal waters. The Japanese contributed much to the economic progress of the country, the development of communications being particularly to their credit. They built 405 miles of railway lines, and also improved the roads sufficiently to allow regular bus traffic. However, the building of communication lines was generally limited to the areas near the coast and the more southern parts of the island, while the greater part of the interior was left more to its own devices (as was also the case in North Sakhalin). The most important coal-fields are also situated near the coast. Production of coal (from a large number of pits) was raised by the Japanese to 2 million tons by the beginning of the last war, of which 500,000 tons were exported to Japan, the remainder being used in the country itself, mainly for the timber industry. The latter was developed on a large scale by the Japanese, who started systematically in 1929 to build up a pulp and paper industry for supplying their home economy with these products. Finally, shortly before the war there were eleven large pulp and paper mills in the country. Their production represented 90 per cent of the industrial output of South Sakhalin, and roughly 60 per cent of the total production. In addition, South Sakhalin produced large quantities of wood in the form of sawn timber and plywood. South Sakhalin was also very important to the Japanese as a fishing base, since it yielded a large surplus. One thing the Japanese did not achieve was to secure self-sufficiency in food production for the area, which remained dependent on imports of food in spite of the strenuous efforts of the Japanese to expand both arable and mixed farming.

As soon as the Soviets had taken over the country following the evacuation of the Japanese, they tried hard to repopulate it and to get production going again. Several reports are available which refer to the founding of *kolkhozes* and *sovkhozes*, and there are frequent reports about the equipping of new fishing bases and fish-processing centres. There is hardly any news about the revival of the coal and timber industries, but since the Soviet Union attaches such great importance to industry, it can be assumed that everything possible has been done to get production started again.

## THE REGION OF THE AMGUN AND THE UD

This region comprises the whole of the heavily indented coastal strip around the south-west corner of the Sea of Okhotsk, from the Amgun river-basin in the south-east to the Ud river-basin in the north-west. The coast is better known than the interior, which has been explored very little—especially between the Bureya Mountains and the coast. The raw climate of Okhotsk with its heavy precipitation, the very marshy character of the valley floors, the dense and almost impenetrable taiga of the mountains, interrupted only by high-altitude moors, and the general loneliness of these areas—all these combine to make the region unattractive.

The landscape is generally very diversified in character. Low wooded mountain ranges alternate with chains of higher mountains, while between them are deeply incised, flat-bottomed valleys which often widen into large plains. The mountain ranges run mainly towards the north-east, and in some parts form faulted continuations of the Bureya Mountains or outliers of the Dzhagdy range. Some mountain ridges extend into the sea as peninsulas, with the intervening bays apparently representing valleys formed by subsidence. The numerous islands lying off-shore, collectively called the Shantar Islands, enhance the impression of a mountainous landscape partially sunk into the sea. Three large bays penetrate southwards far into the country: narrow Nikolya Bay in the east, 30 miles long and up to 12 miles wide; broad Ulban Bay in the centre; and Tugur Bay in the west, into which flows the Tugur River. Compared with these three bays, all of which penetrate deeply into the country with heavily indented coast-lines, the large rounded Bay of Ud pushing westwards at the western end of the region seems rather monotonous. The whole coast, from the mouth of the Amur to the mouth of the Ud, is generally rocky, particularly where the mountain ranges break off steeply towards the sea. The mountains consist mainly of loamy and flinty slates and sandstones, generally folded very steeply with north-easterly lines of strike. Granite and porphyry appear only rarely among the sedimentary rocks, and where they do they are easily recognizable from afar because of the massive dome-shaped outlines they produce. The beaches and the sea floor are littered with remnants of shells, particularly *Balanus*, *Cardium Californiense*, *Natica aperta*, *Trokhus Shantaricus*, &c. (127). The channel between the Great Shantar Islands and the mainland is very shallow, and is nowhere deeper than 13 fathoms. The sea is even shallower between the individual islands, and Yakshina Bay, which penetrates into Great Shantar Island from the south, is not navigable at low tide. The 50-metre (27-fathom) contour line runs directly westwards from the northern tip of Sakhalin peninsula and encloses all the islands, so that in this part it runs 60–75 miles from the continental coast. In contrast with this, the sea along the Okhotsk coast (running north-eastwards from the Bay of Ud) is 110 fathoms deep 3–5 miles from the coast. The tides are very noticeable between the islands, particularly in the bays, with local changes in level of 13–23 feet.

The raw influence of the Sea of Okhotsk, which affects the whole area, is due, among other things, to the current flowing along the coast from the north-east, carrying with it vast masses of ice which accumulate between the islands and the mainland in the spring. This same current is responsible for the formation of the regular coast-line running south-eastwards from Nikolayevsk Bay to the mouth of the Amur, with its attendant lagoons and barrier beaches. The silting up of the Amur *Liman* in the north, between the mainland and the northern tip of Sakhalin, is also one of the disadvantages caused by this current.

The Great Shantar Island consists of the same geological material as the mountains of the mainland, with their north-easterly strike-lines. The whole group of islands can therefore be regarded as parts of the mainland cut off by the sea. Great Shantar Island is formed of a jumbled group of dome-shaped peaks and mountains rising up to 3,300 feet and covered with forests, with the intervening areas covered with mossy moors, bogs, and lakes. The other small islands are also partly covered with woods which, combined with the generally rocky formation, produce a very picturesque landscape. All the islands are uninhabited.

The Amgun, with a total length of more than 500 miles (of which roughly 250 miles are said to be navigable), comes from the eastern slopes of the middle Bureya Mountains, and flows north-eastwards at first between these and the Badzhalsky Mountains. Then it enters a plain, which widens greatly along the middle reaches of the river to become as much as 60 miles across. Here fairly important rivers flow into the Amgun from all sides, among them the Kerbi coming from the west, which has already been mentioned in connexion with the rich gold deposits found along its upper reaches. The plain itself, from which rise occasional isolated hills and mountains, is covered with moors, marshes, and lakes. Among the latter, the best known is Lake Chukchagirskoye, with its numerous islands. Along the rest of its course the Amgun is characterized by a wide and humid valley floor. The valley is accompanied to north and south by mountainous country up to 1,600 feet high, with gentle slopes covered with woods. Occasionally the mountains come quite close to the river and then drop down steeply to the valley floor. Along the lower reaches of the Amgun the valley widens considerably and joins the Amur plain. This part of the river is ill-famed, since the gradient is so negligible that the river divides into an endless number of channels, backwaters, and elongated pools, and meanders tortuously across the area in a series of large and small bends.

The wide, flat marshes and moors here produce a picture totally different from the meadow steppes of the Amur plains. The latter are also generally flat, but are slightly more irregular in their surface formation because of the turf banks and mossy hills which stand between shining stretches of water. However, the greatest difference lies in the long and irregular rows of trees and bushes which wind their way through the wide plains, lining both sides of the rivers and making their courses recognizable from afar. Along the Amgun these trees are mainly deciduous. It is typical of all the cool, humid areas between the Amgun and the Ud that woods grow only where there is relatively better drainage, that is, where both surface and ground waters are moving. In this respect conditions are best along the rivers and on the slopes, while the flat ridges and plateaux are less favourably placed because the sphagnum moors frequently make the trees 'water sick' and cause their slow death. The traveller must keep away from the valley floors and use the slightly elevated hills and ridges. Even here he often meets impassable bogs and sphagnum moors on the level areas of the watershed, and he can therefore progress most easily along the slopes.

The Amgun region is almost uninhabited, with a few people to be met only here and there along the largest rivers. These are mainly Gilyaks in their timber cottages, although there are also a few Tungus (Olches and Nigidales) who live by fishing and hunting. Along the Amgun itself there are also a few Russian settlers who live together in small villages, the most important of which is Kerbi, situated at the mouth of the Kerbi River. The Amgun is navigable up to this point by small steamers, which carry the necessary provisions for further transport up the Kerbi by barges to the gold-fields.

The valley of the Tugur is as wide as 12 miles in some places, and has a similar character. Here, too, mossy moors are found high up in the valley, and marshiness is increased by the presence of permafrost.

The river-system of the Ud is very extensive, since the river collects all the run-off from both the Dzhagdy and the Dzhugdzhur Mountains. (A left-hand tributary—the Maya, which is more than 200 miles long—separates the Stanovoy Mountains from the Dzhugdzhur Mountains.) Here, too, the traveller encounters the greatest difficulties because of the marshy ground. The Ud is a mountain river flowing swiftly in a stony bed and interrupted by numerous rocky islands, becoming calmer only in its lower reaches. Situated here is a small Russian village called Udskoye, which is the centre for trapping fur-bearing animals, still a very profitable occupation in these remote mountain areas.

# THE OKHOTSK COASTAL REGION

This area comprises all the western and northern coastal areas of the Sea of Okhotsk, starting at the Ud in the south and ending at Penzhina Bay in the north. Since this stretch of coast is more than 1,200 miles long, there are local variations in conditions, but, on the whole, the predominant character is retained throughout of a rough forested mountain area adverse to cultivation, with a humid cool climate less suitable for human beings than the harsh contrasts of the continental interior.

The area can be divided into two parts, according to the structure and appearance of the coast-line: a south-western part with a smooth coast-line between the Ud and Okhotsk, the character of which is determined solely by the Dzhugdzhur mountain range lying parallel to the coast; and a north-eastern part with a very irregular coast-line (characterized by numerous peninsulas, islands and small bays) in which mountain ranges run towards the coast at irregular intervals.

In the western part of the Dzhugdzhur coastal area the mountain ranges come very close to the shore, leaving a narrow coastal strip which widens only at the mouths of the rivers to allow room for human settlement. The Primorski range, which extends from the Ud to the Ayan between the Dzhugdzhur range and the coast, breaks off very abruptly and steeply down to the sea. The Dzhugdzhur Mountains consist of several ridges running parallel to the coast, and are composed mainly of granite, gneiss, and porphyry. They form an unbroken wall separating the coast from the interior, with an average height of more than 3,000 feet and a few unsheltered passes situated at almost the same altitude. The watershed lies close to the coast, so that there are numerous short rivers all along the coast which flow very rapidly to the sea down the steep slopes. The deeply incised valleys opening towards the sea form a sharp contrast with the generally horizontal line formed by the rounded domes of the mountain massif. The valleys are filled with taiga and an almost impenetrable undergrowth; their narrow floors are covered with boulders and stones, and they offer human beings little chance of penetrating into the mountains. Since the only possible approaches from the coast into the interior are along these deeply incised and steeply rising valleys, the result is the almost complete isolation of the coastal strip from its hinterland which is especially characteristic of this area. The mountains are covered to any appreciable extent only on the slopes, while the

Y

heights carry nothing but scattered stunted trees and are completely bare at the highest points. Most of the passes are above the tree-line and can hardly be used during the winter because of the heavy snowstorms.

The interior of the mountain range is almost uninhabited, and apart from occasional hunters there are only a few Tungus who pass across the lonely mountains with their small reindeer herds. Along the coast there are a number of Russian fishing settlements, among which the principal place is Ayan, situated on a favourable natural harbour about half a mile long and half a mile wide, and 3–21 fathoms deep. The whole of the Dzhugdzhur coast is blocked by ice during the winter, so that the harbour is usable only during the summer. Even then, constant strong winds from the sea often make it difficult, and sometimes even impossible, for ships to leave the harbour. Starting from Ayan is a road to Yakutsk, which leads by a steep ascent across the mountains as far as Nelkan on the Maya, a left-hand tributary of the Aldan; from there the journey continues along the rivers, first along the Maya and then along the Aldan as far as the Lena. Ayan is ill-famed because of its high annual precipitation, and it therefore does not make much progress in spite of its favourable natural harbour; today it has only about 1,000 inhabitants, although it has been established for quite a long time.

Towards the north, the Dzhugdzhur range turns away from the coast and makes room for a wide coastal plain which advances far into the country. It is along this stretch of coast that the village-town of Okhotsk is situated, at the mouth of the Okhota, which forms a good natural harbour. It is the oldest Russian port on the Pacific. There is an overland route from Okhotsk to Yakutsk, which is a less diffcult route than the one from Ayan, and there is also a telegraph line connecting the town with Yakutsk. Okhotsk is today an important fishing centre. Along the coast as well as in the hinterland there are numerous Russian settlers who are engaged mainly in raising cattle, which thrive on the natural pastures of the alluvial plain; they also grow potatoes and other vegetables. The Russians have been joined by the Tungus Lamutes, who are engaged in the same type of cultivation as the Russians, in addition to their fishing. They now take the same care of their cattle that they used to take of their reindeer in former generations. Farther into the interior the reindeer Tungus still exist in fairly large numbers, living a nomadic life moving between the valley floors and the mountain tundra.

North-east of Okhotsk the coastal landscape becomes more varied in character. Many maps of this area still show an unbroken mountain range running parallel to the coast, but at least between Okhotsk and the Yama (a river to the east of Pyagina peninsula) this does not exist. On the contrary, lateral spurs of the Cherski Mountains meet the coast almost at right angles, separated by comparatively wide and lengthy valleys stretching from the coast into the interior. An additional orographic feature, limited to the peninsulas and islands, appears farther to the east, resulting in an even more interesting picture. This is a very much deranged and badly-broken-up mountain chain running roughly parallel to the coast, which is considered by scientific authorities today to belong to the inner arc of Tertiary folded mountains of East Siberia. It is believed that this mountain chain was once linked with Sakhalin, and parts of it are also supposed to reappear in Taygonos peninsula, in the western part of the Penzhina plain, and in the northern part of the Anadyr region. In the coastal area itself, this mountain chain appears in the Chutnavar Mountains, which form a wide peninsula running from west to east and separated from the mainland mountains by an extensive parallel valley through which flows the Kasa-Tauy River. (The mainland mountains are the lateral spurs of the Cherski Mountains, their ridges and intervening valleys lying at right angles to the Kasa-Tauy valley; thus the contrasting structure is clearly evident here within a small area.) Otherwise, this Tertiary mountain chain appears only on the peninsulas of Koni, Pyagina, and Taygonos, and as island remnants.

East of the Yama River begin the Kolyma Mountains, running north-eastwards parallel to the coast as far as the hinterland of Taygonos peninsula, and then turning north-north-eastwards into the interior of the country. The watershed of this range (in contrast to that of the Dzhugdzhur range) lies far inland, the mountains sloping gradually down towards the coast. The range is divided up by several comparatively wide, eroded valleys which lie roughly perpendicular to the coast. The general impression is therefore the same as farther west between Okhotsk and the Yama, where the spurs of the Cherski Mountains also lie at right angles to the coast. The difference is that in the coastal area of the Kolyma Mountains the valley floors and the coastal plains are less extensive. In the Gizhiga Bay hinterland, between the Kolyma Mountains and the Taygonos ridge, there is an extensive plain of Tertiary deposits, in which coal-bearing strata have recently been discovered. They contain layers of brown coal and lignite of economic importance. Even along the coast of Gizhiga Bay natural outcrops of productive seams can be seen.

The landscape characteristics of the coastal area east of Okhotsk are an obvious reflection of its more northern position. As a rule the sheltered valley floors are covered with good meadows rich in hay which form useful pastures for cows and horses. The water-courses are bordered by willow-bushes and rows of poplars, with birches appearing as well farther upstream. The valley slopes are generally covered with larch-woods, which become thinner and shorter towards the top. The mountain-ridges themselves are either bare or overgrown with brushwood and reindeer moss.

Because of the good variety of conditions offered by the sheltered valley floors together with the ridges covered by moss-tundra, the coastal hinterland is much more inhabited by nomadic Tungus reindeer-herders than is the case along the Dzhugdzhur coast. In spite of its more northerly position there are also a greater number of settlements along this stretch of coast than along the Dzhugdzhur coast. There are fewer Russians to be found here, the chief inhabitants being the sea-Tungus, who, besides fishing, grow a certain amount of potatoes and other vegetables. They also keep cows and horses, which is especially noteworthy because in this respect they are following the Russian example. At present, however, they are far from utilizing all the possibilities for cattle-raising, and the future in this respect looks most favourable, especially as there is sufficient hay to secure adequate winter feeding. The most important places along the coast are Tauysk, Ola, Yamsk, and Gizhiga, all situated on rivers of the same name. Communication between these places is maintained in summer by small coastal steamers, and in winter by reindeer-, horse-, and dog-sledges along the coastal route which runs from Okhotsk to Kamchatka.

More important than all these coastal places is the newly founded city of Magadan, which was built only shortly before the last world war and has already far surpassed old Okhotsk in importance as a harbour. Magadan owes its founding and rapid growth in the first place to the richness of mineral resources in its hinterland. Extraordinarily rich gold-fields were discovered in the upper reaches of the Kolyma, including gold-lodes as well as alluvial gold, and more thorough prospecting led to the discovery of coal deposits and other large deposits of rare elements. Exploitation was started immediately, and led to the development of many new settlements, of which there are now more than fifty in the upper Kolyma basin. The focus of industrial life lies in the area round the head-waters of the Kolyma and its tributaries, the Berelyakh and the Tenka. The most important of the new places are Orotukan and Khatynakh. An all-year motor highway was built leading from Ust-Utinaya to the coast at Magadan, thus opening up the area to the outer world. Since the Kolyma is navigable beyond Ust-Utinaya, this highway has created the shortest connexion with the whole of the Kolyma area. The highway is more than 600 miles long and was built under very difficult conditions presented by the mountains and areas of permafrost. Small highway stations (with farms attached) facilitate its use. The port of Magadan lies on Nagayevo Bay, its piers having been built out from the foot of the steep cliffs. The port is provided with ice-breakers in order to lengthen the shipping season. The rapidly growing town (which already had more than 10,000 inhabitants in 1939 and is estimated to have more than 50,000 today) lies a short distance from the port and is separated from it by a low and rocky hill. It was built using the most modern methods of construction, and by using deep excavation and layers of insulation it has been possible to build blocks of houses six storeys high in spite of the permafrost.

## THE REGIONS OF THE EXTREME NORTH-EAST

These regions are bounded on the west by the Kolyma Mountains, and comprise the Chukchen peninsula, the Anadyr and Penzhina regions, and the Koryak Mountains. The extensive interiors of these regions remain largely unexplored, and only the coastal strips are somewhat better known.

The Chukchen peninsula is separated from the Asian continent by Chaun Bay of the Arctic Ocean on the one side, and by Anadyr Bay of the Bering Sea on the other. The southern boundary is formed by the Anadyr Mountains (more than 3,000 feet high), which form the watershed between the Anadyr River and the rivers flowing into the Arctic Ocean. The area between the Anadyr Mountains and the Arctic coast is almost entirely filled with mountain ranges running in an east–west direction. Farther east the uninterrupted expanse of mountains is replaced by two distinct mountain ranges less than 2,500 feet high. These ranges are broken through by rivers several times before they reach the east coast. The northern range runs towards Cape Deshnev, which lies at a distance of 46 miles from the mainland of Alaska and consists of a single large mountain composed of limestone. It rises to a height of 2,540 feet and is completely isolated, being connected with the mainland by a low, narrow isthmus covered with tundra. Seen from the sea, it looks like an imposing island, resembling the rock of Gibraltar in position. The northern and southern mountain ranges are both composed mainly of gneiss and granite. In the Anadyr Mountains the folds include Mesozoic strata, and south of the Anadyr Mountains there are even Tertiary strata as well. Thus one gets into younger formations as one moves farther south.

Because it is more readily accessible, the coast of the Chukchen peninsula has been quite well explored. On the east side of Chaun Bay is Cape Skelagski, which is about 3,100 feet high. Farther east the mountains (2,000–2,600 feet high) recede to make room for a wide coastal plain containing lakes and lagoon-like beach formations, interrupted here and there by knobbly mountains rising from the alluvial flood-plain. Near Kolyuchin Bay the mountains come close to the sea again, with Cape Serdtse-Kamen rising to 2,000–3,000 feet. Along the Arctic coast of the Chukchen peninsula eight meteorological stations have been set up to make climatic observations, especially on the ice conditions, to assist navigation. The stations are roughly equidistant from each other along the coast and are supplied mainly by aircraft; all of them are provided with wireless equipment. The east and south coasts of the peninsula, where the mountain ranges often come close to the sea, are deeply indented by numerous bays, of which Holy Cross Bay (branching off from Anadyr Bay) penetrates farthest inland. Alongside one of the inlets of this bay is Mount Matachingay, the highest peak of the Chukchen peninsula, which has an altitude of 9,200 feet and towers above the surrounding mountains, which are only 2,000–2,600 feet high. At its foot there is an outcrop of andesite which affords some justification for considering it to be of volcanic formation.

The main part of the Chukchen peninsula is covered with tundra, which varies with the relief to form a very diversified picture. A boggy lowland tundra, interrupted by willow and birch thickets along the rivers, appears only in the valleys and plains. Dry mountain-tundra covers the flat ridges of the mountains and is of much greater value, since it is composed of good reindeer moss which secures the existence of the large Chukchen reindeer herds. The higher mountain ridges and peaks are completely devoid of any vegetation, and are covered with a great deal of rocky debris.

There are hardly any trees except in a few more sheltered places, and it is only in the valleys opening southwards towards the Anadyr region that there appear small copses composed mainly of stunted and deformed trees.

Permanent settlements are found only along the coast, mainly on the shores of the Bering Sea. The coastal Chukches live here, occupied mainly with fishing and hunting marine mammals. In some villages Eskimoes are also to be found. The coastal waters of the Chukchen peninsula are particularly well supplied with walrus, which form the principal catch. There are no larger settlements, and Russians do not live here permanently except for those holding official positions. The interior of the peninsula is inhabited by the reindeer Chukches, a strong and wiry people who possess large herds and are said to be excellent reindeer-breeders. However, they are very few in number, and the general population density is only eight persons per 100 square miles. It is therefore possible to travel over long stretches of the country without meeting a single human being. In recent years research has revealed valuable mineral resources, including iron ore, copper, gold ore, graphite, molybdenum, and coal. There are coal outcrops on the coast of Mechigmenskaya Bay and also in the vicinity of Cape Serdtse-Kamen, and pieces of first-class coal have been found by the Chukches in the interior. Most of the mineral resources established so far lie along the east coast, since this is the only area where more detailed research has been undertaken. However, as the geological structure is similar throughout the peninsula, these finds suggest that there must be further deposits in other places. This may well indicate one aspect of the peninsula's future development.

The Anadyr region lies south of the Chukchen peninsula, and is bounded by the Anadyr plateau in the west and the Koryak Mountains in the south. The central part is occupied by an extensive depression, which is filled with Cretaceous and Tertiary deposits. Most of the depression is absolutely flat, but it is not uniformly so because mountain ranges penetrate into it from both north and south, or rise directly from it. For instance, the Pekulney Mountains (with heights of more than 2,300 feet) run due south into the depression as a spur of the Anadyr range, while the Solotoy Mountains and the Ushkani Mountains rise directly from the plain north of the Anadyr *Liman*. South of the Anadyr and east of its tributary the Mayn there are the Alganskiye Mountains, 1,600 feet high. Very little is yet known in detail about the courses of any of these mountain chains and ridges.

The Anadyr originates in the plateau of the same name, and even in its upper reaches has the appearance of a big mountain river, with a width of up to 550 feet. Fine larch-woods grow along its high banks. A left-hand tributary, the Byelaya, which comes from the Anadyr Mountains in the north, is supposed to have only poplar woods and no larches along its upper reaches. The Anadyr plain widens already above Markovo, the main town in the interior of this area. Here the river-bed is no more than 80 feet above sea level, although still more than 300 miles from the mouth, and the gradient from here on is therefore very slight. The middle course of the river already extends to a width of 1 mile and contains many islands, while the lower course develops into a slow-running stream up to 3 miles wide. Marshy ground is consequently very widespread. The river plain, particularly the middle part immediately adjoining both sides of the river, is covered with wide and slightly hilly marshes overgrown with moss, which are interspersed with many rivulets and lakes of various sizes with almost stagnant waters. There are no woods at all in the plain. Clumps of alders, poplars, and willows still grow on the marshes west of the Byelaya and in the south-western part of the Anadyr basin, but towards the east these, too, disappear completely and there is nothing to break the monotony of the wide-open countryside. The mountain flanks and ridges are also generally flat and covered with a layer of spongy moss, with lakes and gleaming marshes often appearing on the ridges.

Poplars grow in the northern part of the Anadyr plain, but only in the more sheltered spots (resembling the Byelaya river-area in this respect). Larches also appear in the southern part of the plain, but generally they are very rare. However, in the western part which is farther away from the humid and cool influence of the sea, larch-woods spread farther northwards along the valleys and slopes. The transition from the plain to the mountains is the same throughout the whole area. Poplars and willows (but rarely birches) begin to appear on the river-banks, and accompany the rivers up into the mountains. Here they widen into broad belts of woods occupying the whole of the valley floors, while coniferous woods already begin to appear on the slopes. The higher wind-swept slopes and ridges are completely treeless.

The Anadyr plain is so open to the influence of the ocean that its effects are felt far inland. Temperatures of minus 58° F. are no rarity, whereas such low temperatures occur only very rarely in the east. In the summer, however, the coast is cool and rainy, whereas there are some very hot days in the interior, and the cool fogs which surround the coast in summer do not penetrate inland.

The east and central parts of the plain are only very thinly populated, but there are a number of villages along the Anadyr and its tributaries, of which Markovo with its 500 inhabitants is the most important. A few Russians live in these villages, but the chief inhabitants are Koryak fishermen and dog-breeders who are permanently settled there. The peripheral areas are occupied by nomadic reindeer-breeders: Chukches in the north, Koryaks in the south, and Lamutes and Tungus in the west. Their life alternates between the excellent mountain tundra in the summer and the sheltered plains in the winter. The majority are still complete nomads, but the wish for permanent winter dwellings is apparent everywhere, and with some of the tribes (particularly the Koryaks) there is a noticeable transition to semi-nomadic life. Some collectivization has been introduced here too, and in 1948 there were forty reindeer-breeding *kolkhozes* in the Koryak National District. Small quantities of potatoes and vegetables were also grown in some of these. Fishing collectives have been formed by the Koryaks at seventy places along the coast.

There are only a few settlements along the coast, because the terrain is too flat to afford much protection against the prevalent storms. Anadyr, with its 2,000 inhabitants, is the most important centre. It is situated at the mouth of the Anadyr River and forms the entrance to the whole of the Anadyr region. It is a regular port of call for the coastal steamers. Recently, fairly large Eocene brown-coal deposits have been discovered near the town, the principal deposit stretching from the north side of the river-mouth, just opposite Anadyr, to the confluence of the Anadyr with the Ugolnaya at the foot of the Solotoy Mountains. Outcrops on both sides of the mouth of the Ugolnaya belong to two seams 5 feet and 19 feet thick. Mining has already begun, to supply coal for the coastal steamers. Anadyr is also the centre of the nationalized fishing industry for the whole of the north coast, and the catches from the various fish-collection centres are delivered to a very large local factory for tinning.

In the south-west there is only a slightly pronounced watershed (maximum altitude 1,085 feet) separating the Anadyr depression from the Penzhina plain, which is very much smaller and is drained by the Penzhina into the Sea of Okhotsk. Compared with the Anadyr region the climate is slightly milder. The ground also slopes more steeply here, and the extensive moss-steppes are therefore not so boggy. The bigger rivers are generally lined by groves of poplars. The change in vegetation towards the mountains is the same as in the Anadyr plain. At the mouth of the Penzhina is Kamenskeye, a port of call for the coastal steamers. Penzhina itself is a small village in the middle of the lonely moss-steppe in the interior. Most of the small population are Koryaks, either fishermen settled in the villages or nomadic reindeer-breeders living on the good pastures of the moss-steppes. Coal-bearing strata have recently been found in the Tertiary deposits which fill the Penzhina basin. These strata contain good-quality brown coal as well as lighter lignites, and are said to occur throughout most of the area.

The eastern boundary of the Penzhina basin is formed by the flat ridge of the Penzhina Mountains. Beyond the latter is a very long moss-steppe—Parapolsky Dol—which runs from south-west to north-east and is similar in character to the Penzhina plain. It widens in the south to cover the whole of the isthmus connecting Kamchatka with the mainland. In the middle of the isthmus the steppe reaches an altitude of 510 feet.

The area between the Anadyr plain in the north and the isthmus in the south is taken up by a still-almost-unknown group of mountains of medium height, usually called the Koryak Mountains after the Koryak peoples who form the majority of the population in this area. These mountains fill the whole of the east-coast hinterland, and are drained mainly into the Bering Sea. Three ranges—the Pal Mal, the Tingeney, and the Rarytkin—run across the area, which is generally of a plateau-like character. These three ranges, like the rest of the Koryak Mountains, belong to the outer zone of Tertiary folds, and are regarded as a continuation of the Kamchatka Mountains. Towards the coast the rivers are very deeply incised, so that from the sea the area has a more mountainous appearance than the plateau-like interior (average altitude only 1,600 feet) really warrants. Most of the surface is covered with tundra, and only the valleys and other more sheltered places are forested. Koryak reindeer-breeders inhabit the interior, and Koryaks also populate the fishing settlements along the coast. The centre of the fishing industry is Ust-Apuka, west of Cape Olyutorski.

Tertiary brown-coal deposits are found in the Koryak mountain area at Korff Bay in the south and at Ugolnaya Bay in the extreme north-east. The Korff Bay deposits have already been mined for years and are the source of supplies for the coastal shipping. The coal is of Miocene age, and investigations up to the present have revealed eleven seams with a total thickness of 65 feet. The upper seams differ markedly in quality from the lower ones, the former being typical lignites while the latter resemble shining bituminous coal. Mining has also started in the Ugolnaya Bay area, and a coal-mining centre is to be established there.

## THE KAMCHATKA PENINSULA

The peninsula of Kamchatka points southwards like the tip of a spear, separating the Sea of Okhotsk from the Bering Sea. The peninsula has an area of 104,000 square miles and a length of 750 miles—roughly equivalent to the distance from Berlin to Rome.

The first chains of hills appear to the south of Parapolsky Dol plateau, which runs transversely across the isthmus. As the peninsula widens, these develop into two mountain ranges—the western and the eastern—between which is the valley of the Kamchatka River.

The western range is the lower of the two, but increases considerably in height south of the Palana River, and has already reached an altitude of 5,400 feet in the vicinity of the Tigil river-basin. In this area the principal ridge is considerably broken up, and accompanied by subsidiary parallel ranges. Near the head-waters of the Bystraya and the Icha is the truncated volcanic cone, Ichinskaya Sopka, which rises from its base (altitude 4,000 feet) to the gigantic height of 11,831 feet. The enormous dome of the mountain is covered with fields of perpetual snow, from which descend several hanging glaciers. Deep gullies have been cut into the mountain by the melted glacial snows. A constant cloud of smoke rises from the crater of this peak, which is the only active volcano in the western half of Kamchatka. South of the Icha the character of the mountains changes a great deal. Instead of the Tertiary sandstones and igneous rocks which predominate north of the river, it is now slate, granite, syenite, and porphyry which prevail, forming more massive ridges and rounded tops. Slowly the mountains decrease in height, and the western range merges with the eastern to form a single chain of mountains running towards the southern tip of the peninsula. The western promontories and parallel ranges carry numerous volcanic cones which frequently rise far above the limit of vegetation, the slender basalt cones of the Eleuk and the Moreshatnaya being especially noteworthy.

Rising slowly from the sea is a treeless moss-steppe (often called tundra), which reaches a height of 600 feet and then changes quickly into hilly country; the latter rises to an altitude of 2,000 feet and then gives way to the mountain zone. The west coast it-self is steep and rocky in the extreme north where the Penzhina Mountains run towards the sea, but for the rest of its length it is a flat regular coast with many narrow spits and coastal lagoons. There are numerous settlements, generally small, in the humid and partly boggy coastal plain, nearly always situated along the lower reaches of the rivers 5–10 miles from the sea—roughly on the border-line between the moss-steppe and the woods advancing along the valleys from the mountains.

The eastern half of Kamchatka is also composed of a mountain range of medium height, but topped by many high volcanic peaks whose thick andesite masses cover large parts of the area from the middle course of the Yalovka in the north to the southern tip of the peninsula. The volcanoes are located mainly between the prin-cipal ridge and the coast, and there are a far greater number here than on the western side of Kamchatka. Eighteen of them are still active, the most important of these being the following. The Shiveluch is situated in the angle between the Yelovka and the lower Kamchatka rivers, rising to a height of 10,940 feet and car-rying six glaciers: the last eruption took place in 1928. Klyuchev-skaya Sopka, which is also glaciated, is situated south of the point where the Kamchatka River breaks through the eastern moun-tains, and rises to an altitude of 15,660 feet. It is the highest peak of the peninsula and, with its cone-shaped peak rising with a gradient of 30° directly from the Kamchatka river-plain, it is one of the world's most impressive volcanoes. Its last eruption took place in 1931, but its greatest eruption occurred in 1696, even be-fore the arrival of the Russians; a stream of lava then reached the Kamchatka River near the village of Klyuchi, which is about 20 miles from the crater. The summit is usually surrounded by a cloud of smoke which may rise 1–2 miles above it, and sometimes showers ashes and stones on to the slope. The crater has a diameter of 800–1,000 feet and a depth of 160 feet. Russian scientists climbed down into the crater in 1931, and their report (29/277) reads in part as follows:

'Clouds of ashes and stones, many of which had a light red shimmer, were thrown up to a height of 700–1,000 feet and fell down with a great clatter. The opening of the crater was con-tinually filled with dark grey smoke. A strong smell of sulphur dioxide and hydrogen chloride filled the air. Inside the crater dusk and darkness prevailed, accentuating the light from the red-hot stones. The whole place resounded from an indescribable rumbling and clattering. During the 16 hours of our stay in the crater a particularly strong eruption took place, driving upwards an enormous cloud which covered the crater with a shower of red-hot stones.'

Near Klyuchevskaya Sopka are the volcanoes Ploskaya and Samina, both of which are also covered by perpetual snow. Farther south is Tobalchik (12,077 feet high), which is known for its enormous crater and for the largest glaciers of Kamchatka. Even farther south is Kronotskaya Sopka (11,874 feet), which was regarded as extinct until 1922, when it suddenly became active again. At its foot is the lake of the same name, which is 420 feet deep and probably fills the opening of an old crater. Around this lake rise a number of volcanoes, among which Uson requires special mention because of the numerous hot springs (125–185° F.) which rush noisily upwards from its deep crater and emerge through several fissures. The Avachinskaya Sopka (8,557 feet), 20 miles to the north-east of Petropavlovsk, is still continually active. Its last big eruption was in 1926, and since 1927 it has continued to emit gases, steam, and ash. This volcano has a double crater and resembles Vesuvius in structure and appearance, although more than double its height. The lava of the Avachinskaya Sopka is a type of andesite (172). Not far away is a pair of volcanoes, the imposing but dormant Koryatskaya Sopka (10,978 feet) and the Sopka Shupanova (9,607 feet). South of Avacha Bay the mountains are dissected by many valleys, because of the radial drainage of the area, but they continue to be surmounted by many smaller volcanoes (both active and extinct) as far as the southern tip of the peninsula. These mountains are seldom more than 3,000 feet high. The last group of volcanic mountains, including the Ilinskaya (2,805 feet) and the Kambolnaya Sopka (5,298 feet), rise above the gentle slopes of the widely spread and heavily eroded mountains surrounding the southern end of Lake Kurilsk, which fills a former crater and is 1,004 feet deep. Closely associated with the volcanoes of Kamchatka is its abundance of warm mineral springs, among which should be mentioned the Nalychevskiye springs between Avacha Bay and the Sopka Shupanova. These springs emerge from a layer of andesite with a temperature of 162° F., and are rich in boron and arsenic, which are deposited in terraces around the fissures. Interesting scenes are produced in the winter, when steam condenses in the surroundings and solidifies to form fantastic ice formations.

In contrast to the west coast, the east coast is very much indented as the result of subsidence. The projecting promontories generally terminate with a steep and rocky incline towards the sea, while the bays are bounded by a wide, flat, treeless strip of land. This coastal strip is widest along Litke Bay, and somewhat narrower along Avacha Bay, on which Petropavlovsk is situated.

The central Kamchatka valley is fortunate in having a more continental climate, because high mountain ranges surround it and protect it from the cool and humid climate of the coasts with their large amounts of snow and rain. In spite of the severe winters, people prefer it to the perpetually cool damp weather of the coast. The river-valley itself is marshy but accompanied by grass-steppe covered with a sparse growth of birches. This grass-steppe offers good opportunities for cattle-breeding and is even suitable for arable farming. After breaking through the mountains to the east, the Kamchatka river ends in a wide treeless delta which owes its special economic importance to the shoals of salmon which swim up the river in tremendous numbers to spawn.

The vegetation of Kamchatka is of a different character from the wooded coastal areas of Okhotsk, because of the more abundant precipitation and the milder temperatures, and in the southern part of the peninsula the vegetation even becomes very luxuriant. The scene is dominated by the brilliant light green of the deciduous trees, with the dark colour of the Dauric larches and firs to be seen only in the inner reaches of the Kamchatka valley. A forest of the same type as the Siberian taiga does not exist on Kamchatka. The characteristic tree is the birch, mainly the stone birch (*Betula ermani*), with its grey to reddish bark. These trees always grow at some distance from each other, rather than forming dense woods, and thus create a park-like landscape. The stone birch covers the whole of the east-coast area, together with poplars, alders, and mountain ashes. In the late summer the countryside here presents a wonderful picture, with the glowing red colour of the mountain-ash berries showing up against the different shades of green. The tree-line on the eastern slopes is at 1,000 feet in the north and at 1,800 feet in the south, the growth of trees at higher altitudes being prevented by the high humidity and low temperatures. In the interior of the Kamchatka valley, however, the same birch-woods grow up to an altitude of 2,000–2,500 feet. The Kamchatka woodbine (*Lonicera edula*) is particularly prevalent in the undergrowth of these woods, and in August its blackish-brown fruit is gathered in large quantities by the inhabitants for food. At a height of 1,000–1,600 feet the birch-woods generally give way to dwarf timber vegetation, which is very typical of the mountainous parts of Kamchatka. It consists of a tangled mass of creeping alders, cembra pines, and mountain ashes, with several varieties of rhododendron growing in between. This brushwood covers large areas on the slopes and is often so entangled that an axe is needed to clear a way through, unless there is a convenient bear-track which may be preferred. The bear has retreated into this undergrowth and up to the present has survived in fairly large numbers. The brushwood ends at an altitude of about 2,600 feet, and is followed by a zone of alpine flora which generally extends up to 4,600 feet. The permanent snow-line on Kamchatka lies at an altitude of 5,000–5,500 feet, so that most of the volcanoes are snow-capped. Some of them are even half covered in snow, and Klyuchevskaya Sopka is snow-covered for two-thirds of its height. Rising far above the general level of the countryside, these peaks give the landscape of Kamchatka its special character.

The valley floors, where they are not too marshy and consequently covered with moss, carry luxuriant meadows which afford excellent pastures for cattle. These meadows occur most frequently in the south, and the introduction of cattle-breeding has therefore made most progress in this part of the peninsula. The meadows are characterised by very tall plants such as the 'bear berry' (*Angelica ursina*, growing to a height of 10 feet) and the umbrella-shaped 'sweet grass' (*Heracleum tanatum* or *H. dulce*), which can be up to 14 feet high with a stalk 5 inches thick. The native people use the juice of this fast-growing plant to sweeten their food, and the Russians used to extract alcohol from it by fermentation.

Tundra-like moss-steppes run in a wide zone along the whole of the west coast, but in the east form only narrow strips around the bays. Occasionally they are also found in the mountain valleys. Compared with the wooded and park-like mountain areas which have such abundant vegetation, these monotonous areas are very different in character and have a gloomy, depressing effect, especially when they are filled with mist so as to make visibility for any distance impossible.

Before 1914 the population of Kamchatka was estimated to be hardly more than 20,000 people, of which the indigenous peoples formed the majority. During the period from the First World War to the present time, the population has greatly increased, largely because of the great number of Russian immigrants, and was reported to be about 100,000 in 1945. The Russians are now the predominant element in the population, making up about 80 per cent of the total. The present population is estimated to be 150,000, distributed among three main zones of settlement: the east coast, the west coast, and the Kamchatka valley.

The Koryaks and Kamchadals are the main groups of indigenous peoples. The Koryaks inhabit the northern half of the peninsula and the adjoining mainland between the Penzhina plain in the west and the coast of the Bering Sea in the east. On Kamchatka itself they live along the west coast as far south as the Sopochnaya River and in the vicinity of Litke Bay, but no longer in the Kamchatka valley itself. The area inhabited by the Koryaks has been formed into a National District in which, just like the Chukches, they enjoy cultural autonomy. The principal town of the district is Palana, situated near the mouth of the Palana River on the west coast. Nearly half of the Koryaks have permanent homes and live in villages on the coast or along the rivers in timber houses built on the Russian model. They live by fishing and hunting, breeding dogs as their domestic animals, and frequently growing potatoes and vegetables in gardens attached to their houses. The majority of the Koryaks, however, have remained reindeer-breeders, and have the same good qualities in this respect as the Chukches. Apart from the Samoyedes in the northern part of the European tundra, the Koryaks and the Chukches are the best reindeer-breeders of the Soviet Union, and own more than a third of the reindeer herds of the USSR.

The Kamchadals inhabit the Kamchatka valley and the southern part of the west coast, while a fairly large number are also found as workmen in the fishing-places along the east coast. They have succumbed in every way to Russian influence and have completely settled down, although fishing and hunting have remained their main occupations. In some cases they have already given up dog-breeding in order to keep horses as draught animals and for riding, and this practice is becoming more and more common in southern Kamchatka. The growing of potatoes and vegetables has become quite usual. A small number of Tungus Lamutes still live in the more remote central parts of Kamchatka, and are still exclusively reindeer-breeders. Hemmed in by the more progressive Koryaks and Kamchadals, they are the poorest group of people on the peninsula; their herds are only small, and during a hard winter they come to the rich reindeer-Koryaks begging for alms.

The large immigration of Russians is due to the endeavours of the State. Between 1930 and 1933 as many as 15,000 settlers came into the country. By 1939 the capital, Petropavlovsk, had about 28,000 inhabitants—more than the whole population of Kamchatka prior to 1914—and the present population must be about 40,000. One of the main factors aiding the growth of the population has been the development and modernization of facilities for fishing and hunting marine animals. In earlier times there was a shortage of labour, and it was therefore necessary every year during the fishing season to bring thousands of seasonal workers to Kamchatka, among them many Koreans and Chinese. Immigration has done away with this necessity. Many new industries have been developed, especially those which are ancillary to the fish-processing industry. Agriculture, too, has benefited from the immigration, and according to all reports has made great progress. Kamchatka was formerly dependent mainly on imported food supplies, but today the peninsula is self-sufficient to a large extent, and the goal of complete self-sufficiency may soon be reached.

In the south of the peninsula, where the milder climate resembles that of Sweden, there has been a constant increase in the importance of cattle-breeding. In 1939 there were already several thousand head of cattle. A number of cattle *sovkhozes* are responsible for supplying the fishing-places with meat and milk. A start has also been made with arable farming in the Kamchatka valley and in the surroundings of Petropavlovsk, and the acreage of tilled land increases from year to year. *Sovkhozes* and *kolkhozes* successfully grow grain, potatoes, and vegetables, and apples are already harvested from imported fruit trees. There are a number of agricultural research stations both in the interior and in the coastal regions, which have the task of preparing for the further development of agriculture and cattle-raising.

Fishing and the hunting of marine animals take first place in the economy of Kamchatka, which is the most important area of the Soviet Far East in this respect. Of special importance is the occurrence of highly valuable species of salmon. The most important area for catching both salmon and crabs is along the west coast. On the east coast the area around the mouth of the Kamchatka River is a special salmon-fishing area, while Petropavlovsk is the centre for hunting marine animals. The 'passive' and unmethodical system of catching fish by building weirs across the river has largely been replaced by trawling with drag-nets, so that fishing now takes place out in the sea, as well as in the mouths of the rivers.

z

The former method of preserving fish, which was practised along the whole of the Far East coast, consisted merely of sprinkling salt over the heaps of caught fish. This primitive method allowed large quantities of fish to go bad, and has now been replaced mainly by tinning, as well as by smoking and modern methods of salting in barrels. Modern fishing steamers with processing plant on board have helped to make Kamchatka the second most important fishing area of the Soviet Union, surpassed only by the Caspian Sea. As far as crabs are concerned, Kamchatka is foremost in the world. The crabs are very large, with a length of 1½ feet or more, and are brought up from the bottom of the sea in trawling nets. Special mention must be made of the floating crab-tinning factories, which operate along the west coast and carry out the complete process from catching to tinning while afloat.

Petropavlovsk is the principal town of the peninsula and is situated on Avacha Bay, which is surrounded by a semi-circle of high volcanoes and only rarely freezes over. Its favourable natural harbour was recently equipped with a shipyard and a dock for ships of up to 5,000 tons gross. This port has gained more and more in importance, since the ships from the northern sea route spend the winter here before starting on their journey to the north. This applies especially to the ships which ply regularly along the Kolyma River carrying heavy materials to the gold districts on its upper reaches. The town is the centre for all the industries connected with the hunting of marine animals, and in addition there are the fish-processing plants, a brickyard, saw-mills, and a factory for making tins. The latter is of special importance because it provides the tins for all the smaller fish-tinning centres. The second most important place on the peninsula is Ust-Kamchatsk, which is situated in the treeless delta of the Kamchatka River. More than 2,000 workers are employed in the tinning factories here during the summer. The place is also of special importance as the natural entrance to the interior of the peninsula, which can be reached comfortably only along the Kamchatka valley, the alternative access to the valley being over difficult passes. Timber is floated down to the coast along the Kamchatka River to an increasing extent. The timber is processed in Ust-Kamchatsk and shipped on from there. There are a number of villages in the wide north–south valley of the Kamchatka, among which should be mentioned Verkhne Kamchatsk and Milkovo. Horses are kept here instead of dogs, because of the difficulty of supplying fish for the latter in an area so remote from the coast. Situated at the inner end of a transverse valley at the foot of the biggest volcano, is the village of Klyuchi, from which the volcano got its name. The communication lines from the interior converge here and make the village a trading centre, particularly for furs. In addition to the Russians and Koryaks, some Koreans and Chinese have settled here as well. Klyuchi has a scientific observatory for the study and special observation of the Klyuchevskaya Sopka volcano. Below the village the Kamchatka widens into a lake adorned with many islands.

The principal place on the west coast is Bolsheretsk. This is the centre of the crab and salmon-fishing industries, and all the catches from the numerous fish-collecting points are brought together here for processing. The principal fishing areas stretch from Cape Subchaty to the southern tip of the peninsula, and are thus concentrated mainly along the southern half of the coast. Farther to the north is Palana, which is the cultural centre for the Koryaks.

The utilization of mineral resources will play an important part in the future development of Kamchatka. The coal and petroleum deposits have already been dealt with in detail above, so that no more than a reminder is needed here. In addition, there is an abundance of hydro-electric power at man's disposal. So far there are only a few small hydro-electric stations for supplying power to agricultural settlements, but there are possibilities for much greater development. All in all, Kamchatka has had a relatively favourable economic development up to now, and there are good prospects for its future.

## THE KOMMANDORSKI ISLANDS

About 150 miles east of Kamchatka, the Kommandorski Islands rise in isolation out of the sea, separated from the peninsula by a channel 550 fathoms deep. On the Aleutian side of the islands the bottom of the sea is even deeper. This group of islands, which covers an area of 830 square miles, consists of two large inhabited islands—the Bering and Copper Islands—and two small ones on which live only a large number of sea-parrots and *aras*. The islands are of volcanic origin and consist mainly of andesite tuffs and basalt.

Bering Island consists of a low-lying moss-steppe in the north and a wild mountainous area rising up to 2,210 feet in the south. The average yearly precipitation is 20 inches, and there are average monthly temperatures of 25° F. in the coldest month and 52° F.

in July. The damp cold weather, with its constant mist and rain, combined with the strong winds, does not allow for more than a stunted growth of mountain ash and poplar, although the islands are situated on the same latitude as Moscow. However, the grass grows all the more abundantly, the Heracleus species (which grow as tall as a man) being particularly striking.

Copper Island got its name from the copper which is contained in the volcanic rock. It consists of a mountain range which slopes down steeply to the sea, and is divided into two parts connected by a narrow strip of land. The mountain range is further divided up by several cross-valleys. The coasts are rocky and steep, and eroded by the heavy surf into the most weird and picturesque shapes, producing a most romantic and melancholy picture when seen through the mist. Thousands of birds live on the rocks.

The Kommandorski Islands became famous for the seals which were caught here, but today this wealth has been almost completely destroyed. The 600 inhabitants, who are a mixture of Aleutians, Russians, Eskimoes, Kuriles, &c., live almost exclusively on what they can obtain from the sea. There is a great deal of fox-hunting in the interior.

## THE KURILES

The garland of islands constituting the Kuriles was incorporated into the Soviet Union following the Second World War. These islands are generally not very well known, and will therefore be treated here in greater detail.

Together with Hokkaido and Kamchatka, the Kuriles form the most northern arc of the outer 'frame' enclosing the East Asian mainland, representing the link between the volcanic massif of the island of Hokkaido and the volcanoes of Kamchatka. In terms of size there are thirty-six larger islands and twenty smaller ones, as well as many uninhabited rocks which hardly rise above the sea but all belong to the island chain. In terms of relative position the islands can be divided up into two groups: first, the main chain 750 miles long, which starts with Zhumzhu Island in the north and ends with Kunazhiri Island next to Hokkaido; second, a shorter parallel chain situated to the east of the principal chain and only about 60 miles long, starting with Nemuro Island near Hokkaido, and ending with Zhikotan. It has been stated that the total area of the Kuriles is 6,000 square miles, 40 per cent of which is accounted for by the four largest islands—Etorofu, Paramuzhir,

Kunazhiri, and Urup. The northernmost island of the chain, called Alaid, has a latitude of 50° 56′, while the most southern island has a latitude of 43° 26′, so that the Kuriles extend over the same latitudes as between Leningrad and Burgos, Bulgaria.

The foundation of the Kuriles is a submarine mountain ridge, the highest parts of which rise above the surface of the water as a series of islands. Different parts of this submarine ridge differ considerably in inclination. Towards the Sea of Okhotsk it slopes comparatively steeply down to a depth of 1,600 fathoms (maximum depth 1,855 fathoms). The incline towards the Pacific is even steeper, since the Kuriles Deep runs along this side of the island chain, reaching depths between 3,800 and 4,400 fathoms (maximum depth 4,683 fathoms). With some islands the 100-fathom contour line frequently lies very close to the steeply dropping rocky coast. The islands are separated from each other by straits which differ considerably in width and depth. The Bussole Straits (1,100 fathoms) and the Muzhir Straits (990 fathoms) are the deepest. All the other straits are less than 300 fathoms deep, and some of them are very shallow, allowing only a limited interchange of water between the Pacific and the Sea of Okhotsk.

According to the results of research up to the present, the chain of the Kuriles lies on top of a former zone of folding (of Palaeozoic and Mesozoic age) deeply submerged by the sea during the formation of the East Asian geosyncline. The development of the latter started in the Lower Cretaceous period, but the Miocene period was the time of greater subsidence, when thousands of metres of sediment were deposited. Along the eastern edge of the geosyncline (i.e. along the line of the present Kuriles) the subsidence caused folding and fracturing, with an attendant flow of great quantities of magma. By the end of the Tertiary era extensive tear faults and transverse fractures developed; igneous intrusions and further uplift developed along the tear faults, while at the same time the ground on either side continued to subside. The final result was thus a narrow mountain ridge cut up by numerous deep channels. Strong igneous activity followed, resulting in the metamorphism of the injected sediments, and the ejection of enormous masses of lava, which poured out to form volcanic cones which rose as islands above the sea. Movements of the earth's crust, and island formation, have not yet come to an end, and are evident in intense volcanic and seismic activity, and also in uplifting of the islands indicated by numerous beach terraces.

Nearly all the islands consist basically of igneous rocks (andesite lava and tuffs), with only the northernmost and southernmost islands (Zhumzhu and Zhikotan) composed exclusively of sedimentary rocks. On some of the islands, strongly dislocated and metamorphized slates of Palaeozoic and Mesozoic age appear under the lava deposits, while poorly developed Tertiary formations are to be found in some of the synclines.

The Kuriles are typically volcanic formations, containing at least fifty-two volcanoes, of which eighteen are still active. Among the latter, the highest are Syrycheva (4,870 feet) on the island of Matsuva, and Prevo (4,460 feet) on the island of Zhimuzhir. Some of the extinct volcanoes reach greater heights. In structure, most of the volcanoes are composite cones. The various live volcanoes differ greatly in their present volcanic activity. Some (such as Raikoke and Zhimuzhiru) run the full cycle from subterranean rumbling to the eruption of gases, the throwing-up of ashes and bombs, and finally the pouring-out of lava; with others (such as on the islands of Matsuva and Khirinkotan) the lava flows out without any accompanying symptoms. Some have only one crater, while others have lateral parasitic cones. The fumaroles which have developed over the fissures are constantly active.

The north-west Pacific Ocean has a particularly large number of earthquakes. Of all the known seismic occurrences on the earth, 37 per cent happen within this area, and the majority of these affect the Kuriles. Locally the number of earthquakes varies considerably, some of the islands having seven a year while others have a far smaller number. Most of the earthquakes are associated with tectonic processes at the bottom of the sea, and generally have their epicentres deep below the sea floor. Volcanic activity on the islands is often linked with submarine eruptions, which occur quite frequently and have a far greater destructive effect, since they often produce large tidal waves which surge repeatedly against the islands with tremendous power. Tidal waves of this kind have been observed with heights up to 90 feet, and in 1780 a ship which was lying in harbour was carried a quarter of a mile inland by such a wave.

The relief and horizontal outline of the islands vary a great deal. There is usually one single mountain ridge running longitudinally across the larger islands, generally filling the whole of the interior. Sometimes, however, there are two to four mountain ridges, or an island may be occupied by a whole series of separate mountains. The average height of the mountains on the Kuriles is between 1,600 and 3,300 feet, but thirty mountains have been counted with heights between 3,300 and 4,300 feet, as well as twelve mountains which rise above 4,300 feet. The highest peak is the volcano Oyakopa (7,675 feet) on the northern island of Alaid, which is permanently covered with snow down to an altitude of 2,600 feet. Plains and hilly areas are very rare on the islands, the low hills of Zhumzhu in the north and Zhikota in the extreme south forming rare exceptions. As mentioned above, both these islands are composed of sedimentary rock rather than volcanic material, and some geologists therefore consider them as parts cut off from the mainland.

In their vertical profiles the volcanoes exhibit a real museum collection of all types, from the ideal volcanic cone to the ruins of old volcanoes. Along the coasts, craters of old ruined volcanoes filled with sea-water form excellent sheltered bays, such as the Bay of Buroton (110 fathoms deep) on Zhimuzhir Island. The circular arrangement of small island groups often indicates the existence of submarine craters.

Most of the islands have regular shapes. In addition to round and oval islands, which are generally crowned by a group of volcanoes, there are also islands which are oblong in shape. These were probably formed by the merging of adjacent islands, through the rising of the land and consequent widening of the volcanic bases, followed by the filling of the intervening gaps with erupted volcanic matter. Besides these two main types of islands, there are islands here and there which are very broken up in form. The coastal relief is the same almost everywhere. The predominantly steep slopes of the island interiors become gentler towards the coast, and then often terminate in a sheer drop (frequently almost vertical) down to the water. Many of the islands, especially the round and oval ones, are thus almost inaccessible. Lying just off the coasts, and between the islands, there are numerous rocks, reefs and sandbanks which are very dangerous for shipping. Many changes continue to occur as the result of volcanic activity and earthquakes, often in such a short space of time that they are apparent to the human onlooker. For instance, in 1934 a volcanic island rose up from a depth of 440 fathoms about 10 miles from the shores of Alaid Island. Marine erosion is continually active along the coasts, and grottoes and recesses are found everywhere along the steep cliffs. The most important process of change, however, is the general uplifting which is going on at different rates in different parts of the island chain. Beach terraces and abrasion platforms are visible up to heights of 1,000–1,300 feet.

Weathering is very marked, and on the heights and along the slopes are to be found sharp-edged rocks which were loosened and scattered by volcanic explosions. Where the slopes are steep these have rolled down and formed literally 'oceans of stones' at the foot of the mountains. The river valleys are deeply incised into the mountain massifs, and run radially from the highest points to the sea. They often end in bays which are filled with sedimentary deposits, and therefore offer good opportunities for landing. On their way to the sea these rivers have dug deep narrow gorges into the volcanic rocks, but because of the uplifting they frequently have not had time to cut down to sea level, so that they plunge as waterfalls over the steep coastal cliffs into the sea.

The climate of the Kuriles is rigorous, with a cold and long but comparatively dry winter, and a cool humid summer. The islands are completely under the influence of the monsoonal air movements. During the winter very strong north-west winds are predominant (70 per cent), with a monthly average velocity of 31 miles per hour and a small relative humidity of 60 per cent. In the summer south and south-east winds prevail, which are generally not so strong as the winter winds, and are often interrupted by calms; their relative humidity reaches 90 per cent. Towards the end of the summer and in the early autumn there appear very strong winds which are the tail-end of the summer typhoons and can reach a velocity of 46 miles per hour. The range of average temperatures is only 38–41°, the average of the coldest month lying between 19° and 23°, and that of the warmest month between 57° and 63°. The average number of frost-free days is 120 in the north, increasing to 180 in the south. Precipitation varies between 30 and 40 inches, with the maximum in August/September and the minimum in January/February. There is generally precipitation on two-thirds of the days in the year. At the end of October it has already begun to snow, and on the northern islands the snow remains until the beginning of May. The snow cover reaches a thickness of more than 3 feet. The sky is generally very cloudy, and on some of the islands there are only fifteen to thirty cloudless days in the year. The most beautiful season is the autumn, which has the greatest number of days which are calm and dry. Many dense fogs are a characteristic phenomenon of the Kuriles, appearing mainly in the summer and caused by the warm humid air masses coming from the Pacific and flowing over the cold Oyashio current. As a rule the fogs are not very thick, and the summits of the mountains remain bathed in sunshine while the islands below are smothered in fog. There are many difficulties and dangers to shipping as a result of the fogs. Shipping has to stop completely from December to the beginning of April because the whole of the island area is then covered with ice. Even the southernmost island of Zhikotan is completely cut off from the outer world during this time.

The vegetation in the Kuriles shows many variations because of the large spread in latitude covered by the island chain. Of the 768 species of flora established up to now on the Kuriles, 257 have their origin in Japan, and only forty-five on Kamchatka and the adjoining mainland. On the northern islands tundra vegetation is prevalent, with widespread bushy growth of *Pinus pumila*, willows, and birches; fully grown trees are found only in a few sheltered places. The islands in the middle of the chain have the poorest vegetation, since these islands are mostly small and low, and the raw influence of the cold sea currents is therefore most effective here. The southern islands possess a comparatively rich vegetation, and woods with tall trees and an abundance of timber are found on the islands of Urup, Etorofu, Kunazhiri, and Zhitokan. Firs (*Picea Jezoensis* and *P. glehni*) and the Sakhalin pine (*Abies Sachalinensis*) are predominant, interspersed with oaks (*Quercus grosseserrata* and *Q. dentata*), beeches (*Carpinus cordata*), and other deciduous trees. At higher altitudes and near the coasts there are pasture-like grasslands, giving an occasional alpine touch to the countryside. Only a few species of terrestrial animals are represented here. The brown bear and the wolf appear in the woods, and foxes of all kinds are very numerous.

Birds are very much in evidence, with the smaller islands having preference over the larger ones. Migratory birds are rare, since they prefer the Sakhalin route for their flights. The real riches of the Kuriles are the fish and marine mammals, which appear in great numbers although there are only a few different species. Among the fish are found the same species of salmon mentioned above when discussing Kamchatka. Among the marine mammals seals are the most important, although sea-lions and whales are also to be found. The valuable sea-otter has been almost completely destroyed.

Before the Second World War the number of permanent inhabitants in the Kuriles was 13,000 people, mainly Japanese with only a few hundred Kurile Ainos (the indigenous people of the islands). Most of the population was concentrated on the southern islands, where limited cultivation of rye, wheat, barley, and different kinds of vegetables is possible. Judging by 1945 the main occupation of the inhabitants is fishing and hunting marine mammals. In former times the population was increased every summer by about 10,000 fishermen who came from Japan and stayed on the islands for the fishing season. According to the value of the catches, fishing is by far the most important activity, but whaling is fairly important too. The whales, after spending the summer in the Bering Sea, pass along the Kuriles in the autumn on their way to their winter quarters in the southern part of the Sea of Okhotsk. Seals and sea-lions are hunted as well.

Following the acquisition of the islands by the Soviet Union and the evacuation of most of the Japanese, numerous fishing-centres have been set up on the islands. A fleet of whalers has been stationed here, and a whale-processing *kombinat* erected. It is also planned to re-start the breeding of fur-bearing animals originally begun by the Japanese.

Because of their volcanic character, the Kuriles possess numerous hot springs, most of them containing minerals. The islands are poor in natural resources, but the Soviets have plans for making use of the sulphur deposits found on some of the islands.

# Literature

\*

## I. BIBLIOGRAPHIES

Kerner, R. J.: North-eastern Asia. A selected bibliography. 2 vols. Berkeley, 1939.

Leimbach, W.: Nordasien (Northern Asia). General survey of publications during the years 1926–37. Geogr. Yearbook, **53,** 1938.

## II. JOINT WORKS BY VARIOUS AUTHORS

1. Asiatskaya Rossiya (Asiatic Russia). Compiled by the Resettlement Administration. 2 vols. and atlas. St Petersburg, 1914.

2. Atlas der Vereisungsverhältnisse Russlands und Finnlands (Atlas of Glacial Conditions in Russia and Finland). Compiled by the German Naval Observatory. Published by the High Command of the German Navy, 1942.

3. Atlas Energeticheskikh Ressursov SSSR (Atlas of Energy Resources of the USSR). Compiled under the editorship of A. W. Winter, G. M. Krzhizhanovski, and G. I. Lomov. 2 vols. Moscow-Leningrad, 1934.

4. Bolyshaya Sovietskaya Enzikloklopediya (Great Soviet Encyclopedia), 2nd edition, vols. 1–14. In course of publication since 1949. Moscow.

5. Buryat-Mongoliya (Buryato-Mongolia). Works of the Bury. Mong. Expedition of 1932. Moscow-Leningrad, 1937.

6. Buryat-Mongoliya sa 30 Let Sovyetsko Vlasti (Thirty years of Soviet Power in B-M). Ulan-Ude, 1947.

7. Ekonomicheskaya Geografiya SSSR (Economic Geography of the USSR). 2 parts by Balsak, S. S., Vasyutin, V. F., and others. Moscow, 1940.

8. Energeticheskiye Ressursi SSSR (Sources of Energy in the USSR). 2 vols. Academy of Science. Moscow, 1937 and 1938.

9. Mineralyniye Ressursi SSSR: medy, zink, svinets (Mineral Resources of the USSR: Copper, Zinc, Lead). Moscow, 1937.

10. Obsor Glavneyshikh Mestorozhdeni Ugle i Gornizh Slantsev SSSR (General Survey of the Main Sources of Coal and Oil-shales in the USSR). Moscow-Leningrad, 1931.

11. Possevny'e Ploshchade SSSR (The Cultivated Areas of the USSR). The Dynamics of 1928, 1932–8 as compared with 1913. Statistical reference work. Issued by the State Planning Commission. Moscow-Leningrad, 1939.

12. Problemy Buryat-Mongolskoy ASSR (Problems of Buryato-Mongolia ASSR). Works of the first conference of research into the factors of production of B-M ASSR. 2 vols. Moscow-Leningrad, 1935–6.

13. Sozialisticheskoye Stroitelystvo Soyusa SSR (The Socialistic Structure of the Soviet Union), 1933–8. Statistical Cyclopedia. Published by the State Planning Commission. Moscow-Leningrad, 1939.

14. UdSSR in Zahlen–Bevoelkerung–Bodenschaetze–Wirtschaft (USSR in Statistics: Population, Mineral Resources, Economy). Edited by the German Institute for Economic Research. Printed as a manuscript. Berlin, 1941.

### III. WORKS BY INDIVIDUAL AUTHORS

15. Anert, E. E., and Krishtofovich, A. N.: Geolog. Ocherk Primorya (Geological Study of the Coastal Region). Vladivostok, 1923.

16. Anert, E. E.: Kratki Geologicheski Ocherk Priamurya (Short Geological Study of the Amur Region). Geolog. Research into the Gold-bearing areas of Siberia. XVII. St Petersburg, 1913.

17. Ahnert, E. v.: Zwei Ueberquerungen der Stanowoy—Wasserscheide (russ.) (Two Crossings of the Stanovoi Watershed). Geolog. Research into the Gold-bearing Areas of the Amur and the Coastal Region. VIII. St Petersburg, 1908.

18. Arsenyev, A. A.: K Geomorfologii Olekmo-Vitimskoy Gornoy (Geomorphology of the Olekma-Vitim Mountain Region). Bulletin of the Moscow Association of Natural Scientists. Moscow, 1937.

19. Arsenyev, V. K.: Po Ussuriyskom Kraye (Across the Ussuri Region). Vladivostok, 1921.

20. Arsenyev, V. K.: Kitaytsy v Ussuriyskom Kraye (The Chinese in the Ussuri Region). Khabarovsk, 1914.

21. Arsenyev, V. K.: Proisvod, Sily Dalynego Vostoka: Chelovek (The Factors of Production in the Far East—Mankind). Khabarovsk-Vladivostok, 1927.

22. Arsenyev, V. K.: Russen und Chinesen in Ostsibirien. (Russians and Chinese in East Siberia), 2 vols. Berlin, not dated.

23. Arsenyev, V. K.: In der Wildnis Ostsibiriens (In the Wilderness of East Siberia), 2 vols. Berlin, not dated.

24. Baranski, N. N.: Ekonomicheskaya Geografiya SSSR po Rayonam (Regional Economic Geography of the USSR). Moscow, 1939.

25. Baranski, N. N.: Ekonomicheskaya Geografiya SSSR (Economic Geography of the USSR). Moscow, 1947.

26. Berg, L. S.: Die Fauna des Baikalsees und ihre Herkunft. (The Fauna of the Lake of Baikal and its Origins). Archive for Hydrobiology. Stuttgart, 1925.

27. Berg, L. S.: Landschaftno-Geograficheskiye Zony SSSR (The Natural Regions of the USSR). Part 1. Moscow, 1931.

28. Berg, L. S.: Ryby Basseyna Amura (The Fish of the Amur Basin). Moscow, 1909.

29. Berg, L. S.: Priroda SSSR (The Nature of the USSR). Moscow, 1938.

30. Bergmann, St.: Die Tausend Inseln des Fernen Ostens (The Thousand Islands of the Far East). Stuttgart, 1932.

31. Bestuzhev, A. A.: Gussinoye Osero (The Lake of Gussinoye). Verkhne-Udinsk, 1925.

32. Robin, E. S.: Geolog. Issledovanniya v Olekmo-Karlaskom Rayone (Geological Research in the Olekma-Kalar Region). Trudy of the Soviet Geological Research Association. Moscow, 1933.

33. Bobrinski, N. A.: Zhivotny mir i Priroda SSSR (The Animal World and Nature of the USSR). Moscow, 1948.

34. Bogdanovich, K.: Geolog. Skizze von Kamtschatka (Geological Sketch of Kamchatka). Peterm. Geogr. Notes, 1904.

35. Bogoras, W. G.: Nowy'e Sadachi Rossiysko Etnografii v Polyarnykh Oblasyakh (New Ethnographical Publication on the Polar Regions). Trudy of the Scientific and Economic Northern Expeditions. Petrograd, 1921.

36. Bogoras, V.: Lamuty (The Lamutes). Semlevedeniye. Moscow, 1900.

37. Bogoras, V.: The Chukches. New York, 1904–8.

38. Bonch-Osmolovski: Ekonomicheskaya Zhisni Dalynego Vostoka (The Economic Life of the Far East). Planovoye Khosyaystvo, No. 2, 1929.

39. Borissov, A. A.: Klimaty SSSR (The Climate of the USSR). Moscow, 1948.

40. Bubnoff, S. v.: Kohlenlagerstaetten Russlands und Sibiriens (The Coal Deposits of Russia and Siberia). Berlin, 1923.

41. Buchholz, E.: Die Wald- und Holzwirtschaft Sowjetrusslands (The Wood and Timber Economy of Soviet Russia). Agricultural Reports. Berlin, 1932.

42. Buchholz, E.: Die Forst- und Holzwirtschaft der Sowjet-Union nach dem Kriege (The Forest and Timber Economy of the Soviet Union after the War). Bulletin for World Forest Economy, No. 12, 1948.

43. Busch, V. E.: K Morfologii Poluostrova Svaytoy Nos na Baykalye. Isvestiya of the Geogr. Association, LXII, vol. I, 1930.

44. Bykov, G. E.: K Geomorfolgii Vostochnoy Chasti Khrebta Tukuringry (On the Geomorphology of the Eastern Part of Tukuringra). Isvestiya of the Geogr. Association. Leningrad-Moscow, 1935.

45. Khmysnikov, P. K.: Geomorfolog. ocherk Lensko-Yanskogo Kraya (Geomorphological Study of the Lena-Yana Region). Trudy SOPS Series Yakutien I, 1932.

46. Cressy, G. B.: Asia's Lands and Peoples. New York, 1944.
47. Cressy, G. B.: The Basis of Soviet Strength. New York, 1945.
48. Daly, R. A.: Pleistocene Changes of Level. American Journal Sc., ser. 5, vol. 10, 1925.
49. Davies, R. A., and Steiger, A. J.: Soviet Asia. New York, 1942.
50. Dengin, J. P.: Geolog. Issledovaniya v Vostochnom Sabaykalye v 1927 g. (Geological Research in Eastern Transbaikalia in 1927). Moscow, 1931.
51. Dengin, J. P.: Sledy Drevnego Oledeniniya v Yablonovom Khrebte i Problema Golyzovykh Terras (Traces of Old Glaciations in the Yablonovy Mountains and the Problem of the Golez-Terraces). Isvestiya of the Geogr. Association, LXII, vol. II, 1930.
52. Doktorovich-Grebnitskiy: Otchet ob Issledovaniyach v Khamar-Daban v 1919 g. (Report on the Research in the Khamar-Daban in 1919). Isvestiya of the Geolog. Com., No. 2, 1920.
53. Doskach, A. G.: Fisiko-Geograf. Ocherk Seysko-Bureinskoy Rav-niny (Physical Geographical Study of the Seya–Bureya Plain). Trudy of the Georgr. Inst., Academy of Science. Moscow, 1937.
54. Douglas, W. F.: Das Fischereiwesen Russlands (The Fisheries of Russia). Stuttgart, 1930.
55. Dumitrashko, N. V.: Nov Tekton. Shema Vostochnoy Sibiri (New Tectonic Scheme of East Siberia). Priroda, Nos. 8–9, 1933.
56. Dumitrashko, N. V.: Osnovny'e Voprossy Geomorfologii i Pale-ageografii Baykalyskoy Gornoy Oblasti (Basic Factors of the Geomorphology and the Paleontology of the Baikalian Mountains). Trudy of the Geogr. Inst., Academy of Science. Moscow, 1948.
57. Dunikovski, E. H.: Stratigraphische Geologie des Sikhota Alin (Stratographical Geology of the Sikhota-Alin). In 'Scientific Results of the Expedition to the Sikhota-Alin'. Cracow, 1913.
58. Eskola, P.: Beobachtungen ueber die Glazialbildungen in der Gegend der Wasserscheide zwischen dem Barguzin und der ob. Angara in Transbeikalien (Observations on the Glacial Formations in the Region of the Watershed between the Barguzin and the Upper Angara in Transbaikalia). Comtes rendu d.l. Soc. Geolog. d. Finl., 1, 1929.
59. Fedorov, S. F.: Neftyany'e Mestorozhdeniya Sovyetskogo Soyusa (Occurrence of Petroleum in the USSR). Moscow, 1939.
60. Fichell, A.: Géographie Physique et Economique de l'URSS (Physical and Economic Geography of the USSR). Paris, 1946.
61. Fidman, A. I., and others: Maly'e Reki v Narodnom Khosyaystve SSSR (The Small Rivers in the Political Economy of the USSR). Moscow, 1949.
62. Fochler-Hauke, G.: Die Manchurei (Manchuria) Geogr. Geopolitische Landeskunde. Heidelberg-Berlin, 1941.

63. Friedensburg, F.: Gold. Die Metallischen Rohstoffe (Gold, The Metallic Raw Materials), 3rd number, 2nd edition. Stuttgart, 1953.

64. Gagarin, E.: Die Waelder der Sowjetunion (The Forests of the Soviet Union), 2nd edition. Koenigsberg-Berlin, 1943.

65. Gittermann, V.: Geschichte Russlands (The History of Russia), 3rd volume. Hamburg, 1949.

66. Gladzin, I. N.: Solyany'e Osera Burj. Mong. ASSR (The Salt Lakes of Buryato-Mongolia ASSR). Problems of the Burj. Mong. ASSR. Moscow, 1935.

67. Gladzin, I. N.: Sadachi Geomorfolog. Isucheniye v Buryat Mongol ASSR (Tasks of Geomorphological Research in Buryato-Mongolia ASSR). Moscow, 1935.

68. Gladzin, I. N.: Geolog. Ocherk Sabykalyi (Geological Study of Transbaikalia). Trudy of the Arctic Institutes. Moscow, 1938.

69. Gladzin, I. N.: Geomorfologicheski Ocherk Saboykalya (Geomorphologic Study of Transbaikalia). Trudy of the Geogr. Inst., Academy of Science. Moscow, 1938.

70. Glinka, K. D.: O Drevnykh Protsessakh Vyvetrivaniya v Priamurye (Concerning Old Weathering Processes in the Amur Region). Pochvovedeniye, 1911.

71. Gorshenin, K. P.: Geografiya Pochv Sibiri (Geography of the Soils of Siberia). Omsk, 1939.

72. Gozhev, A. D.: Lessa Udskogo Rayona (The Forests of the Ud Region). Moscow, 1934.

73. Gregory, I. S., and Shave, D. W.: The USSR, a Geographical Survey. London, 1944.

74. Grigoryev, A. A.: Geologiya Relyef i Pochvy Sev.-Sap. Chasti Lensko-Aldanskogo Plato i Verkhoyanskogo Khrebta po Dannym Eksped., 1925 g. (Geology Relief and Soils of the NW Part of the Lena-Aldan Plateau and the Verkhoyansker Mountains, according to Information from the Expedition in 1925). Mat. d. Komm. z. Stud. Yakutiens, 4, 1926. (Notes of the Commission Studying Yakutia.)

75. Grigoryev, M. P.: Orogidrograficheskiy Ocherk Aginskoy Stepi (A Hydrographical and Orographical Study of the Steppe of Aginsk). Trudy of the Akinsker Expedition of the Chita Section of the Geog. Assoc., 1913.

76. Grum-Grshimaylo, G. E.: Opissaniye Amurskoy obl. (Description of the Amur Oblast). St Petersburg, 1894.

77. Gubler, A.: Die Kurilen (The Kuriles). Notes of the Geographical-Ethnographical Association, Zurich, XXII. Zurich, 1931–2.

78. Hanisch, E.: Geschichte Russlands (History of Russia). 2 vols. Freiburg, 1941.

79. Hann: Handbuch der Klimatologie (Handbook of Climatology). 3 vols. Stuttgart, 1911.

80. Hassmann, H.: Erdoel in der Sowjetunion (Petroleum in the Soviet Union). Hamburg, 1951.

81. Hultén, E.: Outline of the History of the Arctic and Boreal Biota during the Quaternary Period. Stockholm, 1937.

82. Isbert, H.: Sachalin (Sakhalin). Dissertation. Bonn, 1907.

83. Ivanov, D. V.: Der Sichota Alin Ruecken (russ.) (The Sikhota-Alin Ridge). St Petersburg, 1896.

84. Ivanov, A. P.: Novye Danny'e o Geolog. Stroyenii i Polesnykh Iskopayemykh Orulganskogo Khrebta (New Facts concerning the Geological Structure and Minerals in the Orulgan Mountains). Problemy Arkt. 4, 1938.

85. Jagovkin, I. S.: Tsvetny'e Metally (The Coloured Copper Ores). Moscow, 1931.

86. Jasny, N.: The Soviet Economy during the Plan Era. Stanford, 1951.

87. Jochelson, W.: Peoples of Asiatic Russia. New York, 1928.

88. Jochelson, W.: The Yukaghir. New York, 1910–26.

89. Jochelson, W.: The Koryak. New York, 1905–8.

90. Joffe, J.: Die Planung der Industrieproduktion (The Planning of Industrial Production). Berlin, 1948.

91. Johansen, H.: Der Baikalsee (The Lake of Baikal). Notes of the Geog. Assoc. Munich, 1925.

92. Jorré, G.: The Soviet Union. The Land and its Peoples. 2nd edition. London–New York, 1952.

93. Kamenskiy, J. A.: Zheleso-rudny'e basy SSSR (The Iron Ores Centres of the USSR). Moscow, 1933.

94. Karuts, R.: Die Voelker Nord- und Mittelasiens (The People of North and Middle Asia). Stuttgart, 1925.

95. Kirzhnits, A.: Yevreskaya Avtonomnaya Oblasty (The Autonomous Region of the Jews). Moscow, 1936.

96. Koeppen, W.: Klimakunde von Russland in Europa und Asien (Climatology of Russia in Europe and Asia). Berlin, 1939.

97. Koloskov, P. I.: Klimaticheskiy Ocherk Poluostrova Kamchatki (Climatological Study of the Peninsula of Kamchatka). Isvestija of the Far East Geogr. Inst., 1932.

98. Koloskov, P. I.: Klimaticheskiy Osnovy Selyskogo Khosyayastva Amurskoy gub (The Climatic Factors as a Basis of the Agriculture of the Amur Region). Blagoveshchensk, 1925.

99. Koloskov, P. I.: Klimaticheskiye Rayony Dalynevostochnogo Kraya (The Climatic Regions of the Far East). Moscow, 1927.

100. Kolossovskiy: Khosyaystvo Vostochnoy Sibiri i Dalynego Vostoka v Svyasi s Rayonirovaniyem (The Economy of East Siberia and the Far East in Relation to Regionalism). Planovoye Chosyaystvo, No. 9, 1925.

101. Komarov, V. L.: Putishestviye po Kamchatke (Journeys in Kamchatka). Reports of the Kamchatka Expedition. St Petersburg, 1912.

102. Komarov, V. L.: Tipy Rastitelynosti Yuzhno-Ussuriyskogo Kraya (Vegetational Types of the Southern Ussuri Region). Petrograd, 1917.

103. Konradi, S. A., and Kely, N. G.: Geolog. Otdel Kamchatskoy Eksped. 1908–11 (Geological Section of the Kamchatka Expedition 1908–11). Isvestija of the Geogr. Ges., 1925.

104. Koslov, A. I.: Iskopayemy'e Ugli DKW (The Coal Deposits of the Far Eastern Region). In the Atlas of Energy Resources of the USSR). Moscow-Leningrad, 1934.

105. Krasheninnikov, S. P.: Opissaniye Semli Kamchatki (Description of the Land of Kamchatka). Moscow-Leningrad, 1949.

106. Krasheninnikov, I. M.: K Kharakteristike Landshaftov Vostochnogo Sabaikalya (The Characteristics of the Landscape of East Transbaikalia). Semlevedeniye, 1913.

107. Krasyuk, A. A.: Selyskokhosyaystvenny' Promysel na Sakhalinye v Svyasi s Pochvennymi Uslovyami (The Agriculture on the Island of Sakhalin in Relationship to the Soil Conditions). Notes by the Soil Research Section. Leningrad, 1927.

108. Krishtofovich, A. N.: Geolog. Obsor Stran Dalynego Vostoka (Geological Survey of the Far East). Moscow, 1932.

109. Kropotkin, P. A.: Otchet ob Olekminsko-Vitimskoy Ekspeditsii (Account of the Olekma-Vitimsk Expedition). Sapiski of the Geogr. Assoc., 111, 1873.

110. Krzhishanovskiy, G. M.: Energeticheskiye Ressursy SSSR (The Sources of Energy of the USSR). 2 vols. Moscow, 1937.

111. Kudryavtsev, F. A.: Istoriya Buryat-Mongolyskogo Naroda (History of the Buryato-Mongolian People). Moscow, 1940.

112. Kuminova, A. V., and Vandakurova, E. V.: Stepi Sibiri (The Steppes of Siberia). Novossibirsk, 1949.

113. Kushev, S. L.: Geomorfolog. Ocherk Sev. Chasti Zentr. Kamch. Depressi i Doliny Srednogo Techeniya r. Kamchatki (Geomorphological Sketch of the Northern Part of the Kamchatka Depression and the Valleys of the Middle Reaches of the Kamchatka River). Doklady d. Ak. d. Wiss (Academy of Science). Moscow, 1938.

114. Kushev, S. L., and Liverovskiy, J. A.: Geomorfologicheskiy Ocherk Zentralnoy Kamchatskoy Depressii (Geomorphological Sketch of the Central Kamchatka Depression). Trudy of the Geogr. Inst. Moscow, 1940.

115. Lamakiny, V. V., and N. V.: Sayano-Dzhidinskoye Nagorye (The Mountain Region of Sayano-Dzhida). Semlevedeniye, Moscow, 1930.

116. Lautensach, H.: Korea. Leipzig, 1945.

117. Leimbach, W.: Die Sowjetunion. Natur, Volk und Wirtschaft (The Soviet Union. Nature, People, and Economy). Stuttgart, 1950.

118. Leuchs, K.: Geologie von Asien (Geology of Asia), 1st vol., 2nd part. Stuttgart, 1935–7.

119. Leuchs, K.: Der Asiatische Bau und seine Bedeutung fuer die Tektonik der Erde (The Structure of Asia and its Significance in World Tectonics). Central Paper for Mineralogy, Geology, Palaeontology. Berlin, 1925.

120. Levitskiy, A. P.: K Voprossu ob Evolyutsii Bolot v Amurskoy Oblasti (The Question of the Development of the Marshes in the Amur Region). Pochvovedeniye, 1910.

121. Lyubinov: Ekonomicheskiye Problemy Dalynego Vostoka (The Economic Problems of the Far East). Moscow, 1925.

122. Lyudevig, L.: Amurskoye Semledeliye v Ego Proshlom i Nasto-yashchem (The Agriculture of the Amur—Past and Present). Blagoveshchensk, 1924.

123. Lopatin, Y. A.: Goldydy (The Goldes). Sapiski d. Ges. für Erfor-schung des Amur Geb. Vladivostok, 1922 (Sapiski of the Association for the Exploration of the Amur region).

124. Makhachek F.: Das Relief der Erde (The Relief of the Earth). 2 vols. Berlin, 1938.

125. Maslov, V. P.: Rudny'e bogatstva Malogo Khingana (The Ore Resources of the Small Chingan). In 'Die Expedition der Ak. d. Wiss. 1935'. Moscow, 1937.

126. Matskevich, S.: Roly Elektrifikatsii v Rasvitii Material-notekh-nicheskoy Basy Selyskogo Khosyaystvo SSSR (The Role of Electrification in the Development of Machinery as the Basis of Agriculture in the USSR). Moscow, 1952.

127. Meglitskiy, G.: Das Ufer des Ochotskischen Meeres und das Tungusker Gebiet (The Shores of the Sea of Okhotsk and the Tungus Region) (russ.) Gorny' Zhurnal, No. 8, 1893.

128. Meister, A. K.: Vostochnaya Okraina Lenskogo Soloton. Rayona. (The Eastern Marginal Area of the Lena Gold-fields). Geolog. Forsch. in d. Goldf., Geg. Sibiriens, 10, 1914.

129. Melioranskiy, V. A.: Cheres Sikhote-Aliny k Beregam Tatarskogo Proliva (Over the Sikhota-Alin to the Straits of Tartary). In 'Die Expeditionen der Ak. d. Wiss 1935' (The Expeditions of the Academy of Science). Moscow, 1935.

130. Menyaylov, A. A., and Naboko, S. I.: V Krayu Solota i Platina (In the Territory of Gold and Platinum). In 'Die Expeditionen d. Ak. d. Wiss. 1934'. Moscow, 1935.

131. Mikhaylov: Amur-Dekastri (Amur-De-Kastri). In 'Ekonomiches-kaya Zhisny Dalynego Vostoka', Nos. 7–8. Khabarovsk, 1929.

132. Mikhaylov, N., and Pokshishevski', V.: Reise ueber die Karte der Sowjetunion (Journey across the Map of the Soviet Union). Berlin, 1947.

133. Musylev, S. A.: Geolog. Rasres Cheres Maly' Khingan (The Geological Profile of the Smaller Khingan). Obruchev-Festschrift, I. Moscow, 1938.

134. Novak, Y.: Wiss. Ergebnisse der Expedition nach dem Sikhota-Alin (Scientific Results of the Expedition to the Sikhota-Alin). Cracow, 1913.

135. Novograblenov, P. T.: Katalog Vulkanov Kamchatki (Catalogue of the Volcanoes of Kamchatka). Isvestiya of the Geogr. Ges., 1932.

136. Obruchev, S. V.: Drevneye Oledeneniye i Chetvert. Istoriya Chukostskogo Okruga (Ancient Glaciations and the History of the Quaternary Ice Age in the Chukchen District). Isvestiya of the Ak. der Wiss., 1939.

137. Obruchev, S. V.: Kolymsko-Indigirski' Kray (The Kolyma-Indigirka Region). Trudy SOPS, Serie Yakuten 1, 1931.

138. Obruchev, S. V.: Orograficheski' Ocherk Chukotskogo Okruga (Orographical Study of the Chukchen District). Trudy des Arkt, Inst., 1936.

139. Obruchev, S.: Der Bau NO/Asiens nach neueren Forschungen (The Structure of NE Asia according to more Recent Research). Geolog. Rundschau, 1934.

140. Obruchev, V. A.: Geologie von Sibirien (Geology of Siberia). Berlin, 1926.

141. Obruchev, S. V.: Novaya Orograficheskaya Shema Severo-Vostochnoy Asii (A New Orographical System of North-East Asia. Moscow, 1940.

142. Obruchev, S. V.: Ocherk Tektoniki Severo-Vostochnoy Asii (Study of the Tectonic Forces in NE Asia). Moscow, 1938.

143. Obruchev, S. V.: Materiali Dlya Tektoniki Severo-Vostochnoy Asii (Notes for the Study of the Tectonic Forces in NE Asia). Probleme der Sowj. Geologie. Mowcow, 1934.

144. Obruchev, V. A.: Khrebty Yablonovy' i Stanovoy po Novym Dannym (The Yablonovy and the Stanovoi Mountains According to Recent Information). In 'Sa Industrialisatsiyu Sov. Vostoka', No. 2, 1933.

145. Obruchev, V. A.: Selenginskaya Dauriya (Selenga-Dauria). Leningrad, 1929.

146. Obruchev, V. A.: Geologicheskoye Stroyeniye Buryat-Mongolyskoy ASSR (Geolog. Structure of Buryat-Mongolian ASSR). Probleme d. Bury. Mongol. ASSR I. Moscow, 1935.

147. Obruchev, V. A.: Geologicheskiy Ocherk Pribaykalya i Lenskogo Rayona (Geological Study of Prebaikalia and the Lena Region). Moscow, 1932.

148. Obruchev, S. V.: Kolymsko-Indigirski' Rayon (The Kolyma-Indigirka Region). Compiled work. Yakut ASSR. Moscow, 1932.

149. Parkhomenko, S. G.: Nekotory'e Danny'e o Prirode Nizhnelen-skogo Kraya (Some Facts about the Nature of the Region of the Lower Lena). Trudy d. Komm. zur Erforschung Yakutiens, 1928.

150. Partanski', M. M.: Ossadki Primorya (The Precipitation of the Coastal Region). Moscow, 1927.

151. Pavlovski', E. V.: Geolog. Ocherk Rayona Verchney Chary (Geolog. Study of the Region of the Upper Chara). Trudy der allsowj. geolog. Forschungsvereinigung (Study of the Allsoviet Geological Research Association). Moscow, 1933.

152. Pavlovski', E. V.: O Sledakh Oledeneniya v Sredne-Vitimskoy Gornoy Strane (Traces of Glaciation in the Region of the Middle Vitim). Geolog. Vestnik, Nos. 4–6, 1926.

153. Perlin, B.: Mongolskaya Narodnaya Respublika (The Mongolian Peoples Republic). Moscow, 1941.

154. Petrov, V. G.: Naledi na Amursko-Yakutskoy Magistrali (Super-imposed Ice Formations in the Amur-Yakutsk Area) Ak. der Wiss. (Academy of Science). Moscow, 1930.

155. Polevoy, P. I.: Anadyrski' Kray (The Anadyr Region). Trudy der Geolog. Kommission, 1915.

156. Polutoff, N.: Die Goldlagerstaetten der UdSSR (The Gold Deposits of the USSR). Ostwirtschaft, 1937 (Eastern Economics).

157. Pomus, M. I.: Buryat-Mongolskaya ASSR (Buryato-Mongolia). Moscow, 1937.

158. Postoyev, K. Y.: Geomorfolog. Ocherk Olekminsko-Aldanskogo Rayona (Geomorphological Study of the Olekma-Aldan Region). Moscow, 1932.

159. Prassolov, L. I.: O Vechnoy Merslote v Stepnoy Polosse Sabay-kalya (The 'Permafrost' in the Steppe Zone of Transbaikalia). Pochvovedeniye, 1911.

160. Prassolov, L. I.: Yuzhnoye Sabaykalye (Southern Transbaikalia). Mat. zur Bodenforschung im Asiat. Russland (Notes for the Soil Study in Asiatic Russia). Moscow, 1927.

161. Prigorovski', M. M.: Obsor Glavneyshikh Mestorozhdeni' Ugley i Goryuchikh Slantsev SSSR (Survey of the Main Coal and Oil-shale Deposits in the USSR). Compiled Work. Moscow-Leningrad, 1931.

162. Ratmanov, G. E.: K Gidrologii Beringova i Chukotskogo Morey (The Hydrology of the Bering and Chukchee Seas). Moscow, 1937.

163. Raupach, F.: Stratigraphische und tektonische Entwicklung d. russ. Fernen Ostens, der Mandchurei und zentralen Mongolei (Stratigraphical and Tectonic Development of the Russian Far East, Manchuria, and Central Mongolia). Diss. Wuerzburg, 1934.

164. Redyko, B. A.: Aleuty Komandorskikh Ostrovov (The Aleutians and the Commander Islands). Vladivostok, 1927.

165. Rudovich, L.: Klimat Okhotskogo Morya (The Climate of the Sea of Okhotsk). Sapiski ueber Hydrographie. Moscow, 1916.

166. Romanov, A. A.: Is Geomorfolog. Nabludeniy v Kharaulakhskom khrebte (Geomorphological Observations in the Kharaulakski Region). Trudy des Arkt. Inst. XIII, 1934.

167. Romer, E.: An den Kuesten des Japanischen Meeres (On the Coast of the Sea of Japan). Mitt. d. K. K. Geogr. Ges. Vienna, 1911.

168. Romer, E.: Bericht ueber Geograph. Arbeiten im Gebiete des Sikhota-Alin Gebirges (Report on Geographical Works on the Region of the Sikhota-Alin Mountains). Anzeiger der Ak. d. Wiss. Cracow Reihe A, Cracow 1913 (Gazette of the Academy of Science, Row A).

169. Saks, V. N.: Geolog. Ocherk Chukotskogo Kraya (Geological Study of the Chukchee Region). Trudy des Arkt. Inst. Moscow, 1739.

170. Saks, V. N.: O Chetvert Oledeninii Severa Sibiri (The Quaternary Glaciation of Northern Siberia). Arktika, IV, 1936.

171. Savich, V. M.: Tipy Rastitelynogo Pokrova Severa Primorya (Vegetational Types in the North of the Coastal Region). Vladivostok, 1928.

172. Savritski', A. N.: Pyaty Let Geolog. Issledovaniy Kamchatki (Five Years of Geological Research on Kamchatka). Problems of Soviet Geology. 1935.

173. Scheynman, J. M.: Issledovaniya Okrestnostyack c. Olovyannogo v Vostochnom Sabaykalye (Research in the Area around Olovyannaya). Isvestiya Geolog. Kom., 1927.

174. Scheynman, J. M.: Nekotory'e Cherty Tektoniki Yugo-Vostoka Sibiri (Some Features of the Tectonics of SE Siberia). Problems of Soviet Geology, No. 2, 1933.

175. Shishkin, I. K.: Materialy po Rastitelynomu Pokrovu Shantarskikh Ostrova (Notes on the Vegetation Cover of the Shantar Islands). Vladivostok, 1928.

176. Shostakovich, W. B.: Der ewig gefrorene Boden Sibiriens (The Permafrost in Siberia). Zeitsch. d. Ges. f. Erdk. Berlin, 1927.

177. Shrenk, L.: Ob Inorodtsakh Amurskogo Kraya (The Natives of the Amur Region). 2 vols. St Petersburg, 1883–99.

178. Shtenberg, L. Y.: Gilyaki (The Gilyaks). Ethnograph. Reports. Moscow, 1905.

179. Shcherbakov, A. V.: Dva Geolog. Peressecheniya Poluostrova Kamchatki (Two Geological Profiles through Kamchatka). Trudy SOPS. Moscow, 1938.

180. Schultz, A.: Sibirien. Eine Landeskunde (Siberia, a Geographical Survey). Breslau, 1923.

A A

181. Schultz, A.: Das Ussuri Land (The Land of the Ussuri). Koenigsberg, 1932.
182. Schwarz, H.: Russia's Soviet Economy. London, 1951.
183. Schwind, M.: Die Gestaltung Krafutos zum Japanischen Raum (The Position of Karafutos in Relation to the Japanese Region). Peterm. Geogr. Mitt. Ergaenzungsheft 239, Gotha, 1942 (Geog. Notes—Supplementary Volume).
184. Scott, J.: Jenseits des Ural (Beyond the Urals). Stockholm, 1944.
185. Sergeyev, M. A.: Narodnoye Khosyaystvo Kamchatskogo Kraya (The Peasant Economy of the Kamchatka Region). Moscow, 1936.
186. Sergeyev, M. A.: Sovyetskaya Kamchatka (Soviet Kamchatka). Moscow, 1932.
187. Zhabad, Th.: The Geography of the USSR; a Regional Survey. New York, 1951.
188. Zhdanko, M.: Usvlecheniye is Doklada v Sased IPGO (Extract from the Notes of the Session of the Geographical Association, 1915). Isvestija d. Kais. Russ. Georgr. Ges., 1915.
189. Skorokhod, V. S.: Geolog. Ocherk Uglenosnogo Bureinskogo Basseyna (Geological Study of the Coal-bearing Bureya Basin). Vladivostok, 1935.
190. Shnizharski', T. N.: Geologicheski' Ocherk Leno-Indigirskogo Rayona (Geological Study of the Lena-Indigirka Region). Trudy des Arkt. Inst. I. Moscow, 1937.
191. Sokolov, D.: Russki' Sakhalin (Russian Sakhalin) Semlevedeniye, 1912.
192. Soklov, D. V., and Tikhonovich, N. N.: Sakhalin (russ). Moscow, 1925.
193. Sokolova, E. N., and Danilovich, V. N.: Visovyach Amura (In the Amur Depressions). In 'Die Expeditionen der Ak. der Wiss. 1934'. In 'The Expeditions of the Academy of Science, 1934'. Moscow, 1935.
194. Solovyev, A.: Kurilyskiye Ostrova (The Kuriles). Edition Glavsevmorputy. Moscow, 1945.
195. Sostsava, V.: Das Anadyrgebiet (The Anadyr Region). Ztschr. d. Ges. f. Erdk. Berlin. 1930.
196. Sochava, V. B.: Po Tundram Bass. Penzhinskoy Guby (Across the Tundra of the Penzhina Bay). Isvestiya der Geogr. Ges., 1932.
197. Sochava, V. B.: O Predele Lessov Na Severo-Vostoke Asii (The Tree-line in NE Asia). Priroda. Moscow, 1929.
198. Stalnov, I. I.: Chikoyski' Solotonosny' Rayon (The Gold-bearing Area along the Chikoy River). Notes from 'General and Applied Geology', No. 64. Moscow, 1927.
199. Stille, H.: Urozeane und Kontinente (Former Oceans and Continents). Abh. d. Dtsch. Ak. d. Wiss. Berlin, 1949.

200. Stille, H.: Geotekton. Probleme des Pazifischen Erdraumes (Geotectonic Problems of the Pacific Region) Abh. d. Dtsch. Ak. d. Wiss. (German Academy of Science). Math.-Naturw. Klasse, 1944.
201. Sukachev, V. N.: Rastitelnosty Verkhney Chasti Basseyna Reki Tungira (The Vegetation of the Upper Basin of the Tungir). St Petersburg, 1912.
202. Sumgin, M.: Ueber die Ewige Gefrornis des Bodens (The Permanently Frozen Subsoil). Z. d. Ges. Erdk. Berlin, 1929.
203. Sumgin, M. I.: Vechnaya Merslota ('The Permafrost'). Ausg. D. Ak. d. Wiss. (Academy of Science). Moscow, 1937.
204. Sumgin, M., and Demchinski', B.: Oblasty Vechnoy Mersloty (The Regions of Permafrost). Moscow, 1940.
205. Suslov, S. P.: Fisicheskaya Geografiya SSSR (Physical Geography of the USSR). Moscow-Leningrad, 1947.
206. Taliyev, D. N.: Baykal Biolog.-Geograf. Ocherk (Baikalia, a Biogeographical Study). Moscow-Irkutsk, 1933.
207. Tanfilyev, G. J.: Geografiya Rossii. Relief Asiatskoy Rossii (The Geography of Russia, the Relief of Asiatic Russia), vol. II. Odessa, 1923.
208. Tetyayev, M. M.: K Geologii Bukachinskogo Kamennougolynogo Mestorozhdeniya (The Geology of the Buckachacha Coal-field). Isvestiya d. Geolog. Komm. No. 2, 1929.
209. Tetyayev, M. M.: K Geologii i Tektoniki Sabaykalya (The Geology and Tectonics of Transbaikalia). Westnik. d. Geolog. Komm. Nos. 8–9, 1927.
210. Tetyayev, M. M.: Novy'e Danny'e po Geologii Sabaykalya (New Findings Concerning the Geology of Transbaikalia). Westnik. d. Geolog. Komm., No. 1, 1927.
211. Tetyayev, M. M.: Kontury Problemy DVK Kak Geolog. Tselogo. (Notes on the Geological Problems of the Whole Far East). Moscow, 1934.
212. Thiel, E.: Die Eiszeit in Sibirien (The Ice Age in Siberia). 'Erdkunde', Nos. 1–2. Bonn, 1951.
213. Thiel, E.: Die Elektrifizierung der Sowjetunion (The Electrification of the Soviet Union). Zeitschr. f. Raumforschung, Nos. 3–5. Bonn, 1950.
214. Thiel, E.: Verkehrsgeographie von Russisch-Asien (The Geography of Communications in Russian Asia). Koenigsberg (Pr.)-Berlin, 1934.
215. Tikhonovich, N. N., and Polevoy, P. I.: Geomorfolog. Ocherk Russkogo Sakhalina (Geomorphological Study of Russian Sakhalin). Trudy des Geolog. Komm. Moscow, 1915.
216. Tikhonovich, N. N.: Geomorfolog. Ocherk Russkogo Sakhalina (Geomorphological Notes on Russian Sakhalin). Bull. Com. Geolog. Petersburg, 1916.

217. Tolmachev, A. I.: O Proishozhdenii Tundrogo Landshafts (The Origins of the Tundra Landscape). Priroda, 1927.
218. Tolmachev, A. I.: Flora Tsentral'noy Chasti Vostochnogo Taimyra (The Flora of the Central Region of the Eastern Taimyr Peninsula). Trudy d. Polar. Komm. 8, 1932.
219. Tomashevski, I. J.: Pochvy Yugosapadnoy Chasti Seyskobureinskogo Vodorasdela (The Soils of the South-western Part of the Seya-Bureya Watershed). Arbeiten d. Amur Exped. XV (Notes by the Amur Expedition). St Petersburg, 1912.
220. Chefranov, S. V.: Fisicheskaya Geografiya SSSR (Physical Geography of the USSR). 8th edition. Moscow, 1949.
221. Chefranov, S. V.: Geografiya SSSR (Geography of the USSR). Moscow, 1951.
222. Churakov, A. N.: V Tayezhnikh Debryach Dalynego Vostoka (In the Taiga Forests of the Far East). In 'The Expeditions of the Academy of Science 1934'. Moscow, 1935.
223. Turin, S. P.: The USSR. London, 1944.
224. Vakar, V. A.: Geolog. Issledovaniya V Bass R Beresyovki (Geological Research in the Beresovka Basin). Isvestiya d. Geogr. Ges. 65, 1931.
225. Vandakurova, E. V.: Stepi Sibiri (The Steppe of Siberia). Novossibirsk, 1949.
226. Vasykovski, A. P., and Synatkov, L. A.: Geologicheski' Ocherk Indigirsko-Kolymskogo Kraya (Geological Study of the Indigirka-Kolyma Region). Trudy des Arkt. Institutes. Moscow, 1939.
227. Vereshchagin, G. J.: Osero Baykal (The Lake of Baikal). Moscow, 1936.
228. Wittenburg, P. V.: Geolog. Studien an der Ostsibir. Kueste im Golf Peters des Grossen (Geological Studies on the East Siberian Coast in the Bay of Peter the Great). Stuttgart, 1909.
229. Volarovich, G. P., and Skorokhod, V. S.: Kratki' Geolog. Ocherk Gornoy Oblasti Sikhote-Aliny (Short Geological Study of the Mountain Regions of the Sikhota-Alin). Vladivostok, 1935.
230. Vosnessenski, V. A.: Vitimsko-Nerchinski i Nerchinsko-Olekminski Vodorasdyelny Khrebet (The Watershed Mountains of the Vitim-Nercha and the Nercha-Olekma). Isvestiya d. Geolog. Kom. XXXIII, 1914.
231. Aitchen, K. Wu: China and the Soviet Union. London, 1950.

IV. JOURNALS AND NEWSPAPERS

Planovoye Khosyaystvo (Planned Economy). Six issues annually. Moscow.

Voprossy Ekonomiki (Economic Questions). Twelve issues annually. Moscow.

Isvestiya Akademii Nauk SSSR (Bulletins of the Academy of Science of the USSR). Up to 1951 a Geographical-geophysical series, since then a geographical series. Four issues annually. Moscow.

Isvestiya Vsesoyusnaya Geograficheskogo Obshchestva (Bulletins of the All-Soviet Geographical Association). Six issues annually. Moscow.

Priroda (Nature). Published by the Academy of Science of the USSR. Twelve issues annually. Moscow.

Pravda. Daily paper. Moscow.

Isvestiya. Daily paper. Moscow.

## Transcription of the Russian Alphabet

Below is given the method used for transcribing Russian letters. As a matter of interest the German method is also given.

|  | German transcription | | English transcription | |
|---|---|---|---|---|
| а | a | | a | |
| б | b | | b | |
| в | w | | v | |
| г | g | | g | |
| д | d | | d | |
| е | e | after a consonant | e | after a consonant |
| | je | after vowels and at the beginning of a word | ye | after vowels and at the beginning of a word |
| ж | sh | | zh | |
| з | s | | z | |
| и | i | | i | |
| й | j | | y | |
| к | k | | k | |
| л | l | | l | |
| м | m | | m | |
| н | n | | n | |
| о | o | | o | |
| п | p | | p | |
| р | r | | r | |
| с | s | (ss, when between two vowels) | s | |
| т | t | | t | |
| у | u | | u | |
| ф | f | | f | |
| х | ch | | kh | |
| ц | z | | ts | |
| ч | tsch | | ch | |
| ш | sch | | sh | |
| щ | schtsch | | shch | |
| ъ | | | | |
| ы | y | | y | |
| ь | j | | ’ | |
| э | e | | e | |
| ю | ju | | yu | |
| я | ja | | ya | |

# Index

\*

In the following index only the most important words are mentioned.  For the main subjects see list of contents.